Merchant Ship Construction

Merchant Ship Construction

D. A. TAYLOR
MSc, BSc, CEng, MIMarE
Senior Lecturer in Marine Technology
Hong Kong Polytechnic

Marine Management (Holdings) Ltd for
The Institute of Marine Engineers

Published by Marine Management (Holdings) Ltd for
The Institute of Marine Engineers

The Memorial Building
76 Mark Lane
London
EC3R 7JN

First published by Butterworths, 1980
Second edition 1985
Third edition, published by Marine Management (Holdings) Ltd, 1992

ISBN 0-907206-46-8

British Library Cataloguing-in-Publication Data
A catalogue record for this book is available from the British Library

Printed in Great Britain by BPCC Wheatons Ltd, Exeter

Contents

Acknowledgments

I wish to thank the many firms, organisations and individuals who have provided me with assistance and material during the writing of this book.

For guidance provided in their specialist areas I would like to thank Mr W. Cole, Welding Manager and Mr I. Waugh, Ship Manager, both of Swan Hunter Shipbuilders.

To the firm of Swan Hunter Shipbuilders, now a member of British Shipbuilders, I wish to extend my thanks for their permission to use drawings and information based on their current shipbuilding practices.

The following firms and organisations contributed drawings and information for various sections of this book, for which I thank them:

AGA Welding Ltd
Austin and Pickergill Ltd
Blohm and Voss, A.G.
BOC Cutting Machines
Brown Brothers & Co. Ltd
Cammell Laird Shipbuilders
Cape Boards and Panels Ltd
Clarke Chapman Ltd
Donkin and Co. Ltd
F.A. Hughes and Co. Ltd
Flakt Ltd (S.F. Review)
Glacier Metal Co. Ltd
Hempel's Marine Paints
Hugh Smith (Glasgow) Ltd
International Maritime Organisation
Lloyd's Register of Shipping
MacGregor Centrex Ltd
Moss Rosenberg Verft, A.S.
The Motor Ship
Odense Steel Shipyard Ltd
Oxytechnik
Philips Welding Industries
Phoceenne Sous-Marine, S.A.
Power Blast Ltd
Rockwool Co. (UK) Ltd
Sigma Coatings Ltd
Stone Manganese Marine Ltd
Stone Vickers
Strommen Staal, A.S.
Taylor Pallister and Co. Ltd
The DeVilbiss Co. Ltd
The Naval Architect
Voith GmbH
Wilson Walton International Ltd

Preface

The opportunity has been taken in this, the third edition, to update and add material to a number of chapters. Most of Chapter 1 has been rewritten in order to include additional ship types and more representative illustrations where necessary. Chapter 5 has additional material on anchors and cables, together with illustrations. Chapter 8 now deals with 'Oil Tankers, Bulk Carriers and Container Ships', and a new Chapter 9, 'Liquefied Gas Carriers and Chemical Tankers', has been added. Various changes in IMO legislation have taken place since the second edition and these are outlined in the expanded section in Chapter 11.

This book is intended as an up-to-date review of current ship types, their construction, special features and outfit equipment. The various types of ship are examined in outline and configuration and the current shipbuilding methods and techniques are described. The ship as a stressed structure is examined in relation to the effects and constraints placed upon the structural members and their arrangements.

The major items and regions of structure are illustrated in detail, and the types and methods of strengthening and stiffening are explained. The minor, but nevertheless essential, steelwork items and the various pieces of outfit equipment are also detailed and illustrated.

The statutory and regulatory bodies and organisations involved in shipping and shipbuilding are described and their influence on ship construction is explained. The final chapters deal with the corrosion process and the preventive methods employed for the ship's structure, and also with the examination of ships in drydock, periodical surveys and maintenance.

It is hoped that this text will continue to assist students of naval architecture, marine engineering, nautical studies and those attempting the various Certificates of Competency. The non-technical language and glossary of terms should enable any interested student to progress steadily through this book.

D.A. Taylor

1

The Ship—its Functions, Features and Types

Merchant ships exist to carry cargoes across the waterways of the world safely, speedily and economically. Since a large part of the world's surface, approximately three-fifths, is covered by water, it is reasonable to consider that the merchant ship will continue to perform its function for many centuries to come. The worldwide nature of this function involves the ship, its cargo and its crew in many aspects of international life. Some features of this international transportation, such as weather and climatic changes, availability of cargo handling facilities and international regulations, will be considered in later chapters.

The ship, in its various forms, has evolved to accomplish its function depending upon three main factors—the type of cargo carried, the type of construction and materials used, and the area of operation.

Three principal cargo carrying types of ship exist today: the general cargo vessel, the tanker and the passenger vessel. The general cargo ship functions today as a general carrier and also, in several particular forms, for unit-based or unitised cargo carrying. Examples include container ships, pallet ships and 'roll-on, roll-off' ships. The tanker has its specialised forms for the carriage of crude oil, refined oil products, liquefied gases, etc. The passenger ship includes, generally speaking, the cruise liner and some ferries.

The type of construction will affect the cargo carried and, in some generally internal aspects, the characteristics of the ship. The principal types of construction refer to the framing arrangement for stiffening the outer shell plating, the three types being longitudinal, transverse and combined framing. The use of mild steel, special steels, aluminium and other materials also influences the characteristics of a ship. General cargo ships are usually of transverse or combined framing construction using mild steel sections and plating. Most tankers employ longitudinal or combined framing systems and the larger vessels utilise high tensile steels in their construction. Passenger ships, with their large areas of superstructure, employ lighter metals and alloys such as aluminium to reduce the weight of the upper regions of the ship.

The area of trade, the cruising range, and the climatic extremes experienced must all be borne in mind in the design of a particular ship. Ocean going vessels require several tanks for fresh water and oil fuel storage. Stability and trim arrangements must be satisfactory for the weather conditions prevailing in the area of operation.

The strength of the structure, its ability to resist the effects of waves, heavy seas, etc., must be much greater for an ocean-going vessel than for an inland waterway vessel.

Considerations of safety in all aspects of ship design and operation must be paramount, so the ship must be seaworthy. This term relates to many aspects of the ship: it must be capable of remaining afloat in all conditions of weather; it must remain stable and behave well in the various sea states encountered. Some of the constructional and regulatory aspects of seaworthiness will be dealt with in later chapters.

The development of ship types will continue as long as there is a sufficient demand to be met in a particular area of trade. Recent years have seen such developments as very large crude carriers (VLCCs) for the transport of oil, and the liquefied natural gas and liquefied petroleum gas tankers for the bulk carriage of liquid gases. Container ships and various barge carriers have developed for general cargo transportation. Bulk carriers and combination bulk cargo carriers are also relatively modern developments.

Several basic ships types will now be considered in further detail. The particular features of appearance, construction, layout, size, etc., will be examined for the following ship types:

(1) General cargo ships
(2) Tankers
(3) Bulk carriers
(4) Container ships
(5) Roll-on roll-off ships
(6) Passenger ships.

Many other types and minor variations exist, but the above selection is considered to be representative of the major part of the world's merchant fleet.

General cargo ships

The general cargo ship is the 'maid of all work', operating a worldwide 'go anywhere' service of cargo transportation. It consists of as large a clear open cargo-carrying space as possible, together with the facilities required for loading and unloading the cargo (*Figure 1.1*). Access to the cargo storage areas or holds is provided by openings in the deck called hatches. Hatches are made as large as strength considerations will allow to reduce horizontal movement of cargo within the ship. Hatch covers of wood or steel, as in most modern ships, are used to close the hatch openings when the ship is at sea. The hatch covers are made watertight and lie upon coamings around the hatch which are set some distance from the upper or weather deck to reduce the risk of flooding in heavy seas.

One or more separate decks are fitted in the cargo holds and are known as tween decks. Greater flexibility in loading and unloading, together with cargo segregation and improved stability, are possible using the tween deck spaces. Various combinations of derricks, winches and deck cranes are used for the handling of cargo. Many modern ships are fitted with deck cranes which reduce cargo-handling times and manpower requirements. A special heavy lift derrick may also be fitted, covering one or two holds.

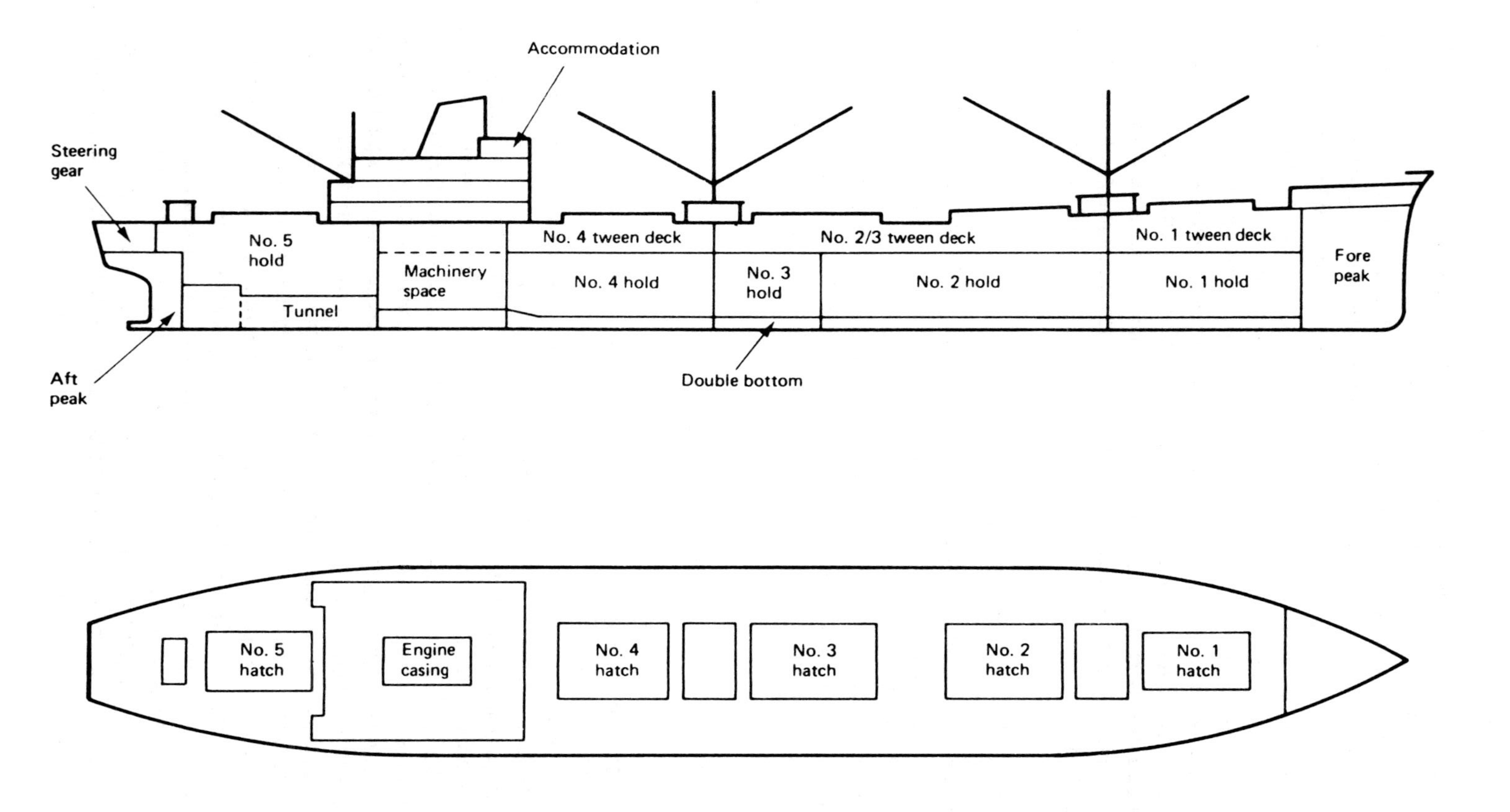

Figure 1.1 *General cargo ship*

Since full cargoes cannot be guaranteed with this type of ship, ballast-carrying tanks must be fitted. In this way the ship always has a sufficient draught for stability and total propeller immersion. Fore and aft peak tanks are fitted which also assist in trimming the ship. A double bottom is fitted which extends the length of the ship and is divided into separate tanks, some of which carry fuel oil and fresh water. The remaining tanks are used for ballast when the ship is sailing empty or partly loaded. Deep tanks may be fitted which can carry liquid cargoes or water ballast.

The accommodation and machinery spaces are usually located with one hold between them and the aft peak bulkhead. This arrangement improves the vessel's trim when it is partially loaded and reduces the lost cargo space for shafting tunnels compared with the central machinery space arrangement. The current range of sizes for general cargo ships is from 2000 to 15 000 displacement tonnes with speeds of 12–18 knots.

Refrigerated general cargo ship

The fitting of refrigeration plants for the cooling of cargo holds enables the carriage of perishable foodstuffs by sea. Refrigerated ships vary little from general cargo ships. They may have more than one tween deck, and all hold spaces will be insulated to reduce heat transfer. Cargo may be carried frozen or chilled depending upon its nature. Refrigerated ships are usually faster than general cargo ships, often having speeds up to 22 knots, and they may also cater for up to 12 passengers.

Tankers

The tanker is used to carry bulk liquid cargoes, the most common type being the oil tanker. Many other liquids are carried in tankers and specially constructed vessels are used for chemicals, liquefied petroleum gas, liquefied natural gas, etc.

The oil tanker has the cargo carrying section of the vessel split up into individual tanks by longitudinal and transverse bulkheads (*Figure 1.2*).

The size and location of these cargo tanks is dictated by the International Maritime Organisation Convention MARPOL 1973/78. This convention and its protocol of 1978 also requires the use of segregated ballast tanks (SBT) and their location such that they provide a barrier against accidental oil spillage. An oil tanker when on a ballast voyage may only use its segregated ballast tanks in order to obtain a safe operating condition. No sea water may be loaded into cargo tanks. The cargo is discharged by cargo pumps fitted in one or more pumprooms, either at the ends of the tank section or, sometimes, in the middle. Each tank has its own suction arrangement which connects to the pumps, and a network of piping discharges the cargo to the deck from where it is pumped ashore. Fore and aft peak tanks are used for ballast with, often, a pair of wing tanks situated just forward of midships. These wing tanks are ballast-only tanks and are empty when the ship is fully loaded. Small slop tanks are fitted at the after end of the cargo section and are used for the normal carriage of oil on loaded voyages. On ballast runs the slop tanks are used for storing the contaminated residue from tank cleaning operations.

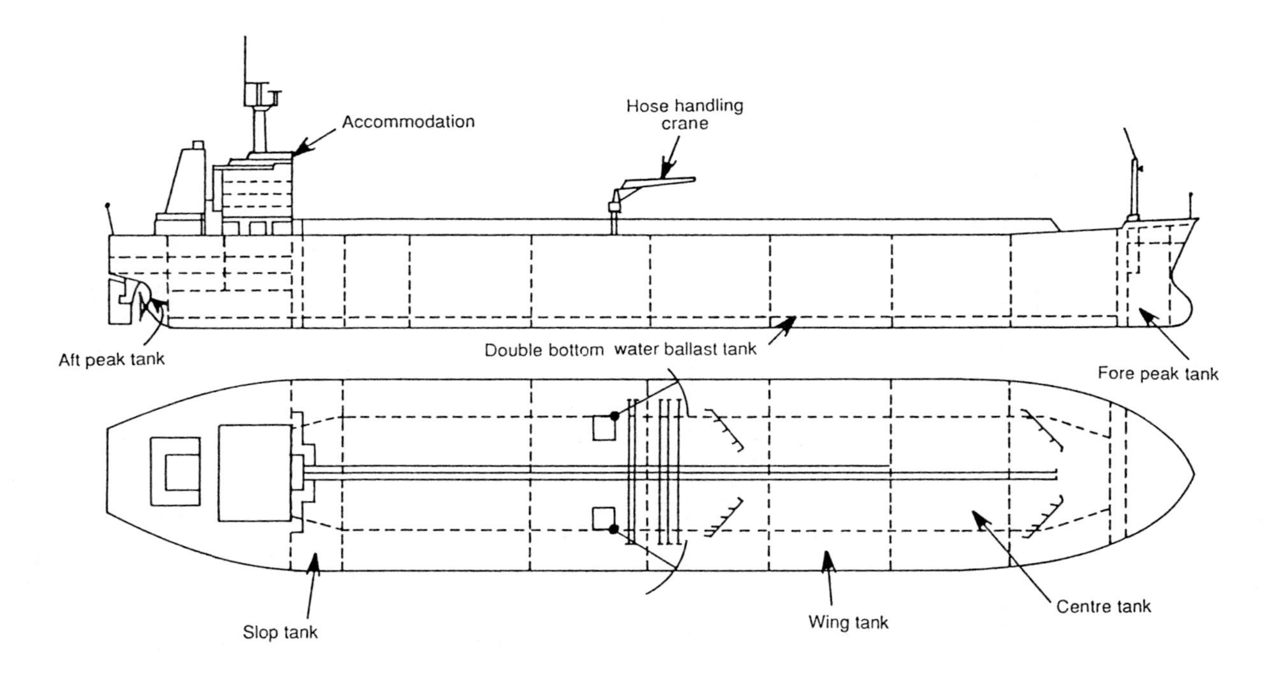

Figure 1.2 Oil tanker

Large amounts of piping are to be seen on the deck running from the pumprooms to the discharge manifolds positioned at midships, port and starboard. Hose handling derricks are fitted port and starboard near the manifolds. The accommodation spaces and machinery spaces are located aft in modern tankers. The range of sizes for oil tankers at present is enormous, from small to 700 000 deadweight tonnes. Speeds range from 12 to 16 knots. Oil tankers are dealt with in more detail in Chapter 8.

Chemical tankers

A chemical tanker is a vessel constructed to carry liquids cargoes other than crude oil and products, or those requiring cooling or pressurised tanks. Chemical tankers may carry chemicals or even such liquids as wine, molasses or vegetable oils. Many of the chemical cargoes carried create a wide range of hazards from reactivity, corrosivity, toxicity and flammability. Rules and regulations relating to their construction consider the effects these hazards have on the ship and its environment with respect to materials, structure, cargo containment and handling arrangements.

The International Maritime Organisation (IMO) has produced the 'Code for the Construction and Equipment of Ships Carrying Dangerous Chemicals in Bulk'. This code provides a basis for all such vessel designs, and the IMO Certificate of Fitness must be obtained from the flag state administration to indicate compliance. Also, Annex II of the MARPOL 73/78 Convention and Protocol is now in force and applies to hazardous liquid substances carried in chemical tankers.

An IMO type II (see Chapter 9) chemical tanker is shown in *Figure 1.3*. A double skin is used to protectively locate all the cargo tanks and even extends over the top. The cargo tank interiors are smooth with all stiffeners and structure within the double skin. Corrugated bulkheads subdivide the cargo-carrying section into individual tanks. The double skin region of the double bottom and the ship sides are arranged as water ballast tanks for ballast only voyages or trimming and heeling when loaded.

Individual deepwell pumps are fitted in each cargo tank and also in the two slop tanks which are positioned between tanks 4 and 5.

Deadweight sizes for chemical tankers range from small coastal vessels up to about 46 000 tonnes with speeds of about 14–16 knots.

Liquefied gas tankers

Liquefied gas tankers are used to carry, usually at low temperature, liquefied petroleum gas (LPG) or liquefied natural gas (LNG). A separate inner tank is usually employed to contain the liquid and this tank is supported by the outer hull which has a double bottom (*Figure 1.4*).

LNG tankers carry methane and other paraffin products obtained as a by-product of petroleum drilling operations. The gas is carried at atmospheric pressure and temperatures as low as −164°C in tanks of special materials (see *Table 2.3*), which can accept the low temperature. The tanks used may be prismatic, cylindrical or

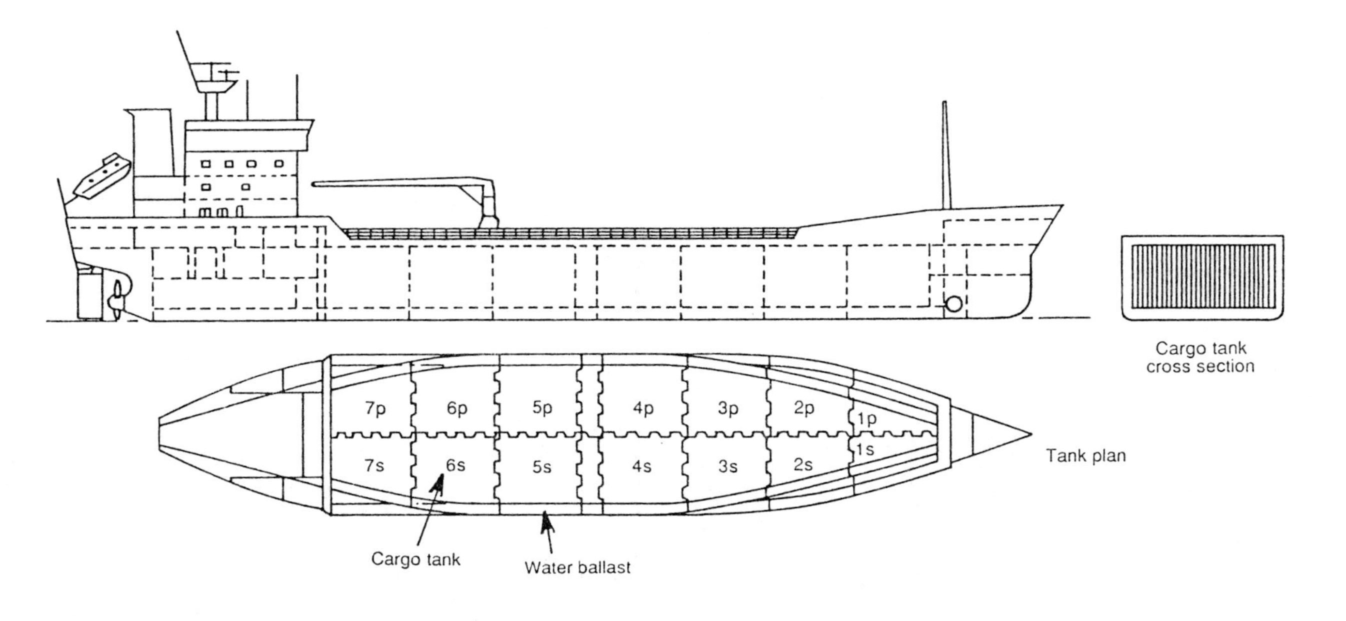

Figure 1.3 IMO type II chemical tanker

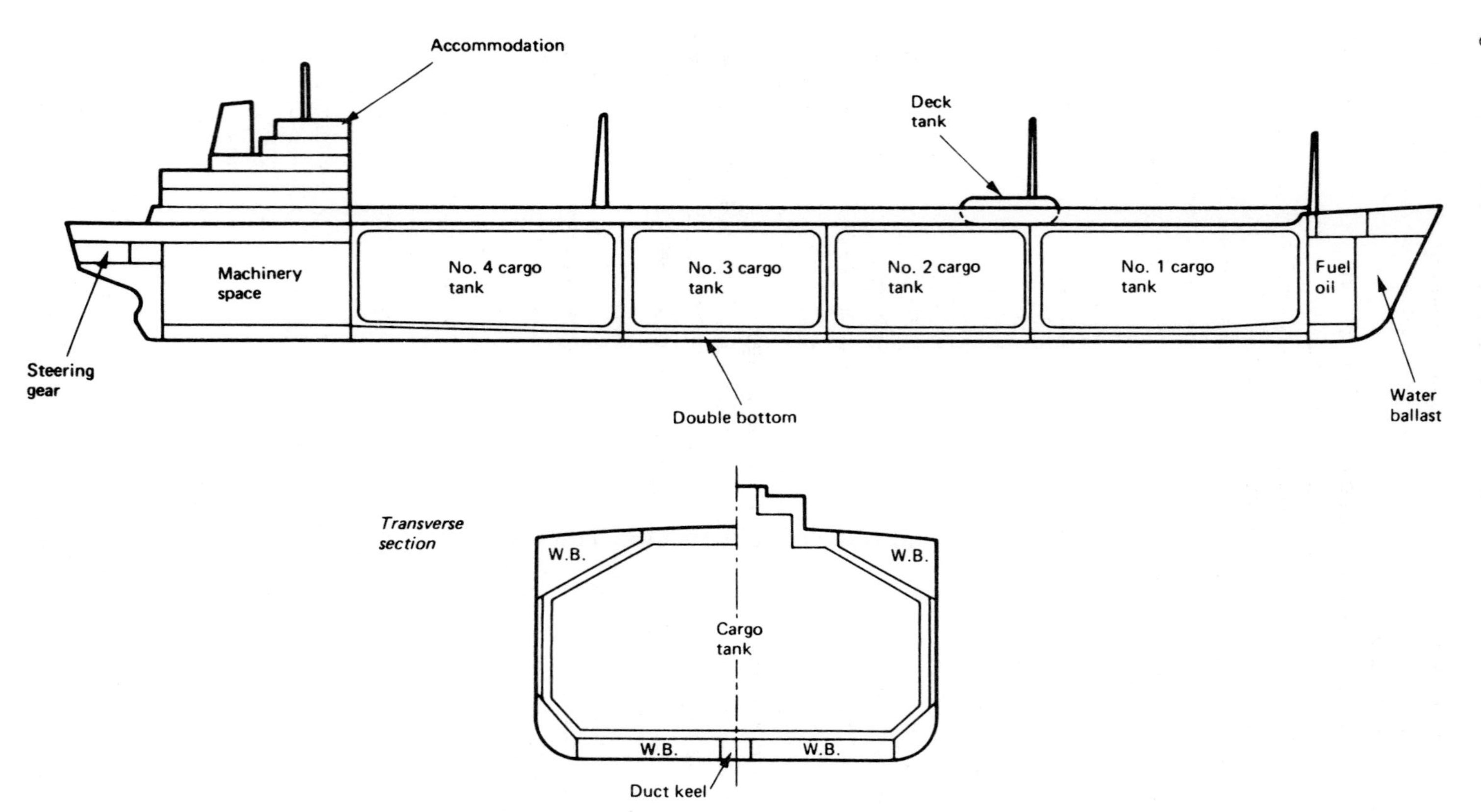

Figure 1.4 Liquefied petroleum gas (LPG) tanker (W.B.; water ballast tanks)

spherical in shape and self-supporting or of membrane construction. The containing tank is separated from the hull by insulation which also acts as a secondary barrier in the event of leakage.

LPG tankers carry propane, butane, propylene, etc., which are extracted from natural gas. The gases are carried either fully pressurised, part pressurised–part refrigerated, or fully refrigerated. The fully pressurised tank operates at 18 bar and ambient temperature, the fully refrigerated tank at 0.25 bar and –50°C. Separate containment tanks within the hull are used and are surrounded by insulation where low temperatures are employed. Tank shapes are either prismatic, spherical or cylindrical. Low temperature steels may be used on the hull where it acts as a secondary barrier.

Displacement sizes for gas carriers range up to 60 000 tonnes, with speeds of 12–16 knots. Liquefied gas carriers are dealt with in more detail in Chapter 9.

Bulk carriers

Bulk carriers are single deck vessels which transport single commodity cargoes such as grain, sugar and ores in bulk. The cargo carrying section of the ship is divided into holds or tanks which may have any number of arrangements, depending on the range of cargoes to be carried. Combination carriers are bulk carriers designed for flexibility of operation and able to transport any one of several bulk cargoes on any one voyage, e.g. ore, or crude oil, or dry bulk cargo.

The general purpose bulk carrier, in which usually the centre hold section only is used for cargo, is shown in *Figures 1.5* and *1.6*. The partitioned tanks which surround it are used for ballast purposes either on ballast voyages or, in the case of the saddle tanks, to raise the ship's centre of gravity when a low density cargo is carried. Some of the double-bottom tanks may be used for fuel oil and fresh water. The saddle tanks also serve to shape the upper region of the cargo hold and trim the cargo. Large hatchways are a feature of bulk carriers, since they reduce cargo-handling time during loading and unloading.

An ore carrier has two longitudinal bulkheads which divide the cargo section into wing tanks port and starboard, and the centre hold which is used for ore. The high double bottom is a feature of ore carriers. On ballast voyages the wing tanks and double bottoms provide ballast capacity. On loaded voyages the ore is carried in the central hold, and the high double bottom serves to raise the centre of gravity of this very dense cargo. The vessel's behaviour at sea is thus much improved. The cross-section is similar to that of the ore/oil carrier shown in *Figure 1.6*. Two longitudinal bulkheads are employed to divide the ship into centre and wing tanks which are used for the carriage of oil cargoes. When ore is carried, only the centre tank section is used for cargo. A double bottom is fitted beneath the centre tank but is used only for water ballast. The bulkheads and hatches must be oiltight.

The ore/bulk/oil carrier has a cross-section similar to the general bulk carrier shown in *Figure 1.5*. The structure is, however, significantly stronger, since the bulkheads must be oiltight and the double bottom must withstand the high density ore load. Only the central tank or hold carries cargo, the other tank areas being

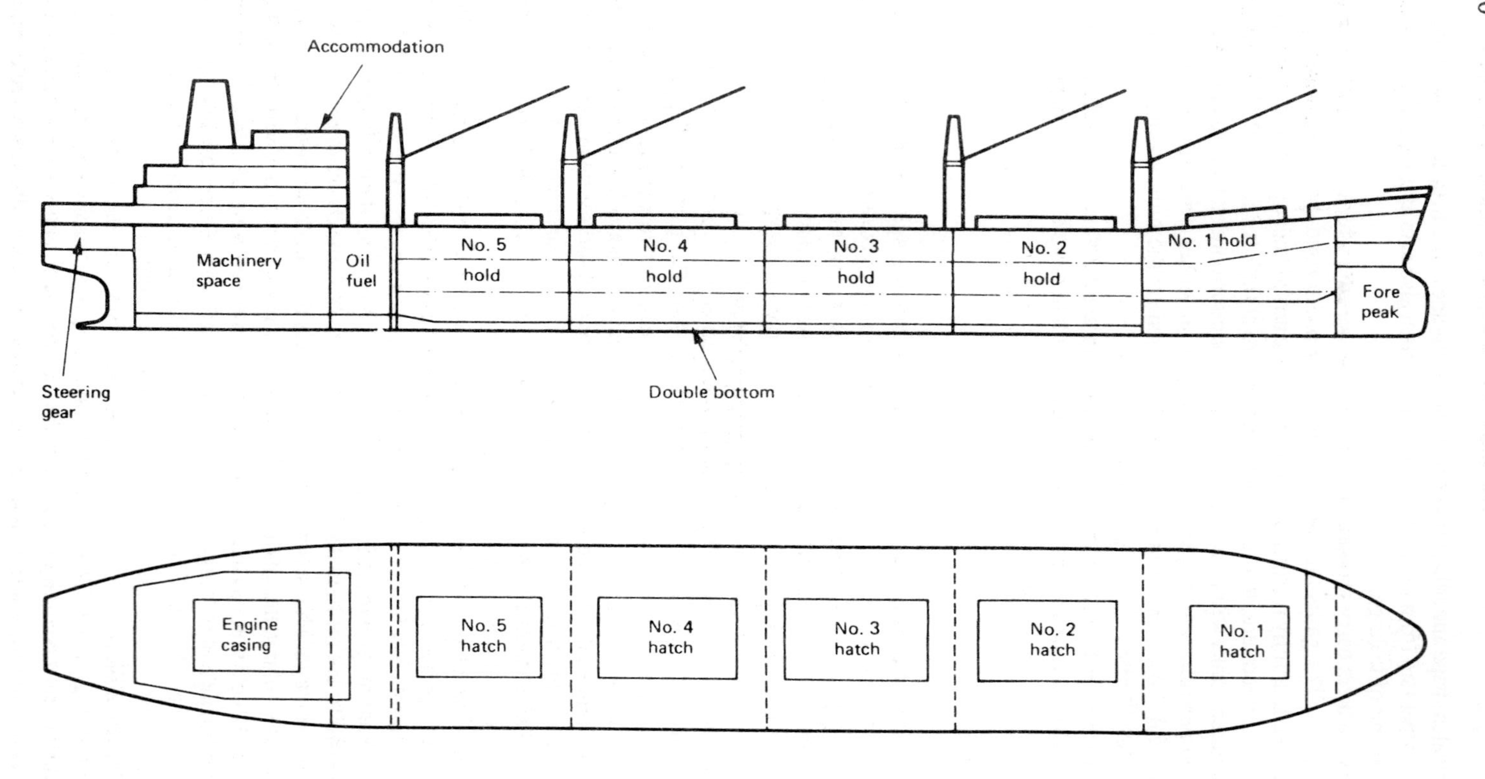

Figure 1.5 ***Bulk carrier***

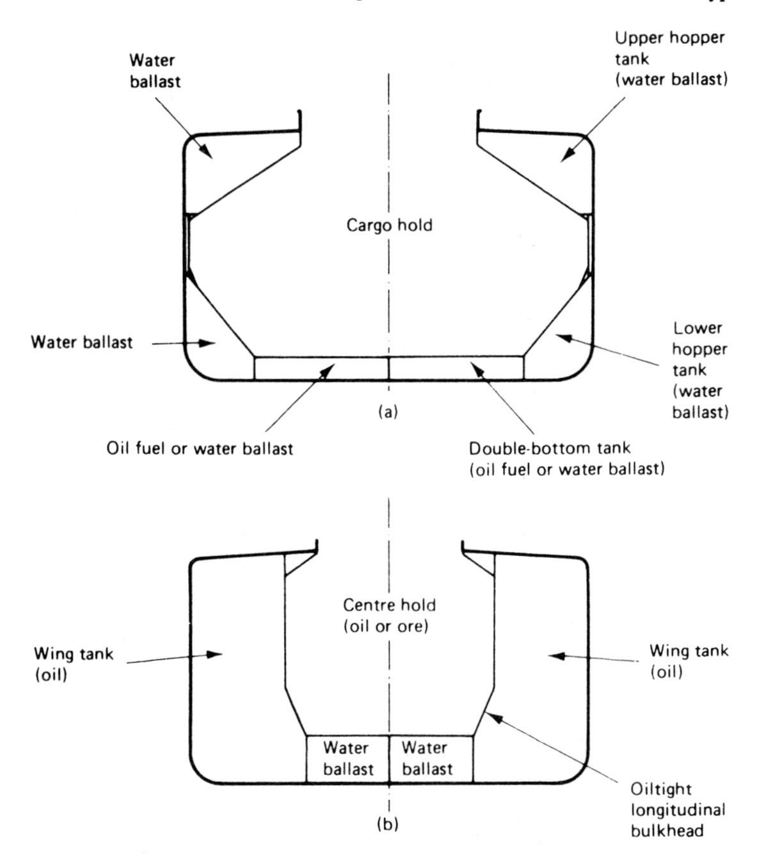

Figure 1.6 Transverse sections: (a) bulk carrier, (b) ore/oil carrier

ballast-only spaces, except the double bottom which may carry oil fuel or fresh water.

Large hatches are a feature of all bulk carriers, to facilitate rapid simple cargo handling. A large proportion of bulk carriers do not carry cargo-handling equipment, because they trade between special terminals which have particular equipment for loading and unloading bulk commodities. The availability of cargo-handling gear does increase the flexibility of a vessel and for this reason it is sometimes fitted. Combination carriers handling oil cargoes have their own cargo pumps, piping systems, etc., for discharging oil. Bulk carriers are dealt with in more detail in Chapter 8. Deadweight capacities range from small to 150,000 tonnes depending upon type of cargo, etc. Speeds are in the range 12–16 knots.

Container ships

The container ship is, as its name implies, designed for the carriage of containers. A container is a re-usable box of 2435 mm by 2345 mm section, with lengths of

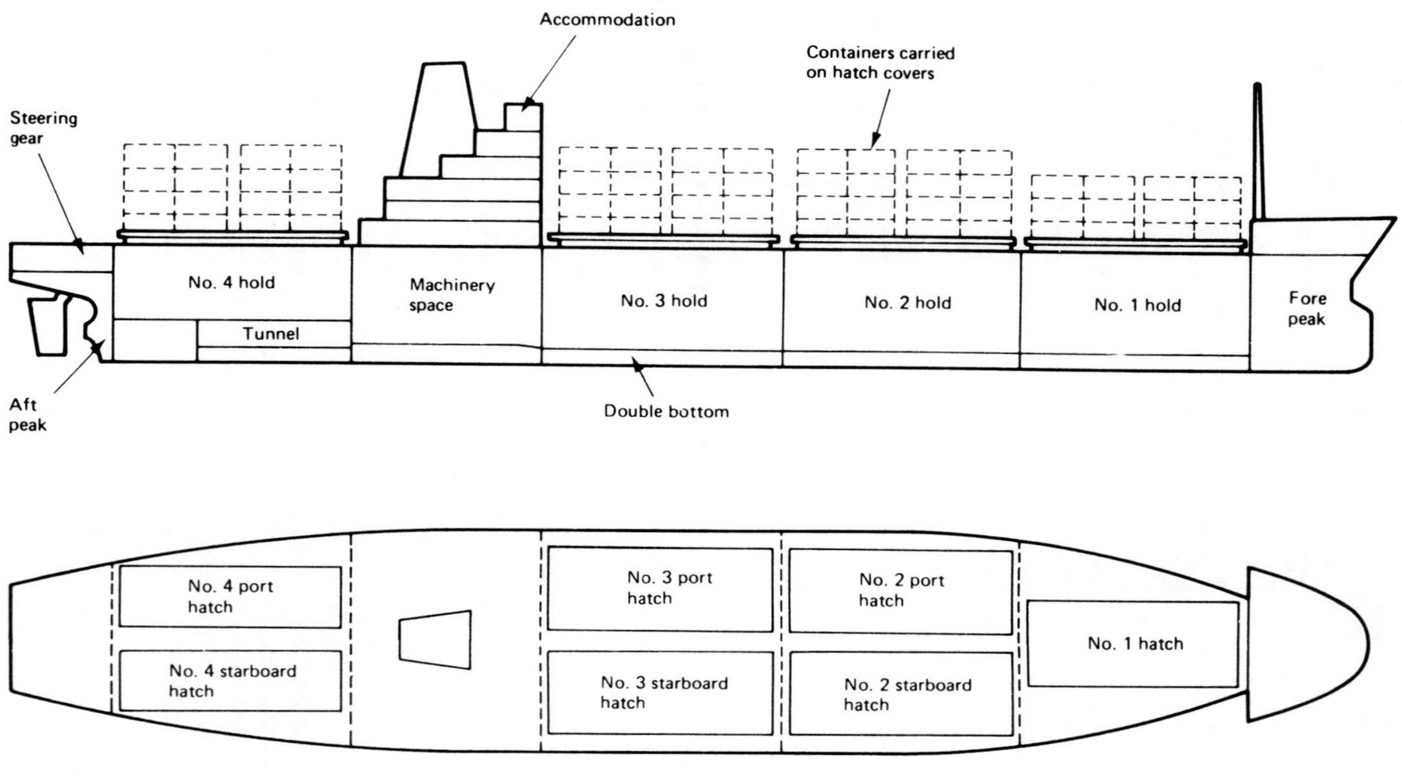

Figure 1.7 Container ship

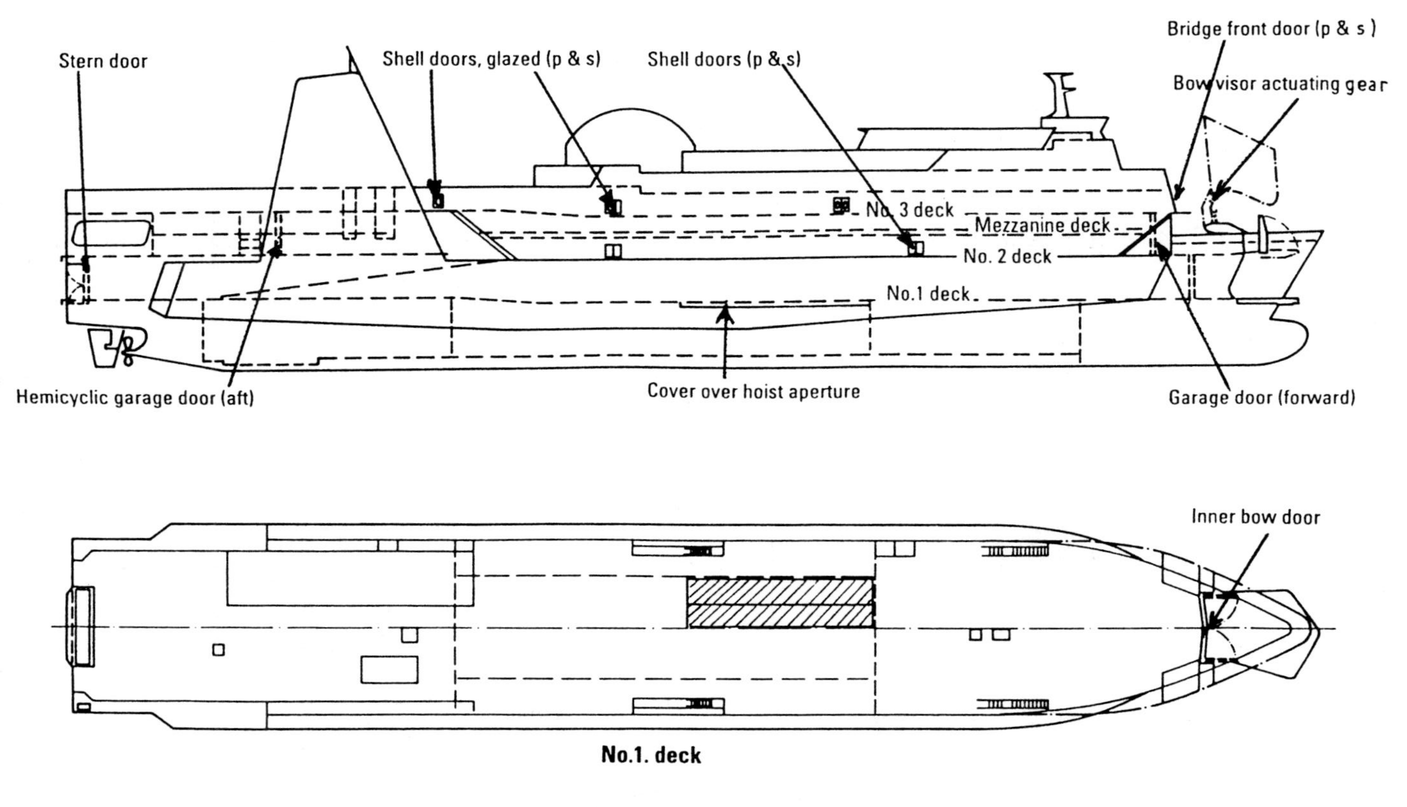

Figure 1.8 Roll-on roll-off ferry

6055, 9125 and 12 190 mm. Containers are in use for most general cargoes, and liquid-carrying versions also exist. In addition, refrigerated models are in use.

The cargo-carrying section of the ship is divided into several holds which have hatch openings the full width and length of the hold (*Figure 1.7*). The containers are racked in special frameworks and stacked one upon the other within the hold space. Cargo handling therefore consists only of vertical movement of the cargo in the hold. Containers can also be stacked on the hatch covers when a low density cargo is carried. Special lashing arrangements exist for this purpose and this deck cargo to some extent compensates for the loss of underdeck capacity.

The various cargo holds are separated by a deep web-framed structure to provide the ship with transverse strength. The ship section outboard of the containers on each side is a box-like arrangement of wing tanks which provides longitudinal strength to the structure. These wing tanks may be utilised for water ballast and can be arranged to counter the heeling of the ship when discharging containers. A double bottom is also fitted which adds to the longitudinal strength and provides additional ballast space.

Accommodation and machinery spaces are usually located aft to provide the maximum length of full-bodied ship for container stowage. Cargo-handling gear is rarely fitted, as these ships travel between specially equipped terminals for rapid loading and discharge. Container ship sizes vary considerably with container-carrying capacities from 100 to 4000 or more. As specialist carriers they are designed for rapid transits and are high powered, high speed vessels with speeds up to 30 knots. Some of the larger vessels have triple-screw propulsion arrangements.

Container ships are described in more detail in Chapter 8.

Roll-on roll-off ships

This design of vessel was originally intended for wheeled cargo in the form of trailers. Rapid loading and unloading is possible by the use of bow or stern ramps. A loss of cargo carrying capacity occurs because of the vehicle undercarriages and this has resulted in the adoption of this type of vessel to either carry containers as a deck cargo or its use as a ferry with appropriate accommodation provided for passengers.

A ro-ro ferry is shown in *Figure 1.8*. The cargo carrying section is a series of large open decks with vehicle hoists and ramps connecting them. A bow visor and flap enables vehicles to leave or enter through the bow and a stern door provides similar arrangements aft.

The ship's structure outboard of the cargo decks is a box-like arrangement of wing tanks to provide longitudinal strength. A double bottom extends throughout the cargo and machinery space. A low height machinery space is necessary to avoid penetration of the vehicle decks. The passenger accommodation extends along the vessels length above the vehicle decks.

Ocean-going ro-ro vessels may be designed for the carriage of containers on deck and with one or more hatches to load containers or general cargo in the vehicle deck space. Sizes range considerably with about 16 000 deadweight tonnes (28 000 displacement tonnes) being common. Speeds in the region of 18–22 knots are usual.

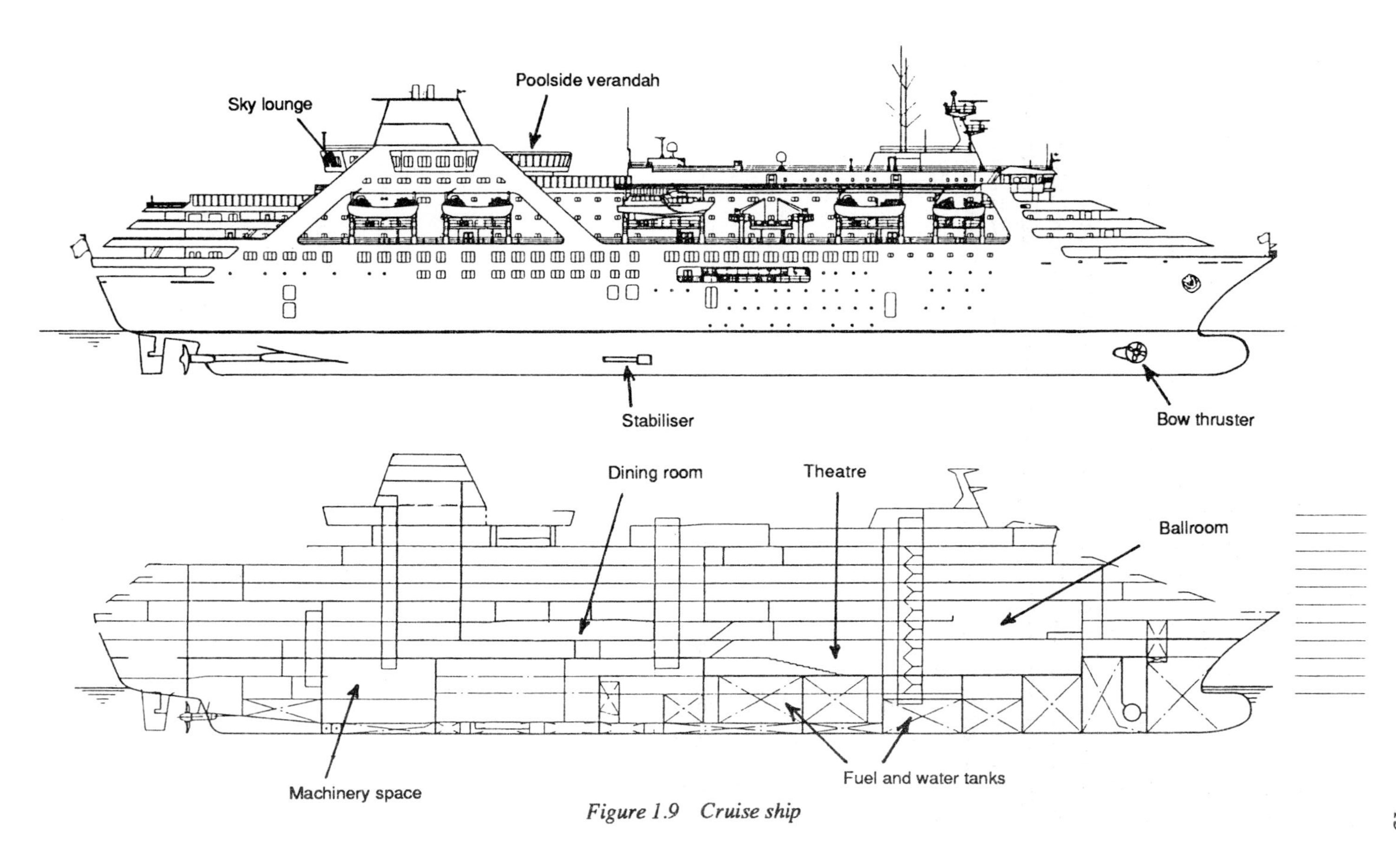

Figure 1.9 Cruise ship

Passenger ships

The passenger liner, or its modern equivalent the cruise liner, exists to provide a means of luxurious transport between interesting destinations, in pleasant climates, for its human cargo. The passenger travelling in such a ship pays for, and expects, a superior standard of accommodation and leisure facilities. Large amounts of superstructure are therefore an interesting feature of passenger ships. Several tiers of decks are fitted with large open lounges, ballrooms, swimming pools and promenade areas (*Figure 1.9*).

Aesthetically pleasing lines are evident, with usually well-raked clipper-type bows and unusual funnel shapes. Stabilisers are fitted to reduce rolling and bow thrust devices are employed for improved manoeuvrability. Large passenger liners are rare, the moderate-sized cruise liner of 12 000 tonnes displacement now being the more prevalent. Passenger-carrying capacity is around 600, with speed in the region of 22 knots.

2

Ship Stresses and Shipbuilding Materials

The ship at sea or lying in still water is constantly being subjected to a wide variety of stresses and strains, which result from the action of forces from outside and within the ship. Forces within the ship result from structural weight, cargo, machinery weight and the effects of operating machinery. Exterior forces include the hydrostatic pressure of the water on the hull and the action of the wind and waves. The ship must at all times be able to resist and withstand these stresses and strains throughout its structure. It must therefore be constructed in a manner, and of such materials, that will provide the necessary strength. The ship must also be able to function efficiently as a cargo-carrying vessel.

The various forces acting on a ship are constantly varying in degree and frequency. For simplicity, however, they will be considered individually and the particular measures adopted to counter each type of force will be outlined.

The forces may initially be classified as static and dynamic. Static forces are due to the differences in weight and buoyancy which occur at various points along the length of the ship. Dynamic forces result from the ship's motion in the sea and the action of the wind and waves. A ship is free to move with six degrees of freedom—three linear and three rotational. These motions are described by the terms shown in *Figure 2.1*.

These static and dynamic forces create longitudinal, transverse and local stresses in the ship's structure. Longitudinal stresses are greatest in magnitude and result in bending of the ship along its length.

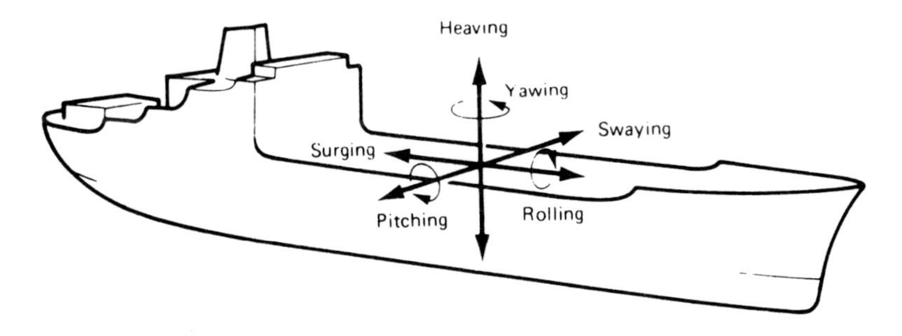

Figure 2.1 Ship movement—the six degrees of freedom

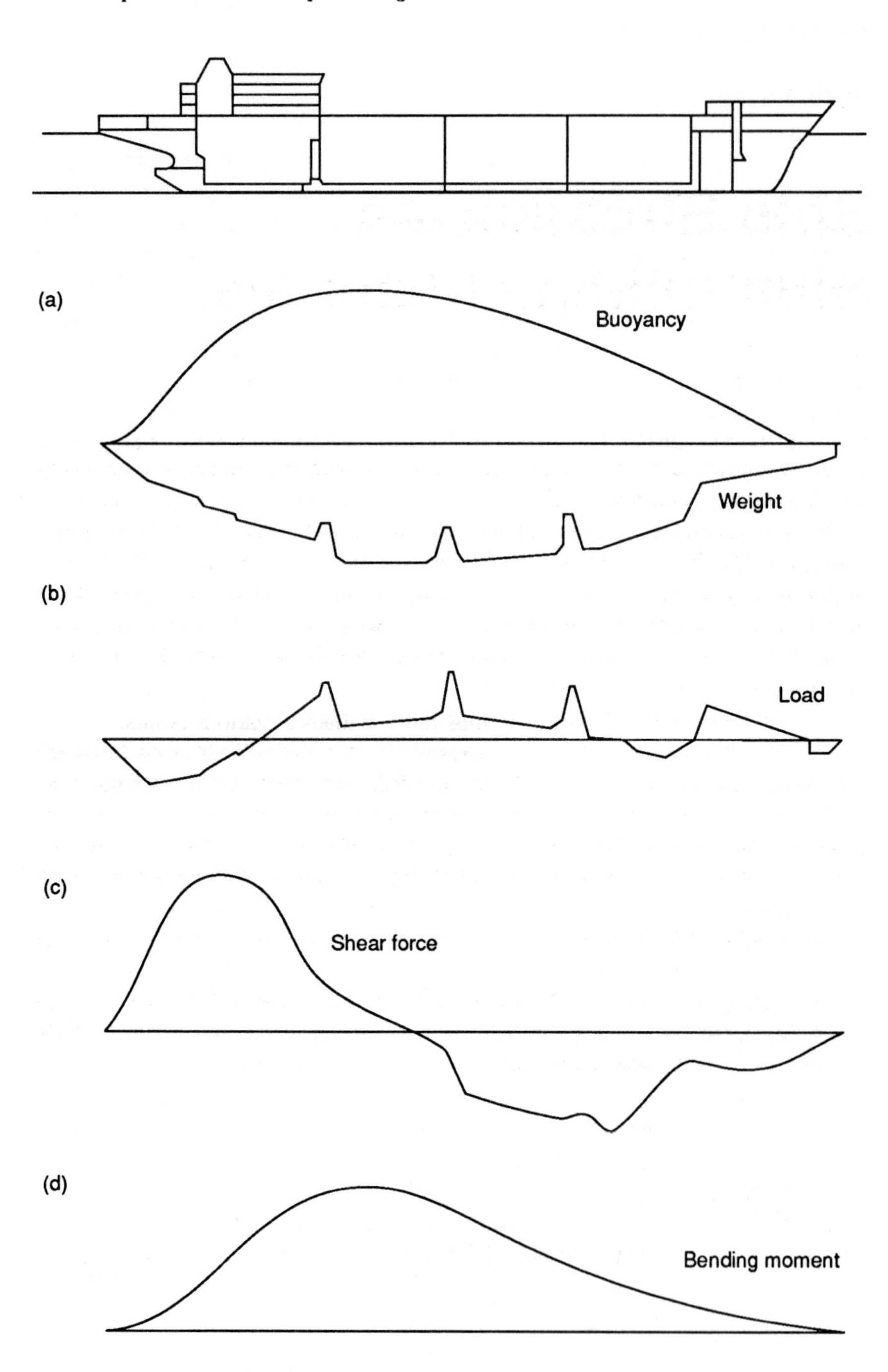

Figure 2.2 Static loading of a ship's structure

Longitudinal stresses

Static loading

Consider a ship floating in still water. Two different forces will be acting upon it along its length. The weight of the ship and its contents will be acting vertically downwards. The buoyancy or vertical component of hydrostatic pressure will be acting upwards. In total, the two forces exactly equal and balance one another such that the ship floats at some particular draught. The centre of the buoyancy force and the centre of the weight will be vertically in line. However, at various points along the ship's length there may be an excess of buoyancy or an excess of weight. Consider the curve of buoyancy, which represents the upward force at various points along the length of the ship, see *Figure 2.2 (a)*. The buoyancy forces increase from zero at the ends of the ship's waterline to a constant value over the parallel middle body section. The area within the curve represents the total upthrust or buoyancy exerted by the water.

The total weight of the ship is made up of the steel structure, items of machinery, cargo, etc. The actual weight at various points along the length of the ship is unevenly distributed and is represented by a weight curve as shown in *Figure 2.2 (a)*. The weight curve actually starts and finishes at the extremes of the ship's structure.

At different points along the ship's length the weight may exceed the buoyancy, or vice versa. Where a difference occurs this results in a load at that point. The load diagram, (*Figure 2.2 (b)*), is used to illustrate the loads at various points.

This loading of the ship's structure results in forces which act up or down and create shearing forces. The shear force at any point is the vertical force acting. It can also be considered as the total load acting on either side of the point or section considered. The actual shearing force at any section is, in effect, the area of the load diagram to the point considered. A shear force diagram can thus be drawn for the ship (*Figure 2.2 (c)*).

The loading of the ship's structure will also tend to bend it. The bending moment at any point is the sum of the various moments to one side or the other. The bending moment at a section is also represented by the area of the shear force diagram to the point considered. A bending moment diagram is illustrated in *Figure 2.2 (d)*, where it can be seen that the maximum bending moment occurs when the shear force is zero.

Since a bending moment acts on the ship then it will tend to bend along its length. This still water bending moment (SWBM) condition will cause the ship to take up one of two possible extreme conditions. If the buoyancy forces in the region of midships are greater than the weight then the ship will curve upwards or 'hog', (*Figure 2.3*). If the weight amidships is greater than the buoyancy forces then the ship will curve downwards or 'sag' (*Figure 2.4*).

Dynamic loading

If the ship is now considered to be moving among waves, the distribution of weight is the same. The distribution of buoyancy, however, will vary as a result of the waves. The movement of the ship will also introduce dynamic forces.

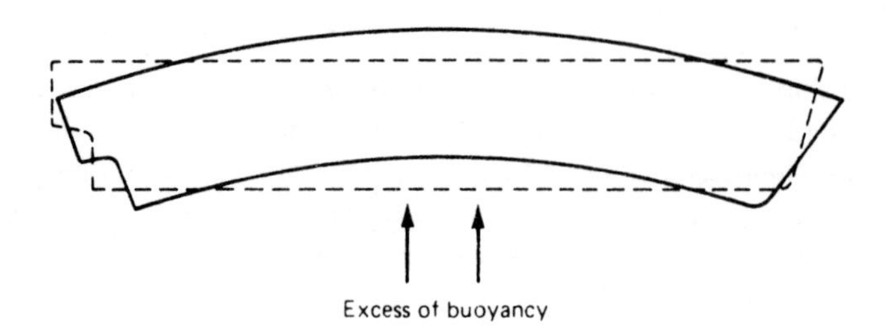

Figure 2.3 Hogging condition

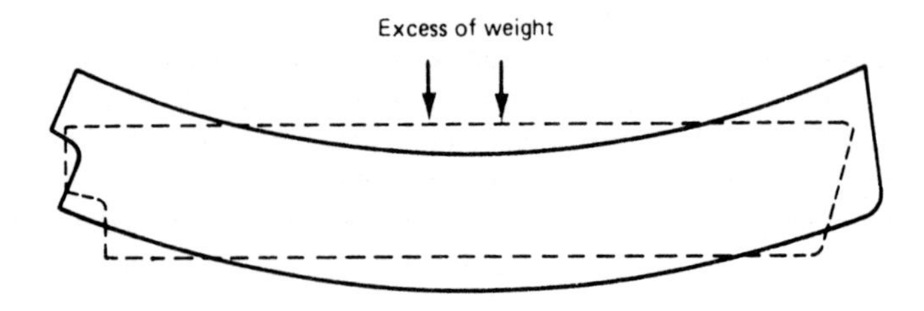

Figure 2.4 Sagging condition

The traditional approach to solving this problem is to convert the dynamic problem into an equivalent static one. To do this, the ship is assumed to be balanced on a static wave the same length as the ship.

If the wave crest is considered at midships then the buoyancy in this region will be increased. With the wave trough positioned at the ends of the ship, the buoyancy here will be reduced. This loading condition will result in a significantly increased bending moment which will cause the ship to hog (*Figure 2.5 (c)*). This will be an extreme condition giving the maximum bending moment that can occur in the ship's structure for this condition.

If the wave trough is now considered at midships then the buoyancy in this region will be reduced. With the wave crests positioned at the ends of the ship, the buoyancy here will be increased. This loading condition will result in a bending moment which will cause the ship to sag (*Figure 2.5 (b)*). Since the ship in its still water condition is considered to hog, then this change to a sagging condition has required a bending moment to overcome the initial hogging bending moment in addition to creating sagging. The actual bending moment in this condition is therefore considerable and, again, it is an extreme condition.

If actual loading conditions for the ship which will make the above conditions worse are considered, i.e. heavy loads amidships when the wave trough is amidships, then the maximum bending moments in normal operating service can be found.

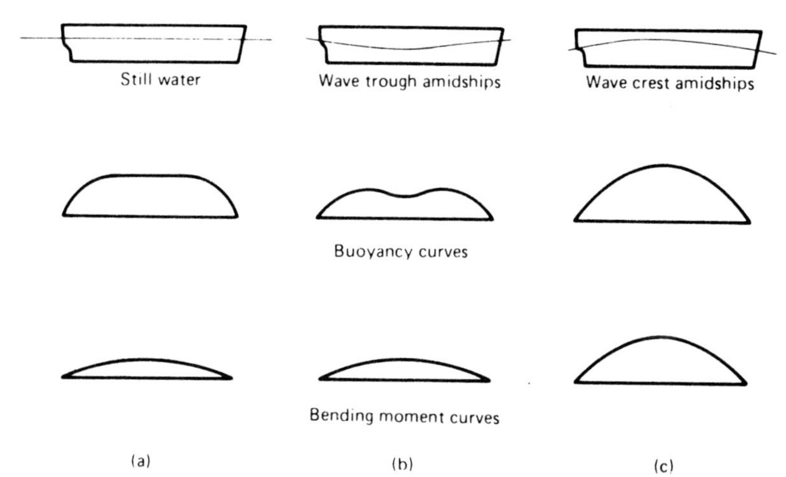

Figure 2.5 Dynamic loading of a ship's structure: (a) still water condition; (b) sagging condition; (c) hogging condition

The ship's structure will thus be subjected to constantly fluctuating stresses resulting from these shear forces and bending moments as waves move along the ship's length.

Stressing of the structure

The bending of a ship causes stresses to be set up within its structure. When a ship sags, tensile stresses are set up in the bottom shell plating and compressive stresses are set up in the deck. When the ship hogs, tensile stresses occur in the decks and compressive stresses in the bottom shell. This stressing, whether compressive or tensile, reduces in magnitude towards a position known as the neutral axis. The neutral axis in a ship is somewhere below half the depth and is, in effect, a horizontal line drawn through the centre of gravity of the ship's section.

The fundamental bending equation for a beam is

$$\frac{M}{I} = \frac{\sigma}{y}$$

where M is the bending moment, I is the second moment of area of the section about its neutral axis, σ is the stress at the outer fibres, and y is the distance from the neutral axis to the outer fibres.

This equation has been proved in full-scale tests to be applicable to the longitudinal bending of a ship. From the equation the expression

$$\sigma = \frac{M}{I/y}$$

is obtained for the stress in the material at some distance y from the neutral axis. The values M, I and y can be determined for the ship, and the resulting stresses in the deck and bottom shell can be found. The ratio I/y is known as the section modulus, Z, when y is measured to the extreme edge of the section. The values are determined for the midship section, since the greatest moment will occur at or near midships (*Figure 2.2*).

The structural material included in the calculation for the second moment I will be all the longitudinal material which extends for a considerable proportion of the ship's length. This material will include side and bottom shell plating, inner bottom plating (where fitted), centre girders and decks. The material forms what is known as the hull girder, whose dimensions are very large compared to its thickness.

Transverse stresses

Static loading

A transverse section of a ship is subjected to static pressure from the surrounding water in addition to the loading resulting from the weight of the structure, cargo, etc. Although transverse stresses are of lesser magnitude than longitudinal stresses, considerable distortion of the structure could occur, in the absence of adequate stiffening (*Figure 2.6*).

The parts of the structure which resist transverse stresses are transverse bulkheads, floors in the double bottom (where fitted), deck beams, side frames and the brackets between them and adjacent structure such as tank top flooring or margin plates.

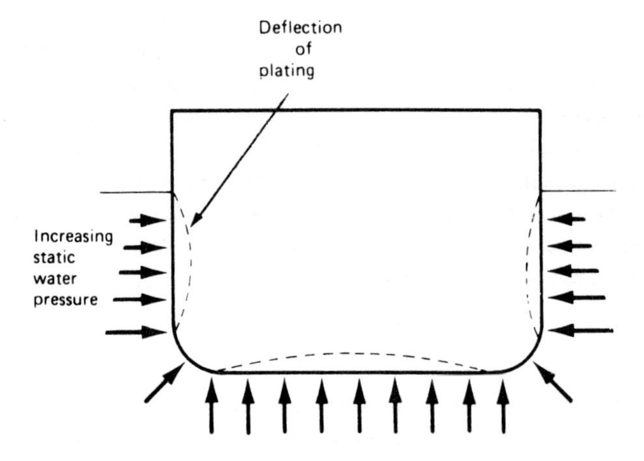

Figure 2.6 Static water pressure loading of a ship's structure

Dynamic stresses

When a ship is rolling it is accelerated and decelerated, resulting in forces in the structure tending to distort it. This condition is known as racking and its greatest effect is felt when the ship is in the light or ballast condition (*Figure 2.7*). The

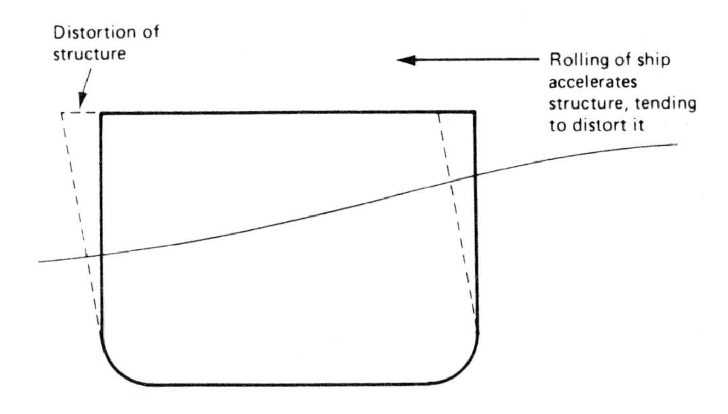

Figure 2.7 Racking

brackets and beam knees joining horizontal and vertical items of structure are used to resist this distortion.

Localised stresses

The movement of a ship in a seaway results in forces being generated which are largely of a local nature. These forces are, however, liable to cause the structure to vibrate and thus transmit stresses to other parts of the structure.

Slamming or pounding

In heavy weather, when the ship is heaving and pitching, the forward end leaves and re-enters the water with a slamming effect (*Figure 2.8*). This slamming down of the forward region on to the water is known as pounding. Additional stiffening must be fitted in the pounding region to reduce the possibility of damage to the structure. This is discussed further in Section A of Chapter 5.

Panting

The movement of waves along a ship causes fluctuations in water pressure on the plating. This tends to create an in-and-out movement of the shell plating, known as panting. The effect is particularly evident at the bows as the ship pushes its way through the water.

The pitching motion of the ship produces additional variations in water pressure, particularly at the bow and stern, which also cause panting of the plating. Additional stiffening is provided in the form of panting beams and stringers. This is discussed further in Section D of Chapter 5.

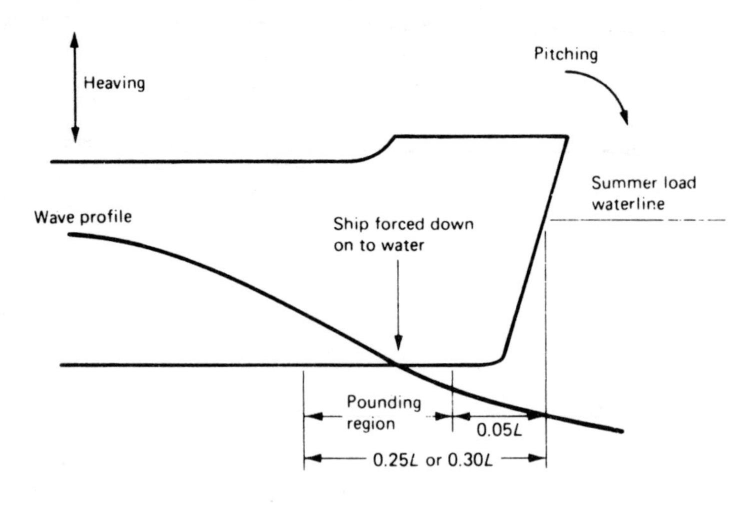

Figure 2.8 Pounding

Localised loading

Heavy weights, such as equipment in the machinery spaces or particular items of general cargo, can give rise to localised distortion of the transverse section (*Figure 2.9*). Arrangements for spreading the load, additional stiffening and thicker plating are methods used in dealing with this problem.

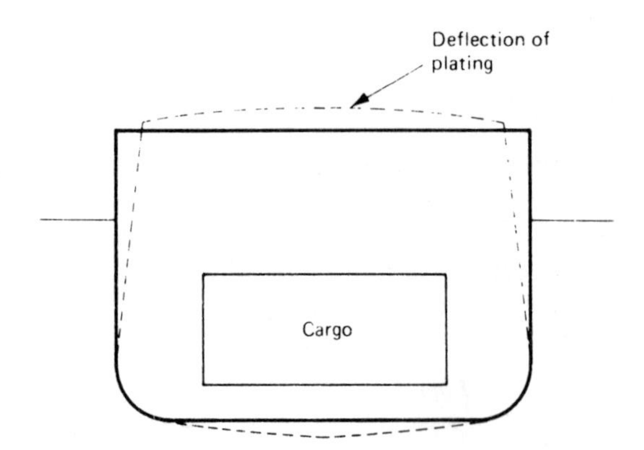

Figure 2.9 Localised loads tending to distort the ship's structure

Superstructures and discontinuities

The ends of superstructures represent major discontinuities in the ship's structure where a considerable change in section modulus occurs. Localised stresses will occur which may result in cracking of adjacent structure. Sharp discontinuities are therefore to be avoided by the introduction of gradual tapers. Thicker strakes of deck and shell plating may also be fitted at these points.

Any holes or openings cut in decks create similar areas of high local stress. Well-rounded corners must be used where openings are necessary, and doubling plates may also be fitted. In the case of hatchways the bulk of the longitudinal strength material is concentrated outboard of the hatch openings on either side to reduce the change in section modulus at the openings. This is discussed further in Sections B and F of Chapter 5.

Vibrations

Vibrations set up in a ship due to reciprocating machinery, propellers, etc., can result in the setting up of stresses in the structure. These are cyclic stresses which could result in fatigue failure of local items of structure leading to more general collapse. Balancing of machinery and adequate propeller tip clearances can reduce the effects of vibration to acceptable proportions. Apart from possible damage to equipment and structure, the presence of vibration can be most uncomfortable to any passengers and the crew.

The design of the structure is outside the scope of this book. The various shipbuilding materials used to provide the structure will now be considered.

Steel

Steel is the basic shipbuilding material in use today. Steel may be regarded as an iron–carbon alloy, usually containing other elements, the carbon content not usually exceeding about 2%. Special steels of high tensile strength are used on certain highly stressed parts of the ship's structure. Aluminium alloys have particular applications in the construction of superstructures, especially on passenger ships.

Production

'Acid' or 'basic' are terms often used when referring to steels. The reference is to the production process and the type of furnace lining, e.g. an alkaline or basic lining is used to produce basic steel. The choice of furnace lining is dictated by the raw materials used in the manufacture of the steel. There are three particular processes currently used for the manufacture of carbon steel, namely the open hearth process, the oxygen or basic oxygen steel process and the electric furnace process. In all these processes the hot molten metal is exposed to air or oxygen which oxidises the impurities to refine the pig iron into high quality steel.

In the open hearth process a long shallow furnace is used which is fired from both ends. A high proportion of steel scrap may be used in this process. High quality steel is produced whose properties can be controlled by the addition of suitable alloying elements.

In the oxygen or basic oxygen steel process the molten metal is contained in a basic lined furnace. A jet of oxygen is injected into the molten metal by an overhead lance. Alloying elements can be introduced into the molten metal and a high quality steel is produced.

In the electric furnace process an electric arc is struck between carbon electrodes and the steel charge in the furnace. Accurate control of the final composition of the steel and a high standard of purity are possible with this process.

Finishing treatment

Steels from the above-mentioned processes will all contain an excess of oxygen, usually in the form of iron oxide. Several finishing treatments are possible in the final casting of the steel.

Rimmed steel is produced as a result of little or no treatment to remove oxygen. In the molten state the oxygen combines with the carbon in the steel, releasing carbon monoxide gas. On solidifying, an almost pure iron outer surface is formed. The central core of the ingot is, however, a mass of blow holes. Hot rolling of the ingot usually 'welds up' these holes but thick plate of this material are prone to laminations.

Killed steel is produced by fixing the oxygen by the addition of aluminium or silicon before pouring the steel into the mould. The aluminium or silicon produces oxides reducing the iron oxides to iron. A homogeneous material of superior quality to rimmed steel is thus produced.

Balanced or semi-killed steels are an intermediate form of steel. This results from the beginning of the rimming process in the mould and its termination by the use of deoxidisers.

Vacuum degassed steels are produced by reducing the atmospheric pressure when the steel is in the molten state. The equilibrium between carbon and oxygen is thus obtained at a much lower level and the oxygen content becomes very small. Final residual deoxidation can be achieved with the minimum additions of aluminium or silicon. A very 'clean' steel is produced with good notch toughness properties and freedom from lamellar tearing problems (lamellar tearing is explained in Chapter 4).

The composition of steel has a major influence on its properties and this will be discussed in the next subsection. The properties of steel are further improved by various forms of heat treatment which will now be outlined. In simplified terms the heat treatment of steels results in a change in the grain structure which alters the mechanical properties of the material.

Normalising The steel is heated to a temperature of 850–950°C depending upon its carbon content and then allowed to cool in air. A hard strong steel with a refined grain structure is produced.

Annealing Again the steel is heated to around 850–950°C, but is cooled slowly either in the furnace or in an insulated space. A softer, more ductile steel than that in the normalised condition is produced.

Hardening The steel is heated to 850–950°C and then rapidly cooled by quenching in oil or water. The hardest possible condition for the particular steel is thus produced and the tensile strength is increased.

Tempering This process follows the quenching of steel and involves reheating to some temperature up to about 680°C. The higher the tempering temperature the lower the tensile properties of the steel. Once tempered, the metal is rapidly cooled by quenching.

Composition and properties

Various terms are used with reference to steel and other materials to describe their properties. These terms will now be explained in more detail.

Tensile strength This is the main single criterion with reference to metals. It is a measure of the material's ability to withstand the loads upon it in service. Terms such as stress, strain, ultimate tensile strength, yield stress and proof stress are all different methods of quantifying the tensile strength of the material. The two main factors affecting tensile strength are the carbon content of the steel and its heat treatment following manufacture.

Ductility This is the ability of a material to undergo permanent changes in shape without rupture or loss of strength. It is particularly important where metals undergo forming processes during manufacture.

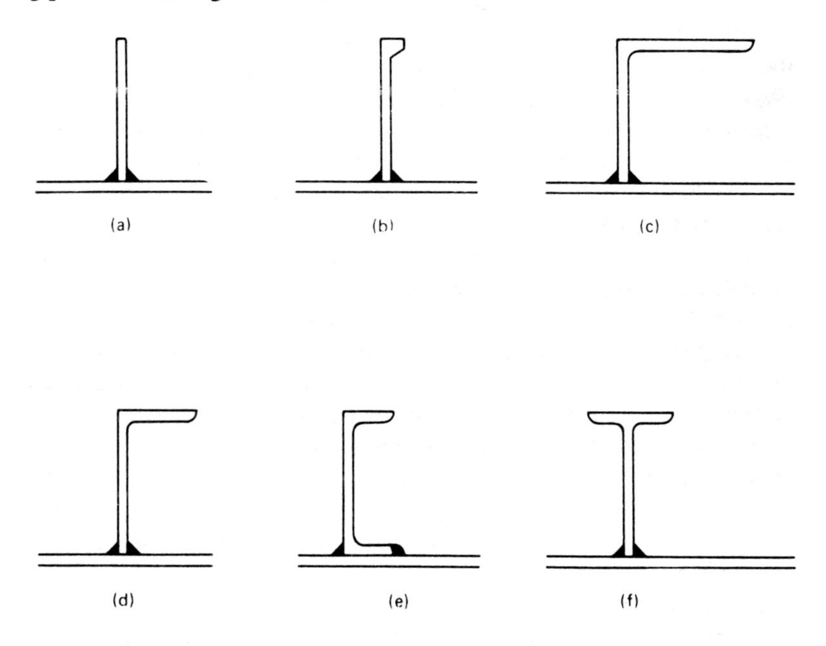

Figure 2.10 Standard steel sections: (a) flat plate; (b) offset bulb plate; (c) equal angle; (d) unequal angle; (e) channel; (f) tee

Hardness This is a measure of the workability of the material. It is used as an assessment of the machinability of the material and its resistance to abrasion.

Toughness This is a condition midway between brittleness and softness. It is often quantified by the value obtained in a notched bar test.

Standard steel sections

A variety of standard sections are produced with varying scantlings to suit their application. The stiffening of plates and sections utilises one or more of these sections, which are shown in *Figure 2.10*.

Shipbuilding steels

The steel used in ship construction is mild steel with a 0.15–0.23% carbon content. The properties required of a good shipbuilding steel are:

(1) Reasonable cost.
(2) Easily welded with simple techniques and equipment.
(3) Ductility and homogeneity.
(4) Yield point to be a high proportion of ultimate tensile strength.
(5) Chemical composition suitable for flame cutting without hardening.
(6) Resistance to corrosion.

These features are provided by the five grades of mild steel (A–E) designated by the classification societies (see Chapter 11). To be classed, the steel for ship construction must be manufactured under approved conditions, and inspected, and prescribed tests must be carried out on selected specimens. Finished material is stamped with the society's brand, a symbol with L superimposed on R being used by Lloyd's Register. The chemical composition and mechanical properties of a selection of mild steel grades are given in *Table 2.1*.

Developments in steel production and alloying techniques have resulted in the availability of higher strength steels for ship construction. These higher tensile strength (HTS) steels, as they are called, have adequate notch toughness, ductility and weldability, in addition to their increased strength. The increased strength results from the addition of alloying elements such as vanadium, chromium, nickel and niobium. Niobium in particular improves the mechanical properties of tensile strength and notch ductility. Particular care must be taken in the choice of electrodes and welding processes for these steels. Low hydrogen electrodes and welding processes must be used. *Table 2.2* indicates the chemical composition and mechanical properties of several high tensile steel grades. A special grade mark, H, is used by the classification societies to denote higher tensile steel.

Benefits arising from the use of these steels in ship construction include reduced structural weight, since smaller sections may be used; larger unit fabrications are possible for the same weight and less welding time, although a more specialised process is needed for the reduced material scantlings.

Table 2.1 PROPERTIES AND COMPOSITION OF SOME MILD STEELS

	C (%)	Mn (%)	Si (%)	S (%)	P (%)	Al (%)	*Minimum yield stress* (N/mm^2)	*Ultimate tensile stress* (N/mm^2)	*Minimum elongation* (%)	*Charpy* (J)
LR 'A' mild steel	0.23 max.	2.5 × C min.	0.50 max.	0.50 max.	0.05 max.	–	230	400–900	22	–
LR 'D' mild steel	0.21 max.	0.70–1.40	0.10–0.50	0.04 max.	0.04 max.	0.015 min.	235	400–900	22	47 at 0°C
LR 'E' mild steel	0.18 max.	0.70–1.50	0.10–0.50	0.04 max.	0.04 max.	0.015 min.	235	400–900	22	27 at -40°C

Table 2.2 PROPERTIES AND COMPOSITION OF SOME HIGHER TENSILE STEELS

	C (%)	Mn (%)	Si (%)	S (%)	P (%)	Al (%)	*Minimum yield stress* (N/mm^2)	*Ultimate tensile stress* (N/mm^2)	*Minimum elongation* (%)	*Charpy* (J)
LR AH32	0.18 max.	0.70–1.60	0.50 max.	0.50 max.	0.04 max.	0.015 min.	315	440–590	22	31 at 0°C
LR AH36	0.18 max.	0.70–1.60	0.50 max.	0.04 max.	0.04 max.	0.015 min.	355	490–620	21	34 at 0°C
LR AH36	0.18 max.	0.70–1.60	0.10–0.50	0.04 max.	0.04 max.	0.015 min.	355	490–620	21	34 at -40°C

Table 2.3 PROPERTIES AND COMPOSITION OF TYPICAL LOW TEMPERATURE CONSTRUCTIONAL MATERIALS

	C (%)	Mn (%)	Si (%)	S (%)	P (%)	Al (%)	Ni (%)	Cr (%)	Mo (%)	*Minimum yield stress* (N/mm^2)	*Ultimate tensile stress* (N/mm^2)	*Minimum elongation* (%)	*Charpy* (J)
Low carbon stainless steel AISI 304	0.03 max.	1.2	0.75	0.02	0.02	–	10.7	18.5	–	235	560	50	103 at –196°C
36% Ni alloy (Invar)	0.09	0.3	0.2	0.01	0.02	–	35.8	–	–	275	480	40	147 at –196°C
5% Ni steel	0.20 max.	0.30–0.60	0.15–0.35	0.035 max.	0.035 max.	–	4.5–5.0	–	–	442	590–740	20	88 at –120°C
9% Ni steel	0.13 max.	0.9 max.	0.15 0.30	0.040 max.	0.035 max.	–	8.5–9.5	–	–	587	690–830	22	34 at –196°C
	Cu (%)	Mn (%)	Si (%)	Mg (%)	Fe (%)	Al (%)	Zn (%)	Cr (%)	Ti (%)				
Aluminium alloy 5083	0.10 max.	0.40–1.0	0.40 max.	4.0–4.9	0.40 max.	Rem.	0.25 max.	0.05–0.25	0.15 max.	126	275	16	

Cryogenic or low temperature materials are being increasingly used as a consequence of the carriage of liquefied gases in bulk tankers. *Table 2.3* details the properties and composition of several of these cryogenic materials. The main criterion of selection is an adequate amount of notch toughness at the operating temperature to be encountered. Various alloys are principally used for the very low temperature situations, although special quality carbon/manganese steels have been used satisfactorily down to –50°C.

Castings and forgings

The larger castings used in ship construction are usually manufactured from carbon or carbon manganese steels. *Table 2.4* details the composition and properties of these materials. Examples of large castings are the sternframe, bossings, A-brackets and parts of the rudder. The examples mentioned may also be manufactured as forgings. *Table 2.4* details the composition and properties of materials used for forgings.

Aluminium alloys

The increasing use of aluminium alloy has resulted from its several advantages over steel. Aluminium is about one-third the weight of steel for an equivalent volume of material. The use of aluminium alloys in a structure can result in reductions of 60% of the weight of an equivalent steel structure. This reduction in weight, particularly in the upper regions of the structure, can improve the stability of the vessel. This follows from the lowering of the vessel's centre of gravity, resulting in an increased metacentric height. The corrosion resistance of aluminium is very good but careful maintenance and insulation from the adjoining steel structure are necessary. The properties required of an aluminium alloy to be used in ship construction are much the same as for steel, namely strength, resistance to corrosion, workability and weldability. These requirements are adequately met, the main disadvantage being the high cost of aluminium.

The chemical composition and mechanical properties of the common shipbuilding alloys are shown in *Table 2.5*. Again these are classification society gradings

Table 2.4 PROPERTIES AND COMPOSITION OF CASTING AND FORGING MATERIALS

	C (%)	Mn (%)	Si (%)	S (%)	P (%)	*Ultimate tensile strength* (N/mm²)	*Yield stress* (N/mm²)	*Minimum elongation* (%)
Steel castings	0.23 max.	1.6 max but not less than 3 × C	0.60 max.	0.04 max.	0.04 max.	400	200	25
Steel forgings	0.23 max.	0.30–1.70	0.45 max.	0.045 max.	0.045 max.	430	215	24 longitudinal 18 transverse
Steel forgings (not intended for weldings)	0.30	0.30–1.50	0.45	0.045 max.	0.045 max.	430	215	24 longitudinal 18 transverse

Table 2.5 PROPERTIES AND COMPOSITION OF ALUMINIUM ALLOY CONSTRUCTIONAL MATERIALS

	Cu (%)	Mg (%)	Si (%)	Fe (%)	Mn (%)	Zn (%)	Cr (%)	Ti (%)	Al (%)	*Minimum proof stress* (N/mm^2)	*Minimum ultimate tensile strength* (N/mm^2)	*Minimum elongation* (%)
AL 1 (LR) Plates and sections	0.10 max.	3.5–5.6	0.5 max.	0.5 max.	1.0 max.	0.2 max.	0.35 max.	0.2 max.	Rem.	125	260	11
AL 2 (LR) Plates and sections	0.10 max.	0.4–1.4	0.6–1.6	0.5 max.	0.2–1.0	0.2 max.	0.35 max.	0.2 max.	Rem.	195	260	8
AL 3 (LR) Rivets	0.10 max.	3.0–3.9	0.5 max.	0.5 max.	0.6 max.	0.2 max.	0.35 max.	0.2 max.	Rem.	90	220	18
AL 4 (LR) Rivets	0.10 max.	0.4–1.4	0.6–1.6	0.5 max.	0.2–1.0	0.2 max.	0.35 max.	0.2 max.	Rem.	120	190	16

where the material must be manufactured and tested to the satisfaction of the society.

Aluminium alloys are available as plate and section, and a selection of aluminium alloy sections is shown in *Figure 2.11*. These sections are formed by extrusion, which is the forcing of a billet of the hot material through a suitably shaped die. Intricate or unusual shapes to suit particular applications are therefore possible.

Where aluminium alloys join the steel structure, special arrangements must be employed to avoid galvanic corrosion where the metals meet (see Chapter 4). Where rivets are used, they should be manufactured from a corrosion-resistant alloy (see *Table 2.5*).

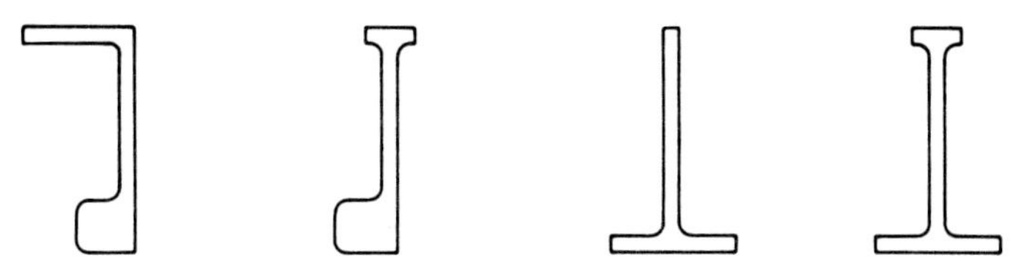

Figure 2.11 Aluminium alloy sections

Materials testing

Various qualities of the materials discussed so far have been mentioned. These qualities are determined by a variety of tests which are carried out on samples of the metal.

The terms 'stress' and 'strain' are used most frequently. Stress or intensity of stress, its correct name, is the force acting on a unit area of the material. Strain is the deforming of a material due to stress. When the force applied to a material tends to shorten or compress the material the stress is termed 'compressive stress'. When the force applied tends to lengthen the material the stress is termed 'tensile stress'. When the force tends to cause the various parts of the material to slide over one another the stress is termed 'shear stress'.

The tensile test is used to determine the behaviour of a material up to its breaking point. A specially shaped specimen piece (*Figure 2.12*) of standard size is gripped in the jaws of a testing machine. A load is gradually applied to draw the ends of the bar apart such that it is subject to a tensile stress. The original test length L_1 of the specimen is known and for each applied load the new length L_2 can be measured. The specimen will be found to have extended by some small amount $L_2 - L_1$. This deformation, expressed as

$$\frac{\text{extension}}{\text{original length}} = \frac{L_2 - L_1}{L_1}$$

is known as the linear strain.

Additional loading of the specimen will produce results which show a uniform increase of extension until the yield point is reached. Up to the yield point the removal of load would have resulted in the specimen returning to its original size. Stress and strain are therefore proportional up to the yield point, or elastic limit as

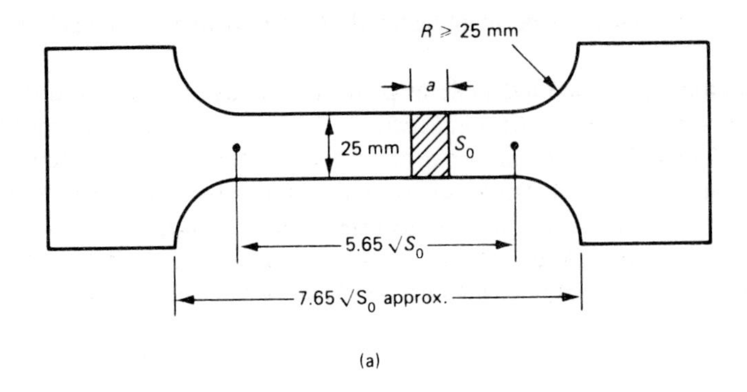

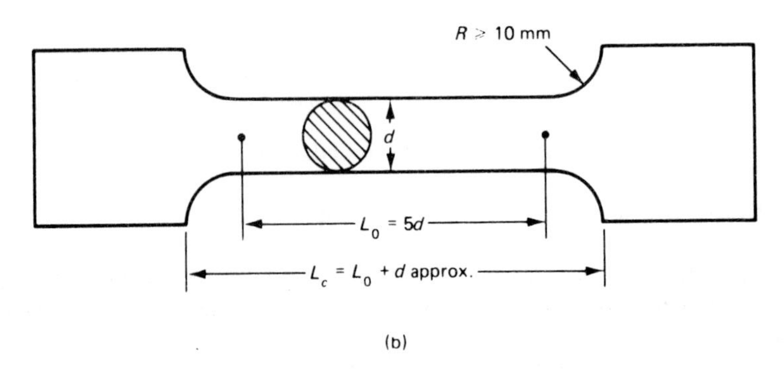

Figure 2.12 Tensile test specimens: (a) for plates, strips and sections (a = thickness of material); (b) for hot-rolled bar

it is also known. The stress and strain values for various loads can be shown on a graph such as *Figure 2.13*.

If the testing were continued beyond the yield point the specimen would 'neck' or reduce in cross-section. The load values divided by the original specimen cross-sectional area would give the shape shown in *Figure 2.13*. The highest value of stress is known as the ultimate tensile stress (UTS) of the material.

Within the elastic limit, stress is proportional to strain, and so

$$\frac{\text{stress}}{\text{strain}} = \text{constant.}$$

This constant is known as the 'modulus of elasticity' (E) of the material and has the same units as stress. The yield stress is the value of stress at the yield point. Where a clearly defined yield point is not obtained a proof stress value is given. This is obtained by a line parallel to the elastic stress–strain line drawn at some percentage of the strain, such as 0.1%. The intersection of this line with the stress–strain line is considered the proof stress (*Figure 2.14*).

The bend test is used to determine the ductility of a material. A piece of material is bent over a radiused former, sometimes through 180 degrees. No cracks or surface laminations should appear in the material.

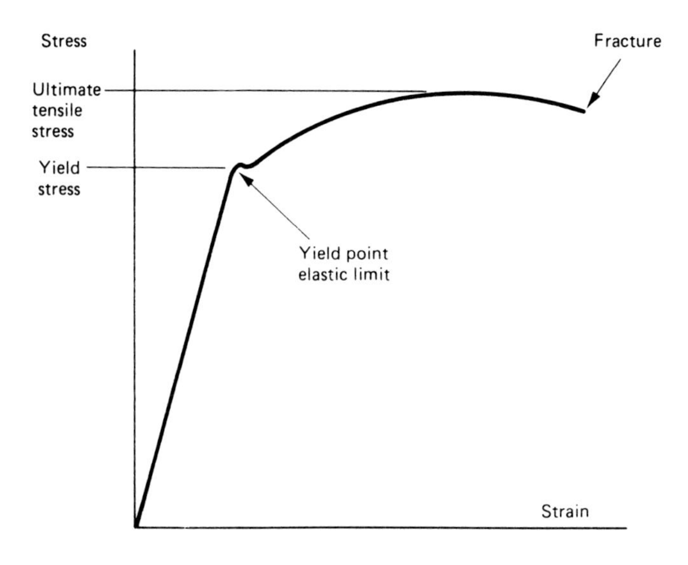

Figure 2.13 *Stress–strain graph for mild steel*

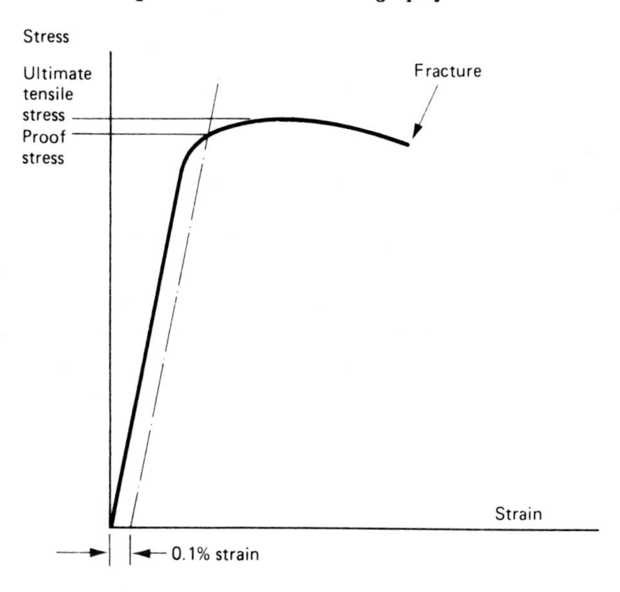

Figure 2.14 *Stress–strain graph for higher tensile steel*

Impact tests can have a number of forms but the Charpy vee-notch test is usually specified. The test specimen is a 10 mm square cross-section, 55 mm in length. A vee-notch is cut in the centre of one face, as shown in *Figure 2.15*. The specimen is mounted horizontally with the notch axis vertical. The test involves the specimen being struck opposite the notch and fractured. A striker or hammer on the end of a swinging pendulum provides the blow which breaks the specimen. The energy

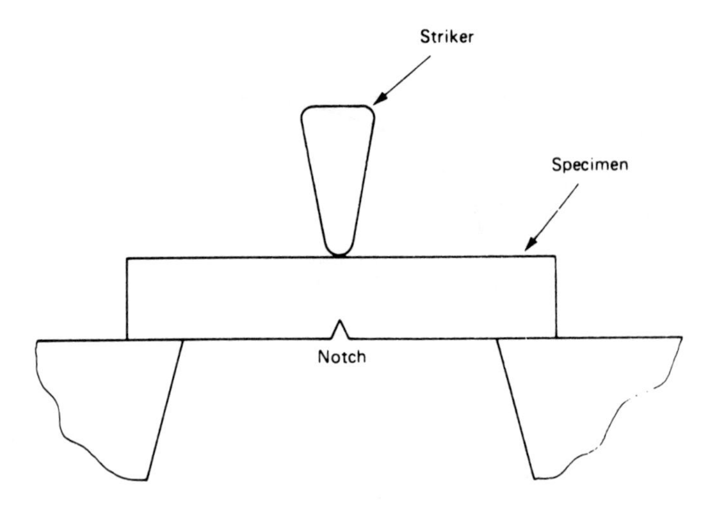

Figure 2.15 Charpy impact test

absorbed by the material in fracturing is measured by the machine. A particular value of average impact energy must be obtained for the material at the test temperature. This test is particularly important for materials to be used in low temperature regions. For low temperature testing the specimen is cooled by immersion in a bath of liquid nitrogen or dry ice and acetone for about 15 minutes. The specimen is then handled and tested rapidly to minimise any temperature changes. The impact test, in effect, measures a material's resistance to fracture when shock loaded.

A dump test is used on a specimen length of bar from which rivets are to be made. The bar is compressed to half its original length and no surface cracks must appear. Other rivet material tests include bending the shank until the two ends touch without any cracks or fractures appearing. The head must also accept flattening until it reaches two and a half times the shank diameter.

3

Shipbuilding

Building a ship is a complex process involving the many departments of the shipbuilding organisation, the arrangement and use of shipyard facilities and the many skills of the various personnel involved. Those departments directly involved in the construction, the shipyard layout, material movement and the equipment used will be examined in turn.

Drawing office

The main function of the shipyard's design and drawing offices is to produce the working drawings to satisfy the owner's requirements, the rules of the classification societies and the shipyard's usual building practices. A secondary, but nevertheless important, function is to provide information to the production planning and control departments, the purchasing department, etc., to enable steelwork outfitting and machinery items to be ordered and delivered to satisfy the building programme for the ship.

Closely following the basic design drawings will be the production of the lines plan. This plan (*Figure 3.1*) is a scale drawing of the moulded dimensions of the ship in plan, profile and section. The ship's length between the forward and after perpendiculars is divided into ten equally spaced divisions or stations numbered 1 to 10. Transverse sections of the ship at the various stations are drawn to give a drawing known as the body plan. Since the vessel is symmetrical, half-sections are given. The station 0 to 5 representing the after half of the ship are shown on the left side of the body plan with the forward sections shown on the right. The profile or sheer plan shows the general outline of the ship, any sheer of the decks, the deck positions and all the waterlines. For clarity, the deck positions have been omitted from *Figure 3.1* and only three waterlines are shown. The various stations are also drawn on this view. Additional stations may be used at the fore and aft ends, where the section change is considerable. The half-breadth plan shows the shape of the waterlines and the decks formed by horizontal planes at the various waterline heights from the keel. This plan is usually superimposed upon the profile or sheer plan, as shown in *Figure 3.1*.

The initial lines plan is drawn for the design and then checked for 'fairness'. To be 'fair' all the curved lines must run evenly and smoothly. There must also be exact

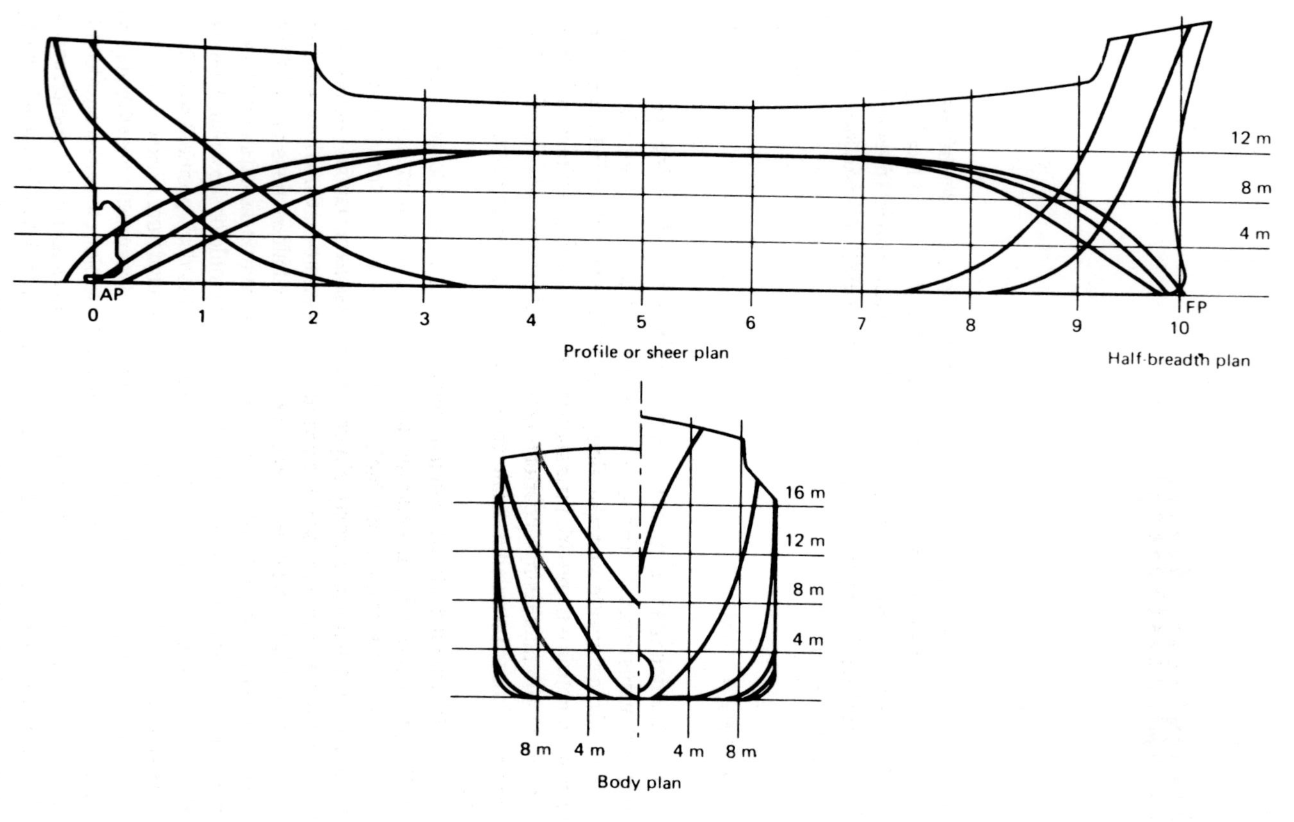

Figure 3.1 Lines plan

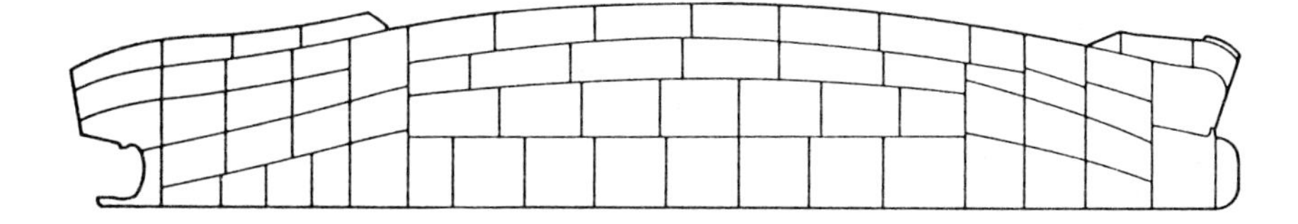

Figure 3.2 Shell expansion by units

correspondence between dimensions shown for a particular point in all the three different views. The fairing operation, once the exclusive province of a skilled loftsman, is now largely accomplished by computer programs.

Once faired, the final lines plan is prepared and a table of offsets is compiled for use in producing the ship's plates and frames.

The traditional practice of drawing plans according to structural areas such as the shell, the deck, the double-bottom framing, etc., is inconvenient in many cases since the ship is nowadays built up of large prefabricated units. A unit may consist of shell plating, some framing and part of a deck. An expansion of a ship's shell is given in *Figure 3.2*, showing the positions of the various units. Plans are therefore drawn in relation to units and contain all the information required to build a particular unit. A number of traditional plans are still produced for classification society purposes, future maintenance and reference, but without the wealth of manufacturing information which is only needed on the unit plans.

The planning and production control departments require drawing information to compile charts for monitoring progress, compiling programmes, producing programmes for material delivery, parts production and assembly and finally unit production and erection.

CAD/CAM

Ship design is now very much a computer aided process and numerous computer aided design (CAD) systems have been developed by companies such as British Maritime Technology, Kockums and Schiffko. The information provided by these design systems has been integrated into computer aided manufacture (CAM) systems. Production information can then be provided directly for use by computer numerical control (CNC) machines. The production processes of cutting plates and sections, panel assembly, etc., can thus be done automatically.

If the BMT Cortec division programs library is considered then most design and production requirements can be met. Design programs include CODES, SFOLDS, COMPGEN and BLINES software packages. CODES is a conceptual design module which is used to obtain the hull, propeller and engine particulars. A techno-economic assessment of possible solutions is performed within a stated set of constraints. The SFOLDS program is a naval architectural design analysis package for hydrostatics calculations and stability determination, which also checks for compliance with national and IMO requirements. The compartmentation of the ship is established using COMPGEN, and BLINES is an interactive system for rapidly defining the ships hull form.

The CAM production requirements are covered by HULLGEN, BRITSHELL, and BRITSHAPE which enable plate development, plate nesting, parts definition and numerical control manufacturing information to be provided. These system packages can also interface with most assembly modelling packages.

In addition to having similar design and production packages Schiffko of Germany is developing engine room, piping and accommodation arrangement packages. These are three dimensional, fully interactive systems for the design of interior layouts. All technical data required for outfit and parts lists can then be generated. This MEPAS program software is being developed in conjunction with shipyards in Belgium, Greece and Germany.

All the above computer programs can be run on desktop personal computers. It is also possible to progressively build up the various programs as a shipyard gradually converts or upgrades CAD/CAM software.

Plan approval

The fundamental design plans and basic constructional details must all receive classification society approval and, of course, the shipowner's approval. Unusual aspects of design and innovations in constructional methods will receive special attention, as will any departures from standard practice. Progress is not hindered by the classification societies, whose main concern is the production of a sound and safe structure.

The shipowner will normally have clearly indicated his requirements from the design inception and his approval of plans is usually straightforward. Most large shipowning companies have a technical staff who utilise their practical experience in developing as near perfect and functional a design as possible.

Plan issue

With plan approval the ordering of equipment, machinery, steel section and plate, etc., will begin and the plans will be issued to the various production departments in the shipyard. The classification society, the owners and their representatives in the shipyard also receive copies of the plans.

During the manufacturing processes, as a result of problems encountered, feedback from previous designs, modifications requested by the owner, etc., amendments may be made to plans. A system of plan recall, replacement or modification in the production departments must be available. This ensures that any future ships in a series do not carry the same faults and that corrective action has been taken.

Steel ordering

The ordering of steel to ensure availability in line with programmed requirements is essential. It must therefore begin at the earliest opportunity, occasionally, where delivery problems may occur, before plan approval. The steel ordering is a key function in the production process, requiring involvement with the drawing office, planning departments, production departments and the steel supplier. The monitoring and control of stock is also important, since the steel material for a ship is a substantial part of the ship's final cost. Stock held by a shipyard represents a considerable capital investment.

Loft work

Loft work takes place in a mould loft. The mould loft is a large covered area with a wooden floor upon which the ship's details are drawn to full size or some smaller more convenient scale. Much of the traditional loft work is now done by computer but some specialist areas still require wooden templates to be made, mock-ups to be constructed, etc.

In the traditional mould loft operation the lines plan and working drawing information is converted into full-scale lines drawn on the loft floor. From these lines the fairing or smoothness of the ship's lines is checked and a scrieve board produced. A scrieve board is a wooden board with the body sections at every frame spacing drawn in. Once the ship's lines are checked and fair, a half-block model is constructed by joiners usually to about one-fiftieth scale. This model has the exact lines of the ship and is used to mark out the actual plates on the shell, giving all the positions of the butts and seams.

The loftsman can now produce templates for marking, cutting and bending the actual plates using the full-size scrieve board markings in conjunction with the plate positions from the model. Finally, a table of offsets is produced for the various frames and plates, giving manufacturing information for the various trades involved in production.

One-tenth scale lofting

With one-tenth scale lofting the mould loft becomes more of a drawing office with long tables. Fairing is achieved using the one-tenth scale drawings. The scrieve board is made to one-tenth scale, perhaps on white-painted plywood. One-tenth scale drawings are then made of the ship's individual plates. These drawings may then be photographed and reduced in scale to one-hundredth of full size for optical projection and marking of the plates. Alternatively, the one-tenth scale drawings may be traced directly by a cutting machine head.

Computer aided manufacture

Numerous integrated ship design, production and management information systems are currently being developed and reference was made to some of these earlier in the chapter.

The Steerbear Hull Option has been developed by Kockums Computer Systems of Sweden. It will be described here as an example of a CAM system. It covers all aspects from lines fairing through to the provision of production information necessary for the manufacture of the hull (*Figure 3.3*).

The input data for the system is obtained from a product model. This is a three-dimensional description of the ship contained in a data base within the computer, together with all functional, technical and administrative properties associated with it. Any required drawings, offset information, material information, etc., can be derived from this model.

A hull system program will be used to define the hull form using a preliminary set of lines. Naval architectural calculations will be required to verify the design and form part of another associated program. Once material size information is available, as a result of the naval architectural calculations, the hull structure will be built up by the computer. Information must then be input regarding butts, seams, longitudinals, etc.

Detailed hull design can now take place in order to refine the product model. A design language is used to input statements which generate hull components such as stiffeners and brackets. Often standards built into the program will simplify the inputs to only one or two parameters.

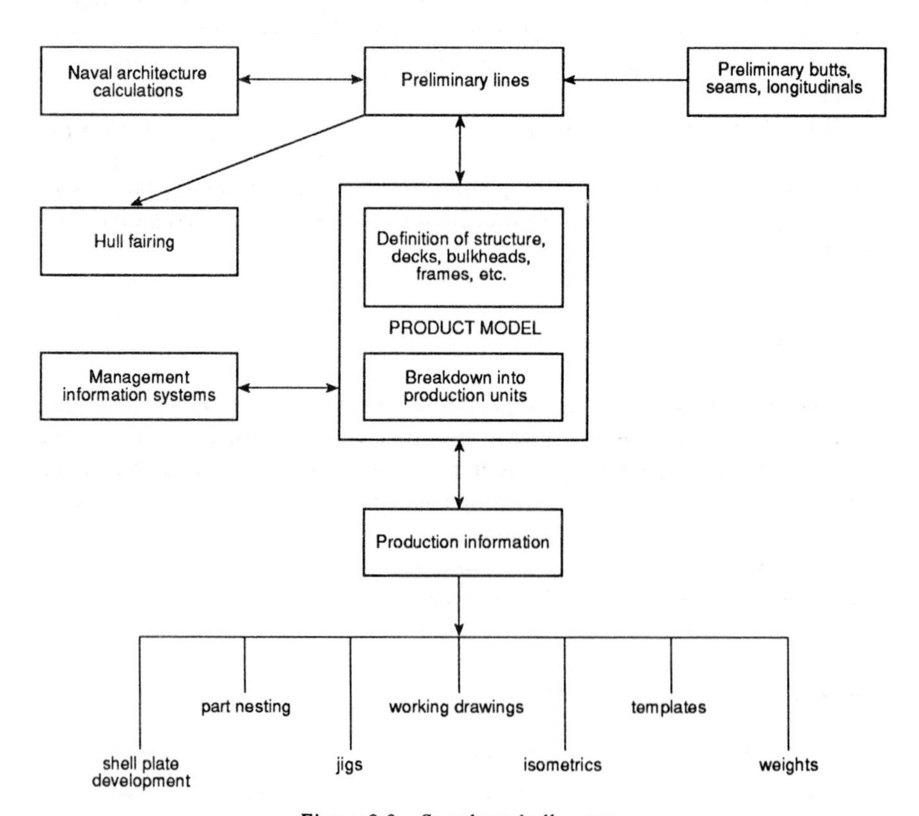

Figure 3.3 Steerbear hull system

This detailed design work will enable the production of various drawings and reports together with the following production information:

(1) Division of the hull structure into plate parts and stiffeners.
(2) Interactive nesting of parts and generation of numerical control tapes for numerical control or computer numerical control machines.
(3) Information regarding the construction of bending templates for shell plates and jigs for block assembly.
(4) Lists for the fabrication of profiles such as longitudinals, frames and stiffeners.
(5) Working drawings.
(6) Perspective drawings of units.
(7) Weights and centres of gravity for units.

The complete integrated system is made up of Steerbear Technical Information Systems and Steerbear Management Information Systems. Steerbear Technical Information Systems has two main functional groups; the hull system, which has been described, and outfitting systems. Outfitting systems deals with equipment, all outfitting design and production including connections for pipework, ventilation and electric cables, and enables accommodation layouts to be made. The Steerbear Management Information System enables planning, materials administration, scheduling and provides production information in various forms.

Numerical control

A numerical control system is one where a machine is operated and controlled by the insertion of numerical data. The numerical data is a sequence of numbers which fully describe a part to be produced. In addition, the use of certain code numbers enables instructions to be fed into the machine to enable it to operate automatically. A reading device on the machine converts the numbers into electrical impulses which become control signals for the various parts of the machine which produce the finished part.

The input data for the machine is produced by a computer aided manufacture system in an appropriate form e.g. punched card, paper tape or magnetic tape, which will contain the numerical data. Where several parts are to be cut from a single plate, they have usually been 'nested' or economically fitted into the plate (*Figure 3.4*).

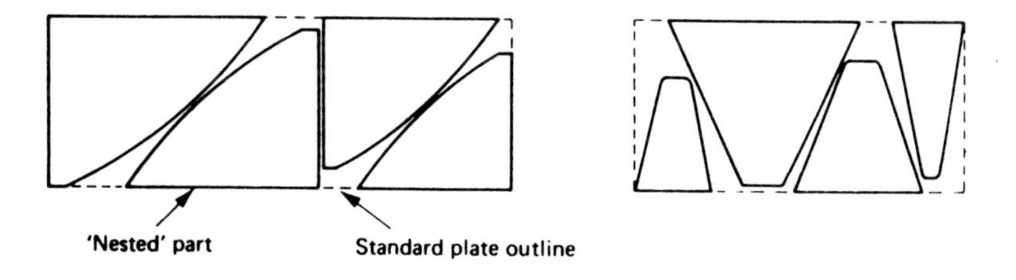

Figure 3.4 Nesting of plates

Shipyard layout

The shipyard layout is arranged to provide a logical ordered flow of materials and equipment towards the final unit build-up, erection and outfitting of the ship. The

Preliminary ship design
↓
Drawing of detailed plans → Steel ordered
↓ ↓
Approval of plans and issue — Steel delivered
↓
Loftwork and production table of offsets
↓
Issue of steel and production begun ← (Steel delivered)
↓
Material preparation—shot blasting and priming
↓
Manufacture of plates and sections—marking, cutting, machining and shaping
↓
Subassemblies and assemblies produced
↓
Units fabricated and delivered to the berth
↓
Units erected, faired and welded

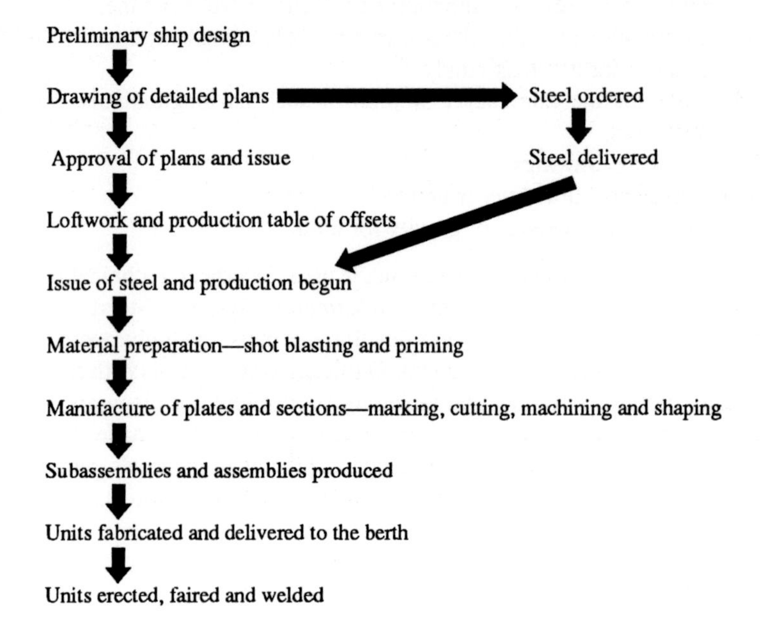

Figure 3.5 Shipbuilding sequence of events

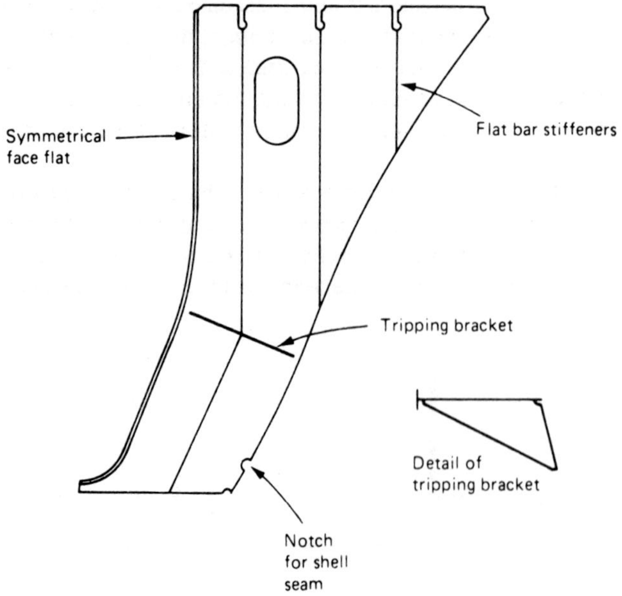

Symmetrical face flat
Flat bar stiffeners
Tripping bracket
Detail of tripping bracket
Notch for shell seam

Figure 3.6 Subassembly—web frame

various production stages are arranged in work areas or 'shops' and, as far as practicable in modern yards, take place under cover. The sequence of events is outlined in *Figure 3.5*.

Steel plates and sections are usually stored in separate stockyards and fed into their individual shot-blasting and priming machines. The plates are cleaned by abrasive shot or grit and then coated with a suitable prefabrication priming paint to a limited thickness for ease of welding. The major areas of steel are therefore protected from corrosion during the various manufacturing processes which follow.

The plates and sections follow their individual paths to the marking or direct-cutting machinery which produces the suitably dimensioned item. Flame cutting or mechanical guillotines may be used. Edge preparation for welding may also be done

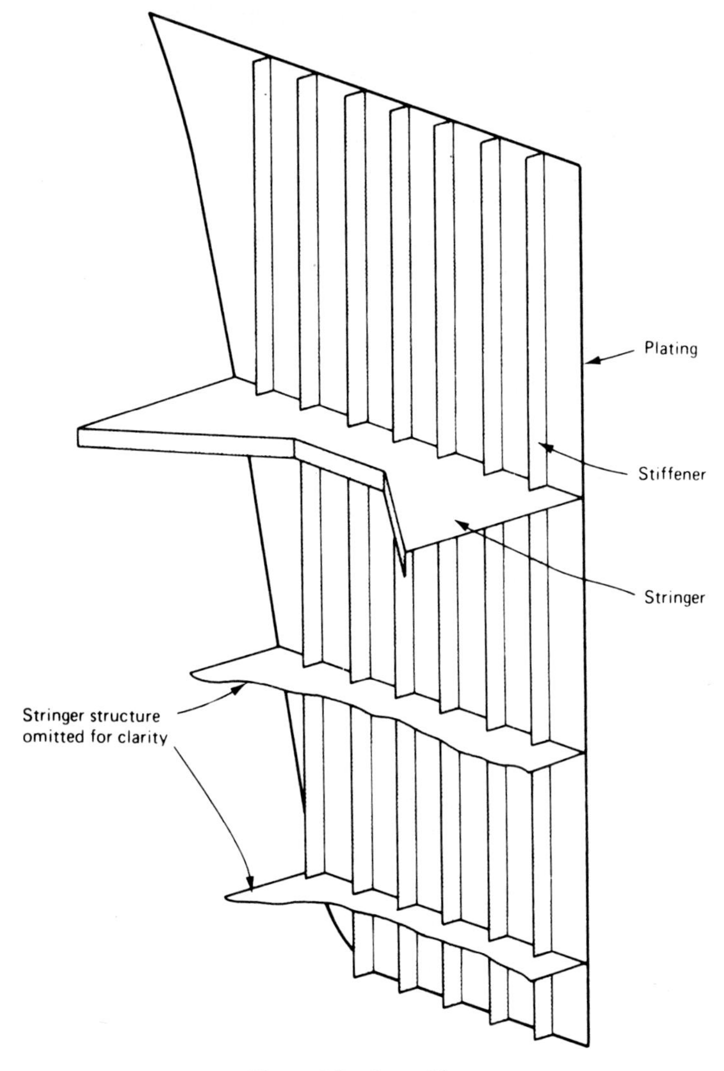

Figure 3.7 Assembly

at this stage. Various shaping operations now take place using plate-bending rolls, presses, cold frame benders, etc., as necessary. The material transfer before, during and after the various processes in shipbuilding utilises many handling appliances, such as overhead travelling cranes, vacuum lift cranes or magnetic cranes, roller conveyors, fork-lift equipment, etc.

The various steel parts in plate and section form are now joined together by welding to produce subassemblies, assemblies and units. A subassembly is several pieces of steel making up a two-dimensional part which, together with other subassemblies, will join to form a unit. Subassemblies may weigh up to 5 tonnes or more and examples would be transverses, minor bulkheads and web frames (*Figure 3.6*). Assemblies consist of larger, usually three-dimensional, structures of plating and sections weighing up to 20 tonnes. Flat panels and bulkheads are examples and consist of various pieces of shell plating with stiffeners and perhaps deep webs crossing the stiffeners (*Figure 3.7*). The flat or perhaps curved panel may form part of the shell, deck or side plating of, for instance, a tanker. Units are complex built-up sections of a ship, perhaps the complete fore end forward of the collision bulkhead, and can weigh more than 100 tonnes (*Figure 3.8*), their size being limited by the transportation capacity of the yard's equipment.

The various subassemblies, assemblies or units are moved on to the building berth or storage area until required for erection at the ship. At this stage, or perhaps

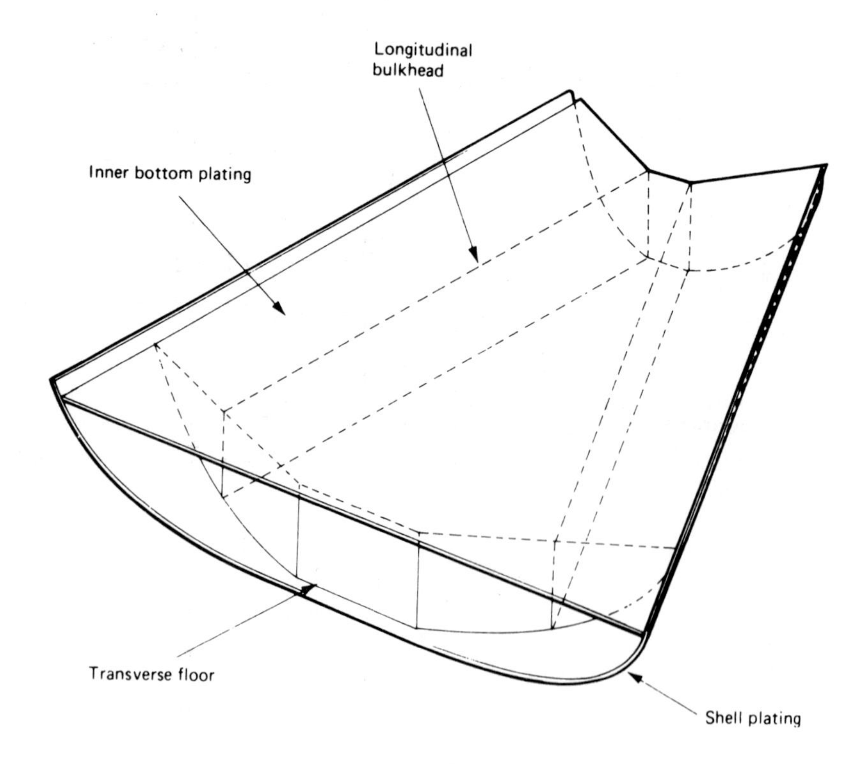

Figure 3.8 Unit

earlier, items of pipework and machinery may be fitted into the unit in what is known as pre-outfitting. Once erected at the berth the units are cut to size, where necessary, by the removal of excess or 'green' material. The units are faired and tack welded one to another and finally welded into place to form the hull of the ship.

Materials handling

The layout of a shipyard should aim to reduce materials handling to a minimum by appropriate location of work stations or areas. The building of large units and the capacity to transport them will reduce the number of items handled but will require greater care and more sophisticated equipment. The building of a ship is as much governed by the shipyard layout as the materials handling equipment and its capacity.

An actual shipyard layout is shown in *Figure 3.9*. The progression of materials through the various production stages can clearly be seen. The various working processes which the plates and sections undergo will now be examined in more detail.

Materials preparation

Plates and sections received from the steel mill are shot-blasted to remove scale, primed with a temporary protective paint and finally straightened by rolling to remove any curvature.

Shot-blasting and priming

A typical machine will first water-wash then heat-dry the plates before descaling. The plates are then simultaneously shot-blasted both sides with metallic abrasive. The plate is fed in horizontally at speeds of up to 5 m/min, and around 300 t/h of shot are projected on to it. Blowers and suction devices remove the shot, which is cleaned and recycled. The clean plates are immediately covered with a coat of priming paint and dried in an automatic spraying machine (*Figure 3.10*). A thickness of about 1 mm of compatible priming paint is applied to avoid problems with fillet welds on to the plating.

Straightening

Plate straightening or levelling is achieved by using a plate rolls machine (*Figure 3.11*). This consists basically of five large rollers, the bottom two being driven and the top ones idling. The top rollers can be adjusted for height independently at each end and the bottom rollers have adjustable centres. A number of smaller supporting rollers are positioned around the five main rollers. The plate is fed through with the

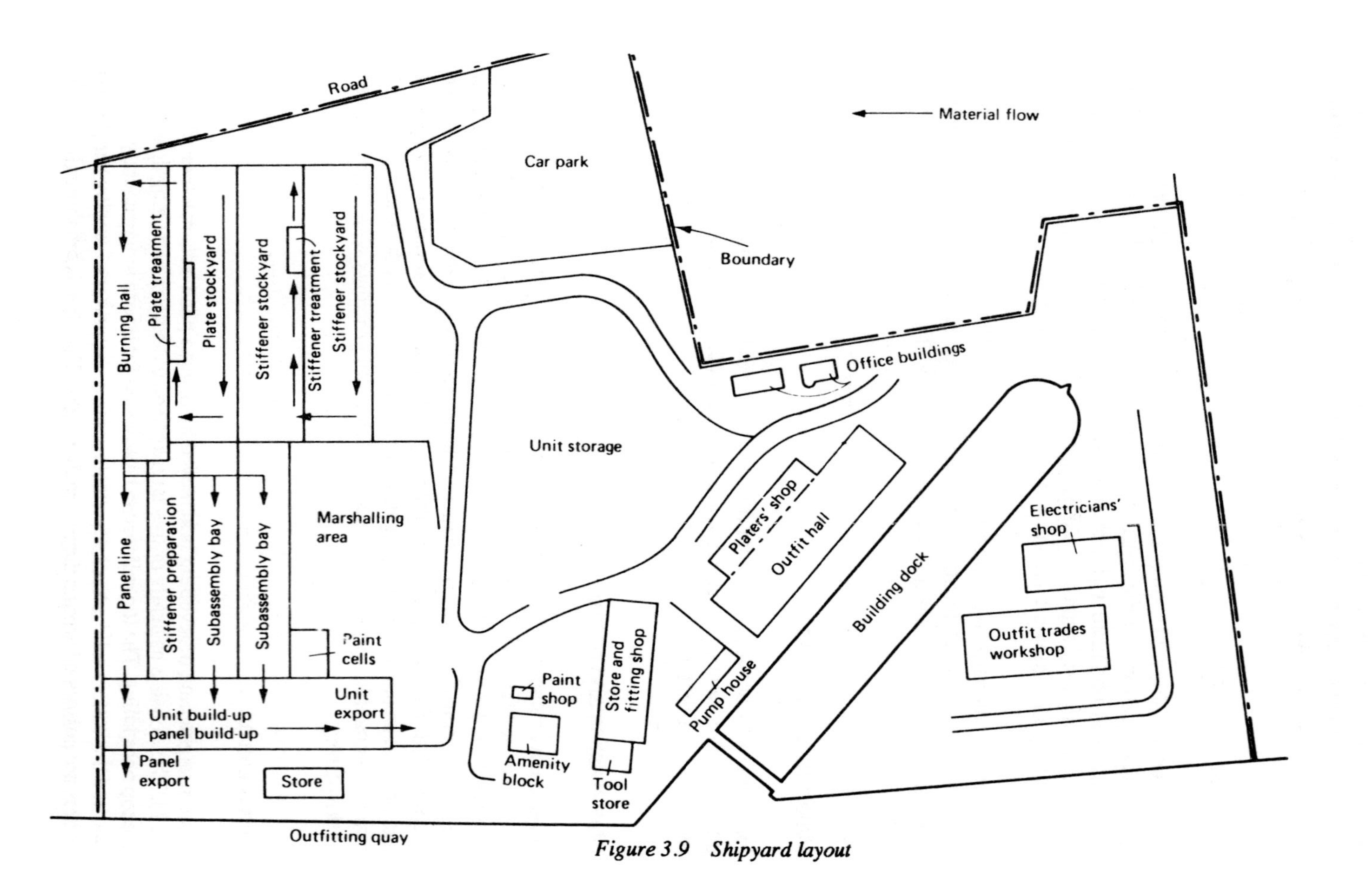

Figure 3.9 Shipyard layout

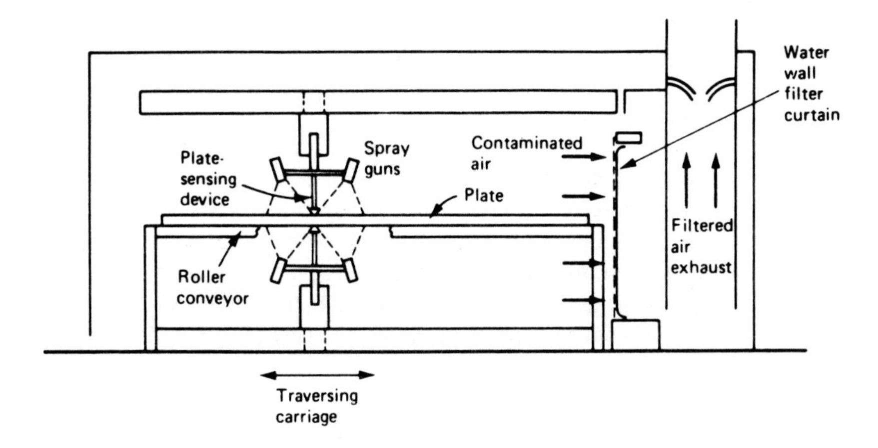

Figure 3.10 Automatic paint-spraying plant

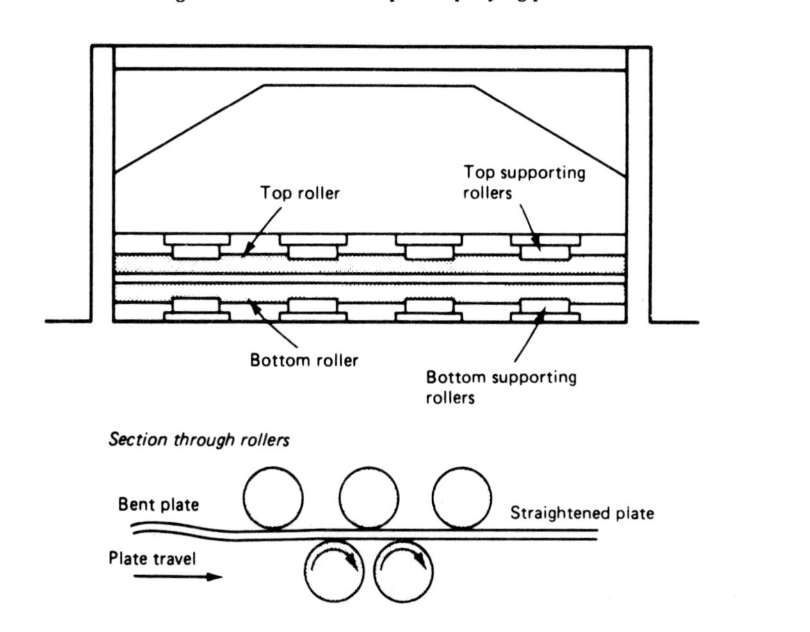

Figure 3.11 Plate straightening

upper and lower rollers spaced at its thickness and is subsequently straightened. This machine is also capable of bending and flanging plate.

Cutting and shaping

Various machines and equipment are used for cutting and shaping the steel parts which form the subassemblies, assemblies and units.

Contour or profile-cutting machine

This machine is made up of a robust portal frame for longitudinal travel which is traversed by several burner carriages, some of which are motorised (*Figure 3.12*). A motorised carriage can pull one or more slave carriages for congruent or mirror-image operation. The burner carriages may be equipped with single burners or up to three heads which can be angled and rotated for edge preparation in addition to cutting, as shown in *Figure 3.12*. Fully automatic operation is possible with punched paper tape input under numerical control. Semi-automatic operation can be achieved by a photoelectric tracing table using 1:1, 1:2.5, 1:5 or 1:10 scale drawings. Complex shapes such as floor plates in double bottoms can be cut with these machines, and also plate edge preparation may be carried out while cutting shell plates to the required shape.

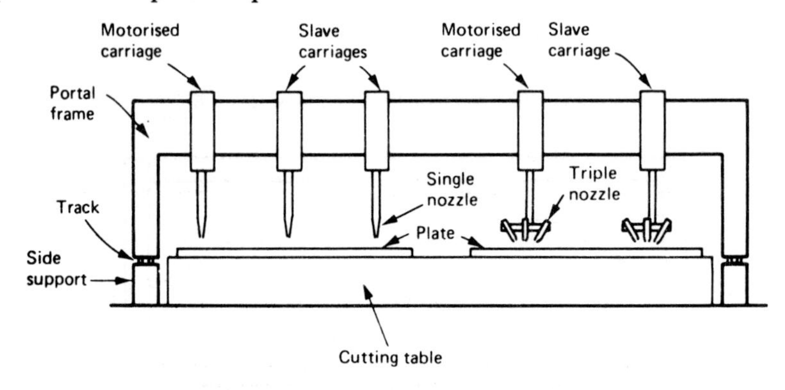

Figure 3.12 Profile-cutting machine

Flame planer

A typical flame planer can have up to three gantries which run on supporting carriages. The gantries are traversed by one or two burner heads (*Figure 3.13 (a)*). With triple-nozzle heads, cutting to size and edge preparation of one or more edges of a plate can take place simultaneously. The operation of the machine is largely automatic, although initial setting up is by manual adjustment. With a three gantry machine, the longitudinal plate edges can be cut to size and also the transverse edges (*Figure 3.13 (b)*). The transversely cutting gantries will operate once the longitudinal gantry is clear. The flame planer can split or cut plates to a desired length or width by straight-line cuts. The use of a compound or triple-nozzle head enables simultaneous cutting and edge preparation of plates. All straight-line edge preparations, such as V, X, Y or K, are possible with this machine.

Mechanical planer

Steel plate can also be planed or cut to size using roller shears, as in the mechanical planer. The plates are held by hydraulic clamps. Setting-up time is somewhat longer than for flame planing, although the actual mechanical cutting operation is much

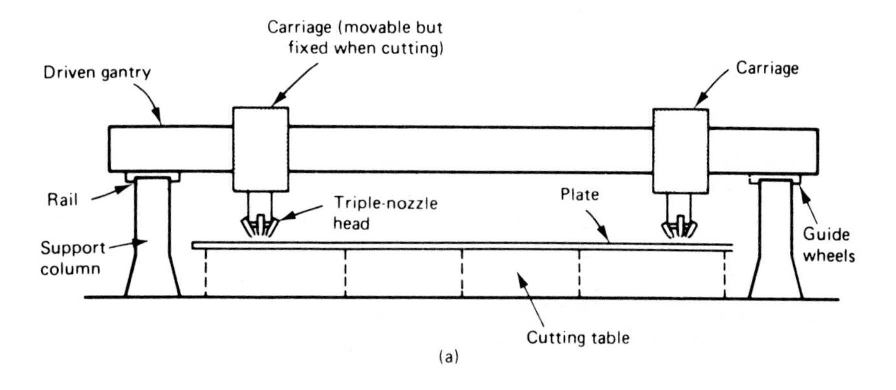

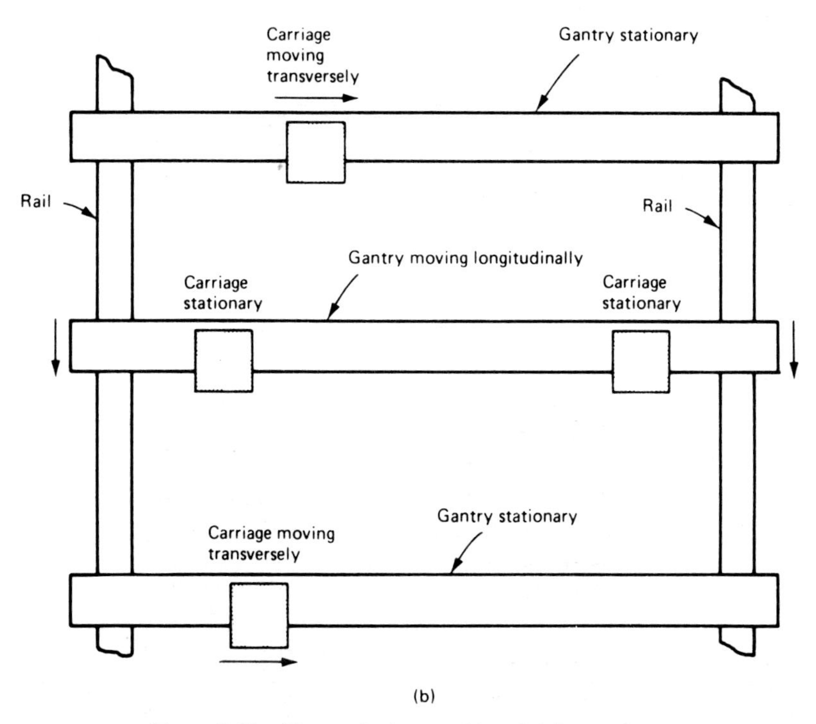

Figure 3.13 Flame planing machine: (a) flame planer; (b) three-gantry operation of flame planer

quicker. Modern machines use milling heads for edge preparation to produce an accurate high standard of finish far superior to gas-cutting techniques (*Figure 3.14 (a)*). These machines can also achieve high speed shearing on the lighter gauges of plating. The most complex edge preparations can be obtained by the use of the rotatable head and assorted cutter shapes (*Figure 3.14 (b)*).

(a)

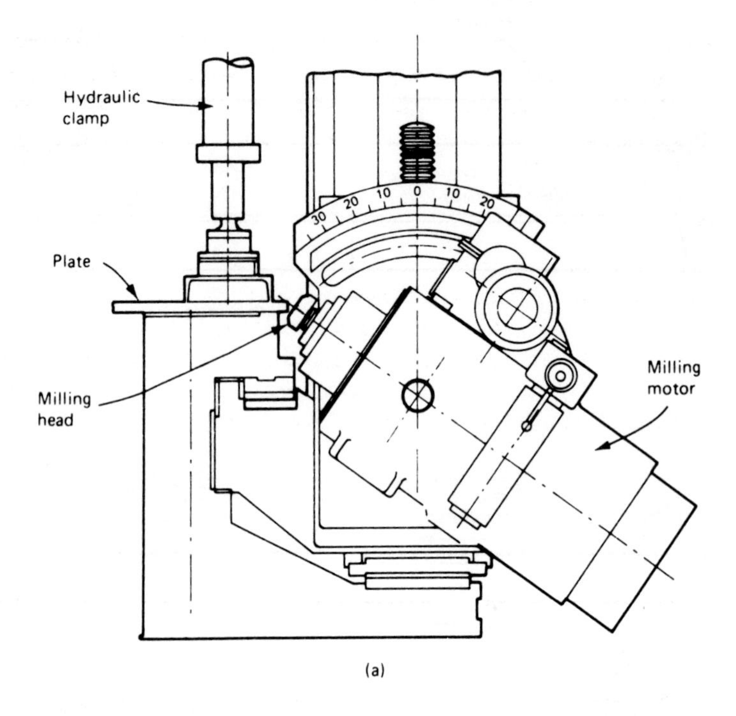

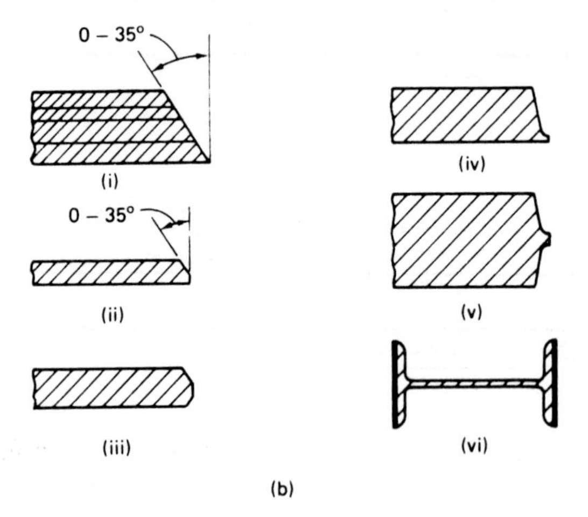

Figure 3.14 Mechanical edge planer: (a) assembly; (b) mechanically cut edge preparation—(i) single bevel without nose, suitable for batches of plates; (ii) single bevel with sheared nose 15 mm maximum or milled nose; (iii) double bevel and nose; (iv) J preparation and nose using 'circular' cutter; (v) double-J preparation; (vi) facings on flanges of structural sections

Gap or ring press

The gap or ring press is a hydraulically-powered press which cold works steel plate. The operations of bending, straightening, dishing and swedging of steel plates can all be achieved by the use of the different die blocks on the bed and the ram (*Figure 3.15*). The gap press provides better access all round and is more versatile than the plate rolls.

Plate rolls

This machine has already been described with reference to plate straightening. It is also used for rolling shell plates to the curvature required. By adjusting the height of the top roller and the centre distance of the bottom rollers, large or small radius bends can be made. Bulkhead flanging is also possible when the machine is fitted with a flanging bar and bottom block. The various arrangements are shown in *Figure 3.16*.

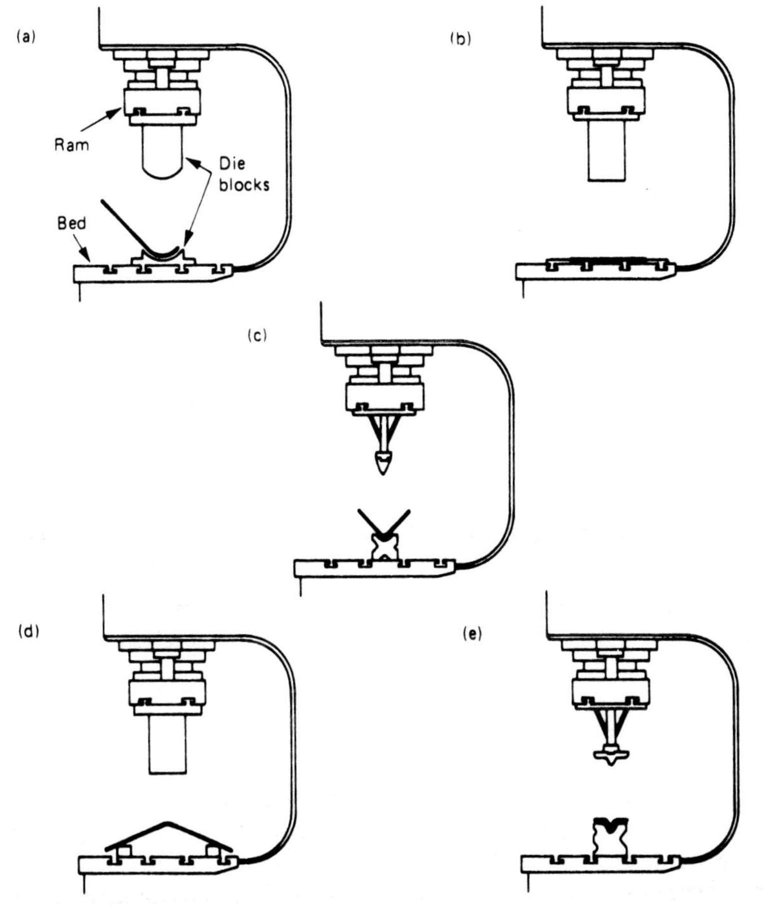

Figure 3.15 Gap press operations: (a) edge curving; (b) plate flattening; (c) plate flanging or bending; (d) plate straightening; (e) plate swaging

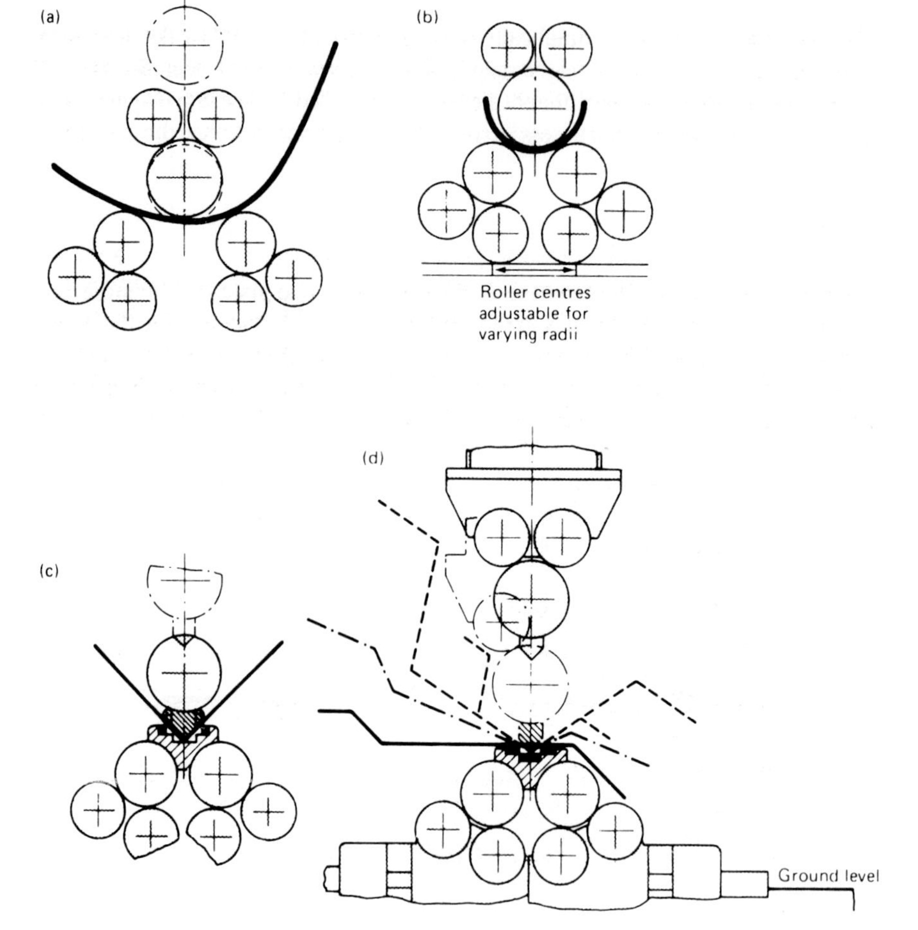

Figure 3.16 Roll press operations: (a) sheer strake rolling; (b) half-round rolling for masts, derrick posts, etc.; (c) 90-degree flanging; (d) bulkhead flanging

Control of the machine is by manual settings and operations carried out from a console located nearby. A shaped metal or wooden lathe is used to check the finished shape.

Punching and notching press

Air holes and drain holes required in many plates and sections can be cut on a profile burner or by a punching press. A fully automated press can be used to punch round the elliptical holes, as well as rectangular and semicircular notches, at preset pitches along a plate or section. The machine is hydraulically powered and fed. Setting up is against datum rollers on the machine. Manual operation is possible, in addition to the automatic mode.

Guillotines

Hydraulically-powered shearing machines or guillotines are used for small jobbing work. The plates are fed, positioned and often held by hand. Small items, such as brackets and machinery space floor plates, may be produced in this manner.

Frame bender

Ship's frames are shaped by cold bending on a hydraulically-powered machine. Three initially in-line clamps hold part of the frame in position. The main rams then move the outer two clamps forward or backwards to bend the frame to the desired shape (*Figure 3.17*). The clamps are then released and the frame is advanced through the machine by a motorised drive. The next portion is then similarly bent. Offset bulb and angle bar plates can be bent two at a time, placed back to back. In this way, port and starboard frames are produced simultaneously.

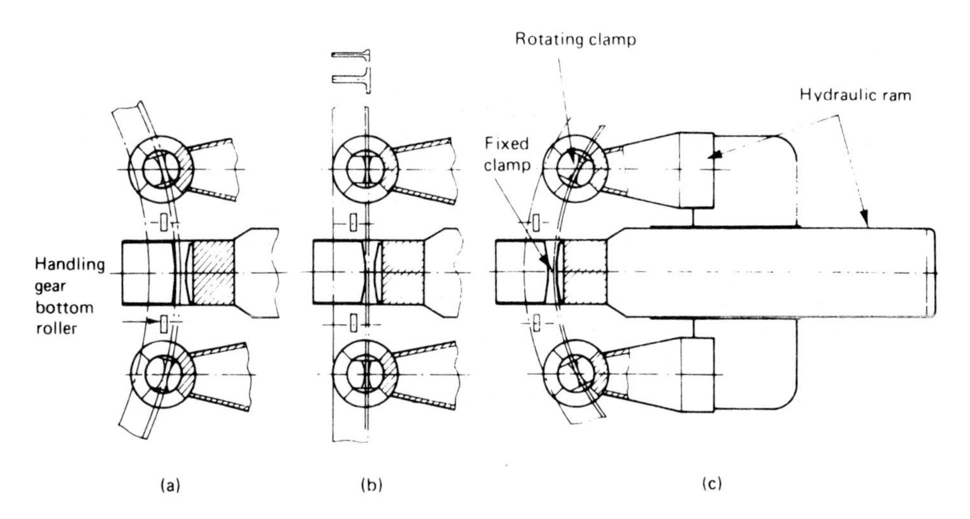

Figure 3.17 Frame bender operation: (a) bow flare bend; (b) initial position; (c) bilge turn bend

The machine can be controlled by hand and the frame bent to match a template made of wood or steel strip. Modern machines are now equipped for the numerical control of frame bending which enables fully automatic operation without the use of templates.

Materials handling equipment

Between the various machines and during build-up of the plates and sections into units, numerous items of materials-handling equipment are used.

Cranes of various types are used in shipyards. The overhead electric travelling crane (OETC) will be found in burning halls and fabrication shops. This crane traverses a gantry which is itself motorised to travel along rails mounted high on the walls of the hall or shop. Using this type of crane the sorting, loading and unloading operations can be combined and maximum use is made of the ground area. Lifting is usually accomplished by magnet beams, vacuum devices or grabs.

Goliath cranes are to be seen spanning the building docks of most new shipyards. Although of high first cost, this type of crane is flexible in use and covers the ground area very efficiently. Some degree of care is necessary in the region of the rails which run along the ground. Mobile cranes are used for internal materials movement, usually of a minor nature.

Special motorised heavy-lift trailers or transporters are used to transfer units and large items of steelwork around the shipyard and to the berth or building dock. Fork-lift trucks, trailer-pulling trucks, roller conveyor lines and various other devices are also used for materials movement of one kind or another.

Panel lines

Most modern shipyards use panel lines for the production of flat stiffened panels. A number of specialist work stations are arranged for the production of these panels.

The plates are first fed into the line, aligned, clamped and manually tack welded together. The plate seams are then welded on one side and the plate turned over. The second side welding of the plate seams then takes place. Some panel lines use a one-sided welding technique which removes the plate-turning operation. The panel is now flame planed to size and marked out for the webs and stiffeners which are to be fitted. The stiffeners are now injected from the side, positioned, clamped and welded on to the panel one after another. The stiffened panel is then transferred to the fabrication area if further build up is required, or despatched directly to the ship for erection. The process is shown in *Figure 3.18*.

Shipyard welding equipment

The equipment required for the manual welding of a ship's hull should enable the operator to use high amperages with large-gauge electrodes and yet still have adequate control of current for the various welding positions adopted and the plate thicknesses being welded. It should also be robust in construction and safe in operation.

Multi-operator systems, in which a three-phase transformer supplies up to six operators, are favoured in shipyard. Each operator has his own regulator and a supply of up to 150 A. The regulator is fed from an earthed distribution box on the transformer and provides a range of current selections. The regulator should be positioned fairly close to the welder both to reduce power losses and the time taken when changing current settings. Remote-controlled transformers, whose current can be altered by the welder through his electrode holder cable, are now fitted in some shipyards. The various welding processes are described in Chapter 4.

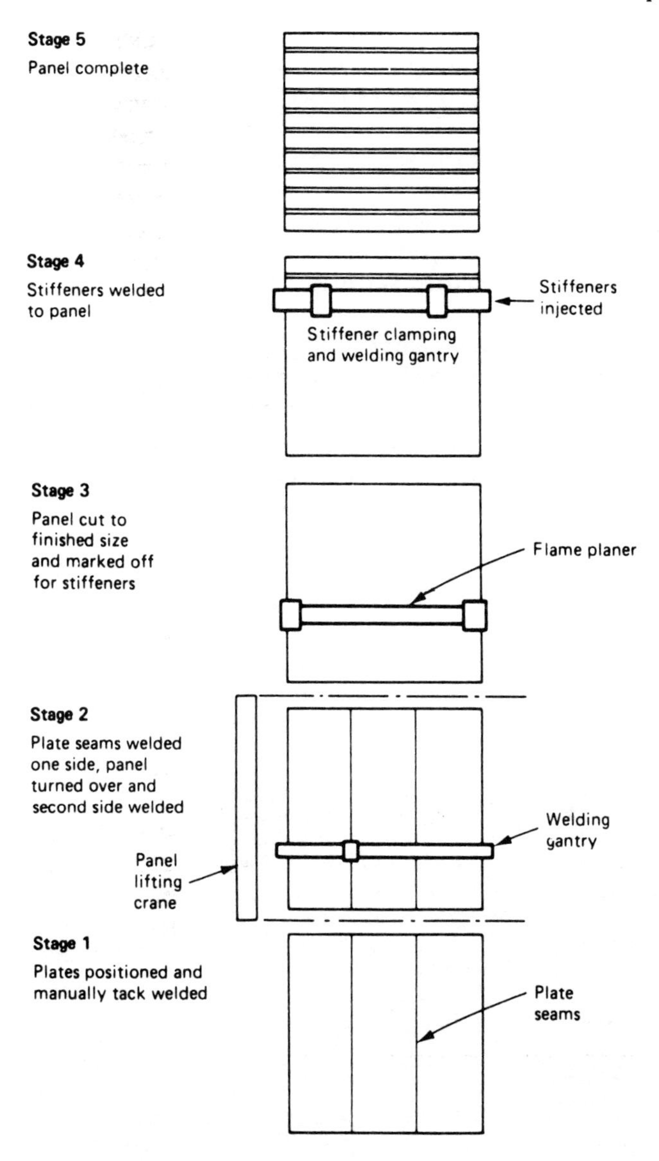

Figure 3.18 Panel line

Robots and automated manufacture

Computers have been in use for ship design for many years and numerous computer aided design (CAD) systems exist. Manufacturing has also benefited from computer applications and computer aided manufacture (CAM) has resulted in considerable savings in manpower and expenditure. Further developments continue and a more specific computer integrated manufacturing (CIM) approach is now being considered in many shipyards.

The computer support and control of many manufacturing and assembly processes may be seen in the use of robots, the design of workstations, flexible manufacturing systems and interfaces and links between various computer controlled machines and applications.

Robots were initially developed for welding to replace equipment such as gravity welders. Most now incorporate adaptive control whereby they can adjust to certain environmental conditions, recognise and also track the joint using tactile sensors or various forms of vision. The development of 'off-line programming' has speeded up the learning process and avoided the need to lead the robot through its operations before they are performed.

Robots designed for shipbuilding are generally large gantry structures or small portable units. The smaller units may be manually transported, self-propelled or even transported by another robot. Various shipyards have developed robots for such diverse purposes as flame cutting of shaped steel, welding, blasting and painting of steel sheet and even ship block assembly.

The first installation of a robot in a UK shipyard took place in 1982. All major shipbuilding nations now have robots in use and further development is progressing rapidly. A robotic beam processing line developed by Oxytechnik of Germany is shown in *Figure 3.19*. Work piece data is first loaded into the computer in the planning department. An input conveyor then automatically measures and feeds sections to a cutting robot. Cut-outs and edge preparation are made and then an output conveyor transfers the finished material to a storage area. Numerous different configurations can be programmed off-line and used from the shop floor as required.

Figure 3.19 Robotic section cutting

The one-off nature of much of today's shipbuilding will perhaps limit the large-scale application of robots in this industry. There still remain, however, many unpleasant, dangerous and difficult production tasks that can be undertaken by uncomplaining cost-effective robots.

4

Welding and Cutting Processes

In shipbuilding, welding is now the accepted method of joining metal. Welding is the fusing of two metals by heating to produce a joint which is as strong or stronger than the parent metal. All metals may be welded, but the degree of simplicity and the methods used vary considerably. All shipyard welding processes are of the fusion type, where the edges of the joint are melted and fuse with molten weld metal. The heat source for fusion welding may be provided by gas torch, electric arc or electric resistance.

Gas welding

A gas flame produced by the burning of oxygen and acetylene is used in this process. A hand-held torch is used to direct the flame around the parent metal and filler rods provide the metal for the joint (*Figure 4.1*). Gas welding is little used, having been superseded by the faster process of electric arc welding. Outfit trades, such as plumbers, may employ gas welding or use the gas flame for brazing or silver soldering.

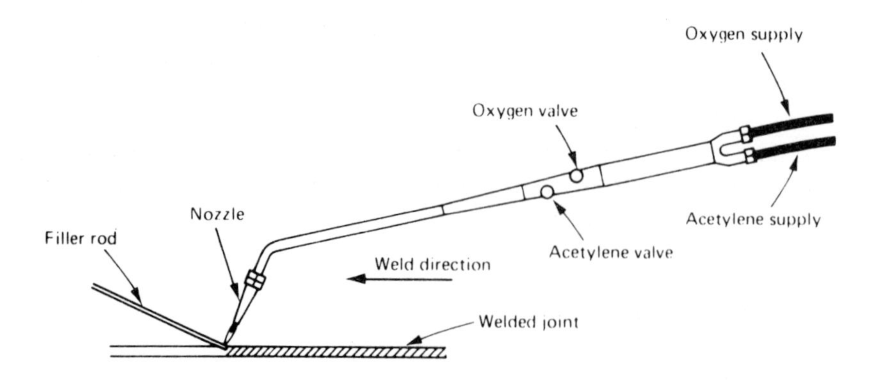

Figure 4.1 Gas welding with an oxy-acetylene torch

Electric arc welding

An electric arc is produced between two metals in an electric circuit when they are separated by a short distance. The basic circuit is shown in *Figure 4.2*. The metal to be welded forms one electrode in the circuit and the welding rod or wire forms the other. The electric arc produced creates a region of high temperature which melts and enables fusion of the metals to take place. Electric power is supplied via variable voltage a.c. transformers which may supply one or more welding operations.

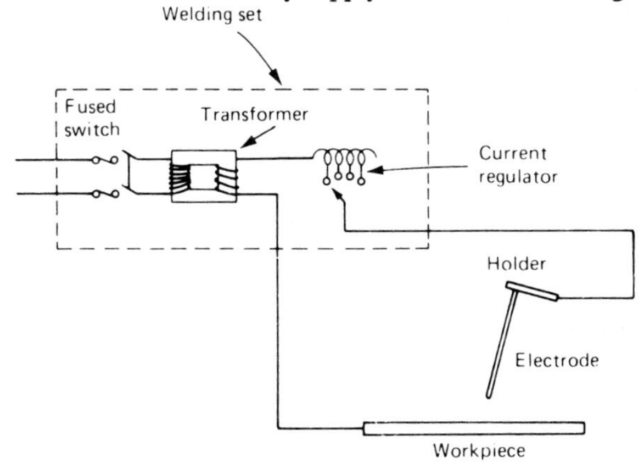

Figure 4.2 Electric arc welding circuit

In the actual welding operation the welding rod and plate are first touched together and quickly drawn apart some 4–5 mm to produce the arc across the gap. The temperature produced is in the region of 4000°C and current flow between the metals may be from 20 to 600 A. The current flow must be preset or adjusted, depending upon the metal type and thickness and the supply voltage. The voltage across the arc affects the amount of penetration and the profile or shape of the metal deposited. The current to a large extent determines the amount of weld metal deposited. A high quality weld is produced with several thin layers of weld metal, but it is less costly to use a single heavy deposit of weld metal.

If excessive current is used weld spatter, i.e. tiny blobs of metal deposited around the weld, may occur.

For a satisfactory weld, atmospheric gases must be excluded and the control of the arc must be easily achieved. This is done by shielding the arc during the welding process. A gas shield is produced by one of two basic methods, either by the burning of a flux or the provision of a gas shield directly.

Processes using flux

Manual welding

In the manual welding process a consumable electrode or welding rod is held in a holder and fed on to the parent metal by the operator. The welding rod is a flux-coated mild steel electrode. The metal of the electrode is normally rimming steel. This is a ductile material which does not contain silicon or aluminium, both of which tend to affect the electric arc. The rod coatings are made up of cellulose, mineral silicates, oxides, fluorides, basic carbonates and powdered metal alloys. The particular constituents used are held together with a binding material such as sodium silicate. The coating covers the length of the core wire, except where it fits into the holder.

Electrodes are classified according to their flux coatings as given in the International Standard ISO 2560:1973(E). The two basic types are the rutile-coated electrode and the hydrogen-controlled electrode. Rutile is an almost pure mineral form of titanium oxide and is the principal ingredient of rutile-coated electrodes. It increases slag viscosity, decreases spatter and improves slag detachability. Rutile electrodes are general-purpose, giving a good finish and a sound weld. Hydrogen-controlled or basic electrodes deposit weld metal which is low in hydrogen content. They are used for the welding of highly stressed joints and the higher tensile steels. The coatings contain major proportions of carbonates and fluorides which are baked on to reduce the water content of the coating to a very low level.

Manual welding may be accomplished in any direction, the three basic modes being downhand, vertical and overhead, and some combinations of these modes are shown in *Figure 4.3*. The correct type of electrode must be used, together with considerable skill, in particular for the overhead and vertical welding positions. As far as possible, welding is arranged in the downhand mode.

The gravity welder is a device consisting of a tripod, one leg of which acts as a rail for a sliding electrode holder (*Figure 4.4*). Once positioned and the arc struck, the weight of the electrode and holder cause it to slide down the rail and deposit weld

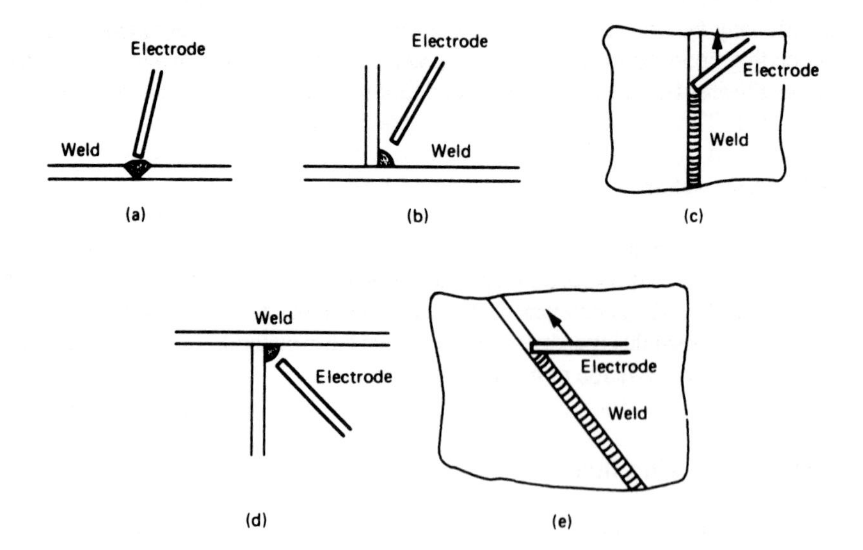

Figure 4.3 Welding positions: (a) horizontal or downhand; (b) horizontal/vertical; (c) vertical; (d) overhead; (e) inclined

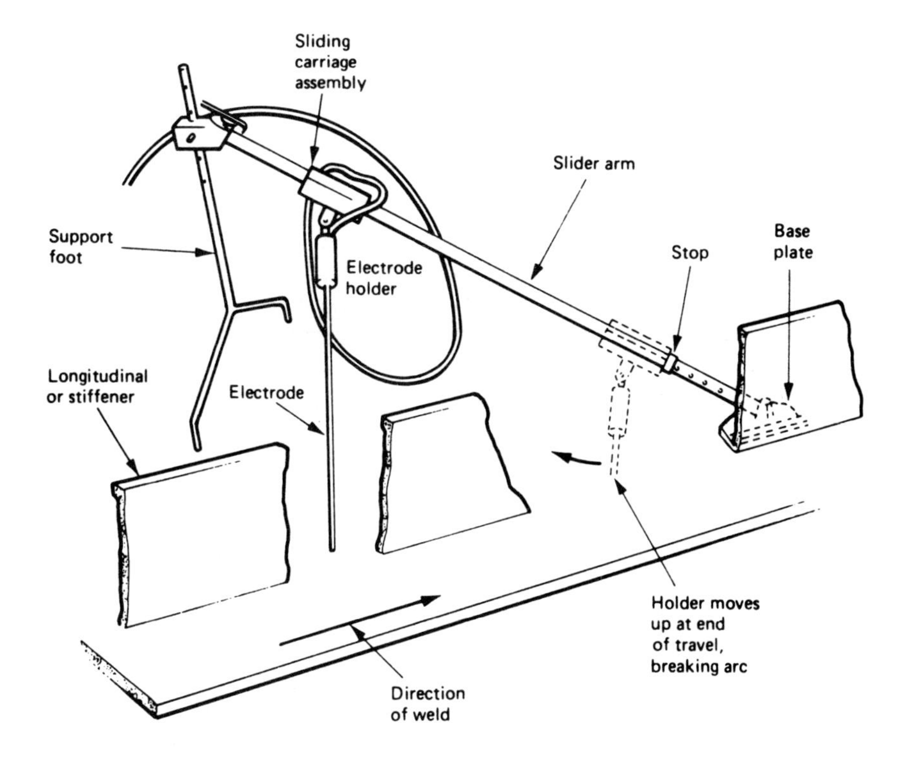

Figure 4.4 Gravity welder

metal along a joint. The angle of the sliding rail will determine the amount of metal deposited. At the bottom of the rail a trip mechanism moves the electrode to break the arc. One man is able to operate several of these devices simultaneously.

Automatic welding

In the automatic machine welding process, travel along the metal takes place at a fixed speed with a flux-covered electrode fed on to the joint. The correct arc length and metal deposition are achieved by the machine, the specially spiralled flux coating providing the shield during welding. Only downhand welding of horizontal joints is possible with this machine.

The arc may be additionally sealed with carbon dioxide gas to permit higher currents for high speed welding. A twin-fillet version is also available for stiffener welding to flat plates or panels (*Figure 4.5*).

Another automatic machine welding process, submerged arc welding, uses a bare wire electrode and separately fed granulated flux. The flux melts to produce a gas shield for the arc and a molten covering. Large metal deposits at high speeds, without air entrainment, are therefore possible in this very efficient process. The process is shown diagrammatically in *Figure 4.6(a)*. The unused flux may be re-

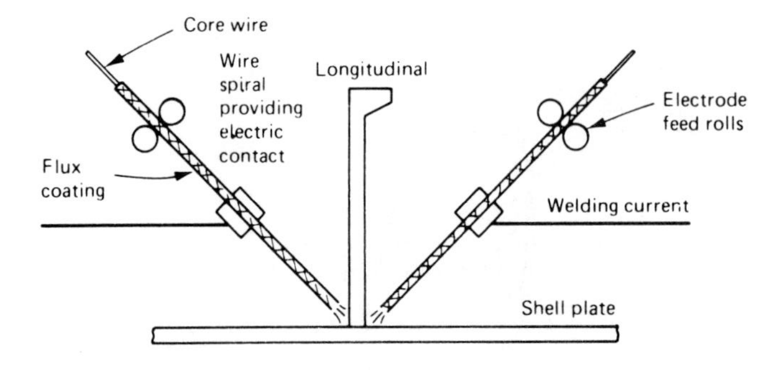

Figure 4.5 Automatic flux-coated electrode welding using a twin-headed machine

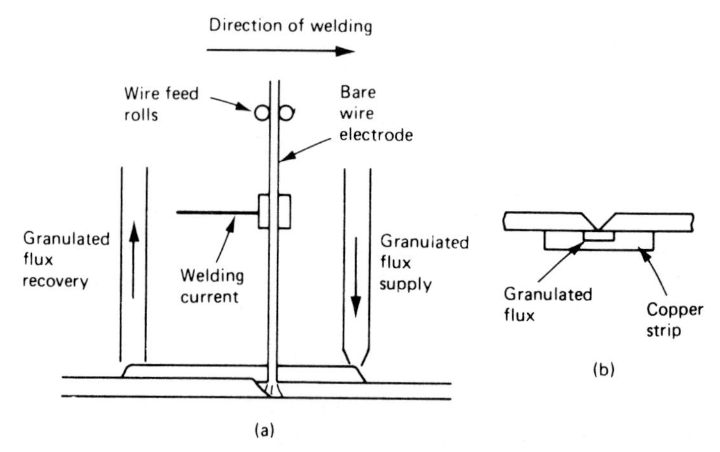

Figure 4.6 (a) Submerged arc welding; (b) backing plate arrangement for one-sided welding

covered for re-use. This is a process for horizontal, i.e. downhand, operation only and may be operated normally, welding both sides, or as a one-sided welding process. In the normal process the downhand weld is made and the plate is turned over, or an overhead weld is made from below. Some veeing out of the joint may be necessary for the final run. In the one-sided process various forms of backing plate can be used; one example is shown in *Figure 4.6(b)*. Any defects in the weld will then have to be repaired by veeing out the welding from the other side. This process is limited to indoor undercover use and is unsuitable for use on the berth.

Electroslag welding

The vertical welding of plate thicknesses in excess of 13 mm is efficiently achieved by this process. Initially an arc is struck but the process continues by electrical resistance heating through the slag. The weld pool is contained by cooled shoes

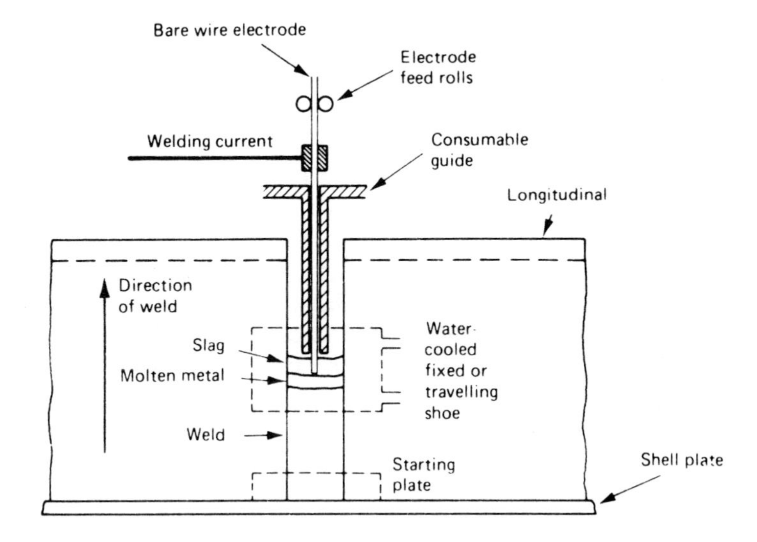

Figure 4.7 Electroslag welding

placed either side of the plate which may be moved up the plate mechanically or manually in separate sections. Alternatively, shoes the height of the weld may be fixed in place either side. The bare wire electrode is usually fed from the top through a consumable guide and acts as the electrode of the circuit. Run-on and run-off plates are required at the beginning and end of the weld and no stoppage must occur during the process. The arrangement is shown diagrammatically in *Figure 4.7.*

Electrogas welding

This process is particularly suited to shipbuilding since vertical plates of thicknesses in the range 13–40 mm are efficiently joined. Cooled shoes are again used but a flux-coated electrode is now employed. Fusion is achieved by an arc between the electrode and the metal, and a carbon dioxide gas shield is supplied through the upper region of the shoes. The arrangement is similar to *Figure 4.7* (electroslag welding) with the carbon dioxide supplied through the top of the shoes.

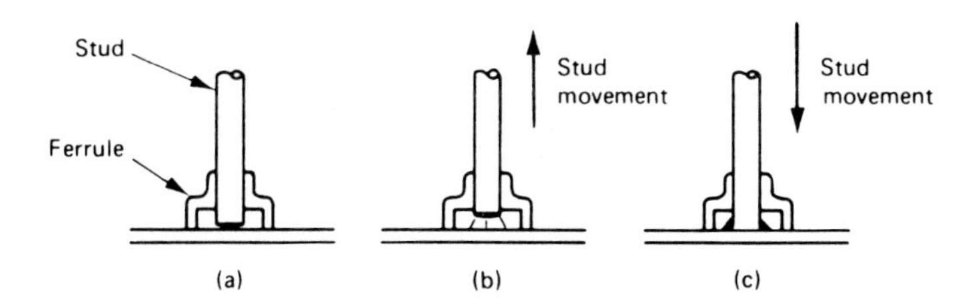

Figure 4.8 Stud welding: (a) stud and ferrule placed on plate; (b) arc drawn; (c) weld completed

Stud welding

A machine or gun as part of the electric circuit is used in stud welding. In one method the stud is fed into the clutch and a ceramic ferrule is placed over the end. The stud is placed against the metal surface and the operation of the gun trigger withdraws the stud to create an arc (*Figure 4.8*). After a period of arcing, the stud is driven into the molten metal pool and welding takes place. The ferrule concentrates the arc, reduces the access of air and confines the molten metal area. Flux is contained in the end of the stud.

Another method uses a fusible collar over the end of the stud which conducts electricity to create the arc and then collapses, forcing the stud into the molten metal pool and forming the weld. Welded studs are used for securing insulation to bulkheads and for other sheathings. Other types of stud, in the form of bolts, hooks and rings, are also available.

Processes using gas

These are welding processes employing a bare electrode or welding wire with a gas shield. Automatic or semi-automatic operation is usual. With automatic operation, once set the process is controlled by the machine. In semi-automatic operation certain machine settings are made but the torch is hand held and the process is to some extent controlled by the operator.

Tungsten inert gas (TIG)

This is a process for thin sheet metal such as steel or aluminium. A water-cooled non-consumable tungsten electrode and the plate material have an arc created between them by a high frequency discharge across the gap. The inert gas shield is usually argon gas. The process is shown in *Figure 4.9*.

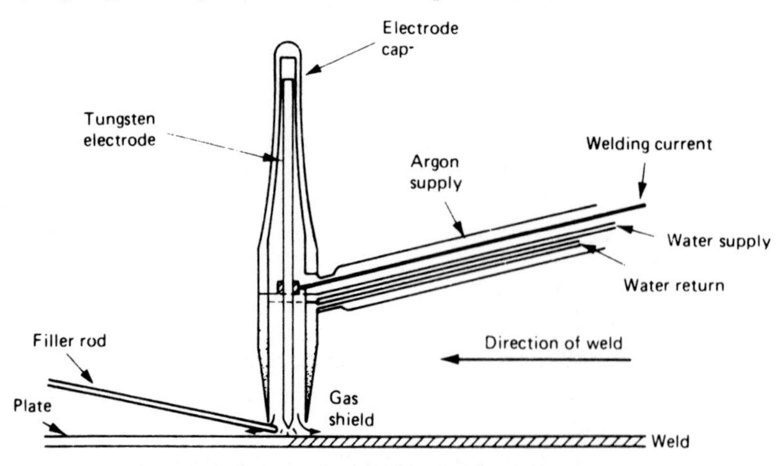

Figure 4.9 Tungsten inert gas process

Metal inert gas (MIG)

A consumable metal wire electrode is used in this process and is fed through the holder or torch from a feed unit (*Figure 4.10*). An inert gas is fed through the torch to shield the arc and the torch and plate are part of an electric circuit. The supply source is usually d.c. and the process may be fully or semi-automatic in operation.

In steel welding using this process, carbon dioxide may be the shielding gas and plating of any thickness may be welded. Controls within the wire feed unit enable a range of constant wire feeds related to the current to be selected. With carbon dioxide gas, the arc characteristic changes with the current from a short-circuiting (dip transfer) arc at low currents to a spray arc at high currents. Dip transfer allows all positions of welding, but the spray arc is downhand only. Dip transfer is ideally suited to thinner materials, since it produces less distortion effects. This process is being used increasingly in shipbuilding.

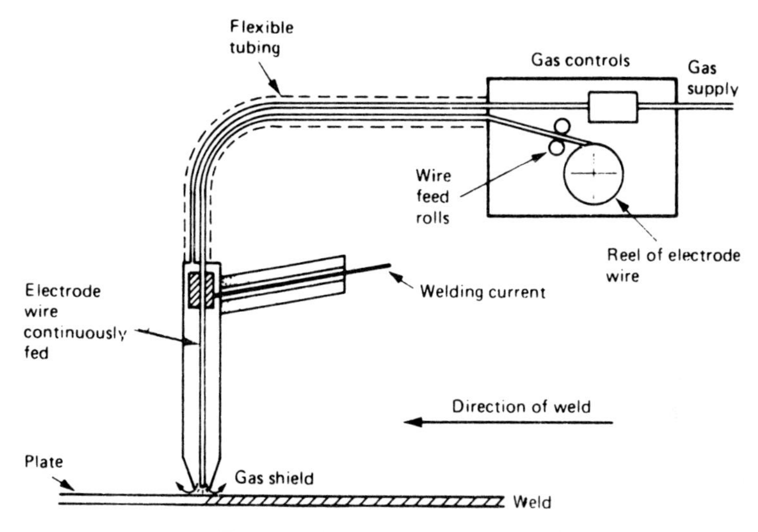

Figure 4.10 Metal inert gas process

Plasma metal inert gas

This is a further development of the metal inert gas process which incorporates a plasma arc around the MIG arc. The plasma is an ionised stream of gas which surrounds the MIG arc and concentrates its effect on to the metal. The plasma arc has its own set of controls for its electric circuit. It is initially ignited by the MIG arc and with both arcs individually controlled the process can be finely 'tuned' to the material requirements. Automatic and semi-automatic versions are available. The semi-automatic version uses a dual-flow nozzle arrangement, as shown in *Figure 4.11*, with a single supply of gas, usually argon, as the shielding and the plasma gases. The torch used is no heavier than a conventional MIG torch and the process has the advantages of higher weld metal deposition rates and the use of a narrower vee preparation, which may be as small as 30 degrees.

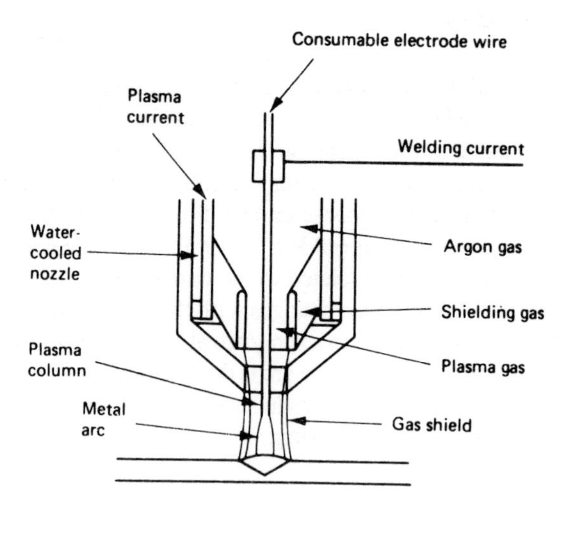

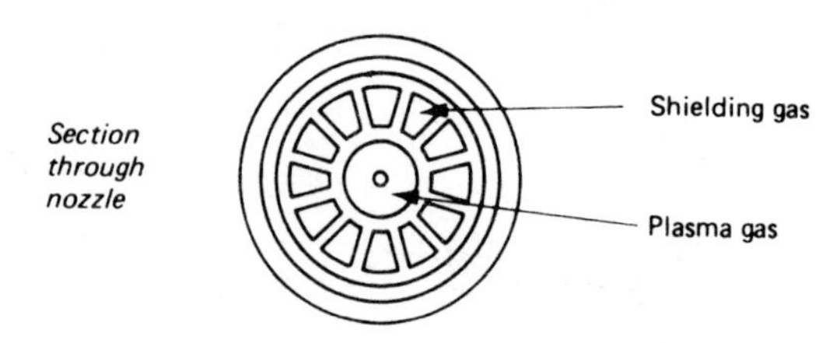

Figure 4.11 Plasma metal inert gas process

Thermit welding

This is a fusion process taking place as a result of the heat released in a chemical reaction between powdered aluminium and iron oxide ignited by barium peroxide. The parts to be welded are usually large sections, such as a sternframe, and they are positioned together in a sand or graphite mould. The molten steel and slag from the chemical reaction is first formed in a crucible and then run into the mould.

Types of weld

A number of different welded joints are used, depending upon their situation, material thickness, required strength, etc. The depth of weld may require more than one pass or run of weld to build up to the workpiece thickness. Reversing the workpiece, gouging out and a final back-run will also be necessary unless a one-sided technique is employed.

The butt weld is the strongest joint when subjected to tension and is illustrated in *Figure 4.12*. The single-V type of preparation is used for the butt weld for plate thicknesses in excess of 6 mm up to a maximum of 20 mm. Below 6 mm, a square

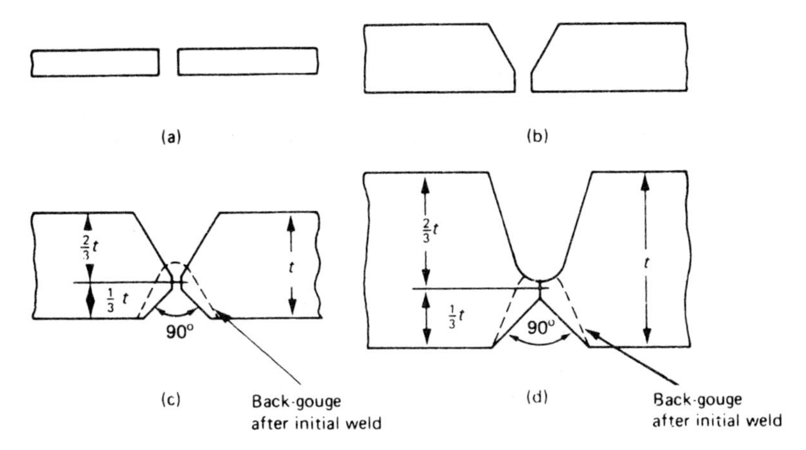

Figure 4.12 Butt weld preparations: (a) square butt joint; (b) single-V butt joint; (c) double-V butt joint; (d) double-U butt joint

edge preparation may be employed and for very thick plates a double-V preparation is used. A U-weld preparation is also used which requires less weld metal and gives a better quality joint in return for a more expensive edge preparation.

Fillet welds are used for right-angled plate joints and lapped joints, as shown in *Figure 4.13*. Two particular terms are used in relation to fillet welds—the leg length, *L*, and the throat thickness, *T*—as shown in *Figure 4.13(a)*. The leg length is related to the thickness of the abutting plate and the throat thickness must be at least 70%

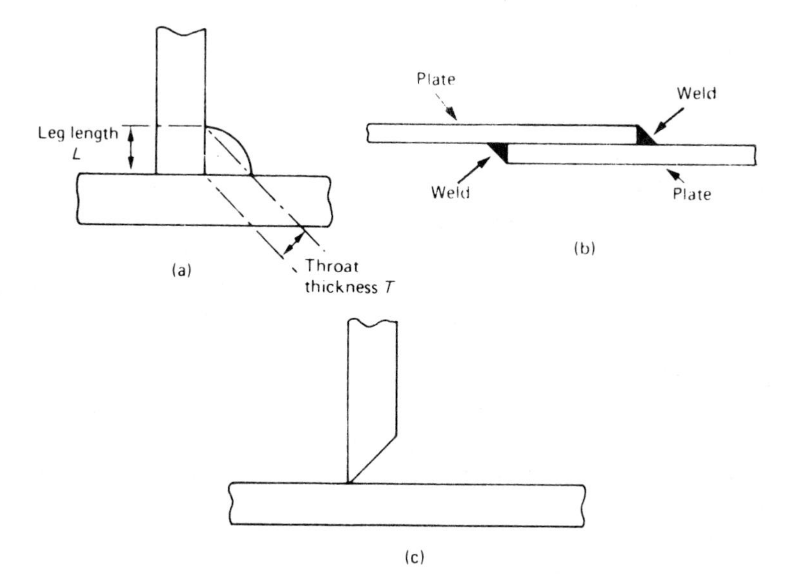

Figure 4.13 Fillet welds: (a) fillet weld; (b) lap weld; (c) fillet weld with full penetration preparation

of *L*. A full penetration type of fillet weld may be used where special strength is required. A full penetration joint is shown in *Figure 4.13(c)*. The abutting plate is of V or J preparation to ensure full penetration when welding.

The fillet welds described may be arranged in a number of ways, depending on structural requirements. Fully continuous welds are used in important strength connections and for oiltight and watertight connections. Chain and intermittent welds are spaced sections of welding and are shown in *Figure 4.14*. Some savings in weight and distortion are possible for lightly stressed material which does not require watertight joints.

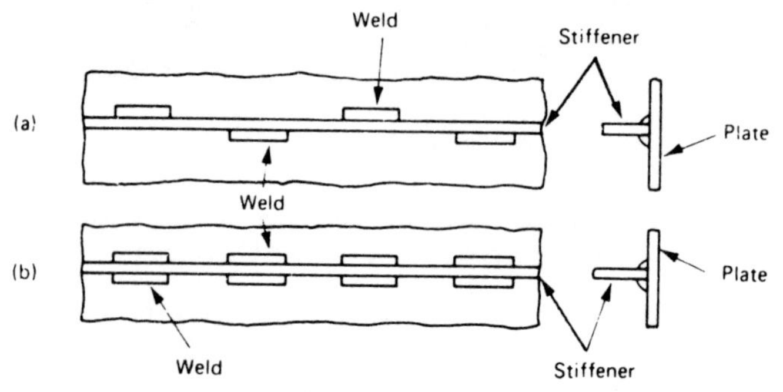

Figure 4.14 Non-continuous fillet welds: (a) intermittent welding; (b) chain welding

Tack welds are short runs of weld on any joint to be welded. They are used to initially align and hold the material prior to the finished joint. They are assembly welds and must be subject to a full welding procedure. They should not be less than 75 mm in length to ensure a sufficient heat input, and should not be welded over.

Welding practice

The welding of the metal, because of the localised concentration of heat, gives rise to areas of plating which first expand and later contract on cooling. The effect of this, and the difference in deposited weld metal and parent metal properties, results in distortion of the workpiece. The appearance of distortion may be in one or more of the following forms—longitudinal shrinkage, transverse shrinkage, and angular distortion. *Figure 4.15* illustrates these various effects.

The cause of distortion may be attributable to several possible factors acting individually or together. The concentrated heating of the welded area and its subsequent later contraction will affect the weld metal and the workpiece in different ways. As a consequence, stresses will be set up in the weld, the two joined workpieces and the overall structure.

The degree of restraint permitted to the welded joint will affect its distortion. Where welded joints are unrestrained their subsequent weld shrinkage will relieve any stresses set up. Restrained joints, by virtue of the rigidity of the structure or some applied form of clamping, induce high stresses to the weld and cracking may occur if the correct welding sequences are not adopted.

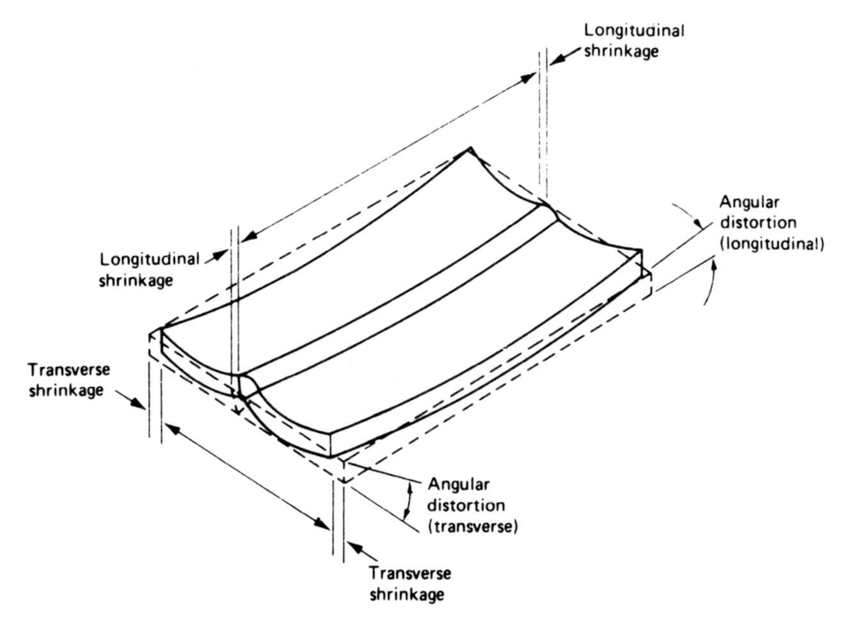

Figure 4.15 Distortion effects

The properties of the workpiece and the possible stresses 'locked in' it due to manufacturing processes may be altered or affected by welding and lead to distortion.

Distortion prevention

Good design should ensure as few welded joints as possible in a structure, particularly when it is made up of thin section plate. Where they exist, welded joints should be accessible, preferably for downhand welding.

The edge preparation of the joints can be arranged to reduce distortion, as shown in *Figure 4.16*. A single-V preparation joint with four runs of welding will distort as shown. A double-V preparation joint welded with four runs in the order shown will only exhibit slight shrinkage of the joined plates.

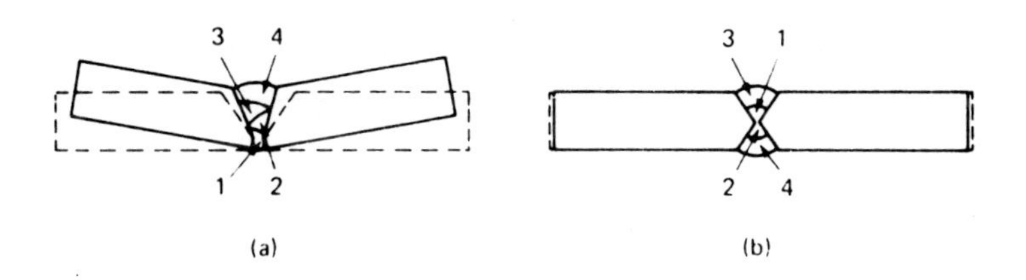

Figure 4.16 Edge preparation to reduce distortion: (a) single-V preparation giving considerable distortion (1 first welding run, 2 second welding run, 3 third welding run, 4 final welding run); (b) double-V preparation giving only slight shrinkage

Restraint is the usual method of distortion prevention in shipbuilding. Where units are faired ready for welding they are tack welded to hold them in place during welding. The parts will then remain dimensionally correct and the rigidity of the structure will usually restrain any distortion. Strongbacks or clamping arrangements are also used on butt and fillet welds, as shown in *Figure 4.17*.

All welds 'shrink', so the use of the correct procedure in welding can do much to reduce distortion. The fewer runs involved in a welded joint, the less will be the distortion. Symmetrical welding either side of a joint with a double-V preparation will produce a distortion-free weld. Simultaneous welding by two operators is therefore a useful technique which should be practised whenever possible. Welding should always take place towards the free or unrestrained end of a joint. For long welding runs several techniques are used to minimise distortion. The back-step method is illustrated in *Figure 4.18*. Here the operator welds the joint in sections in

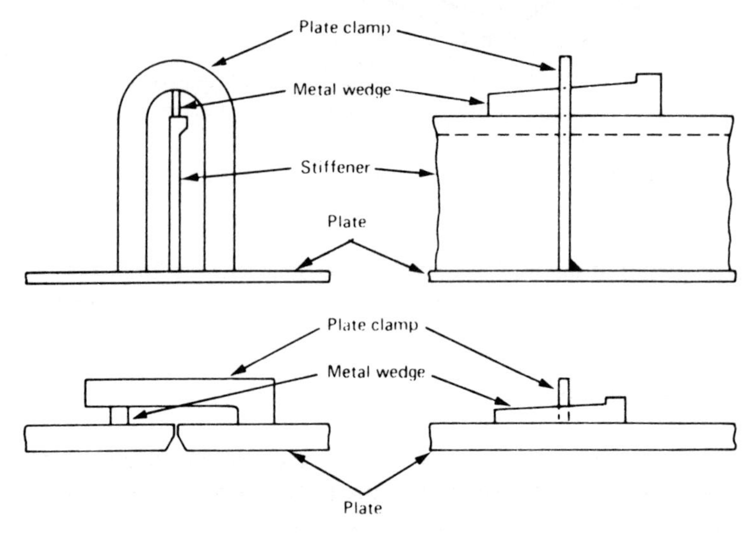

Figure 4.17 Clamping arrangements

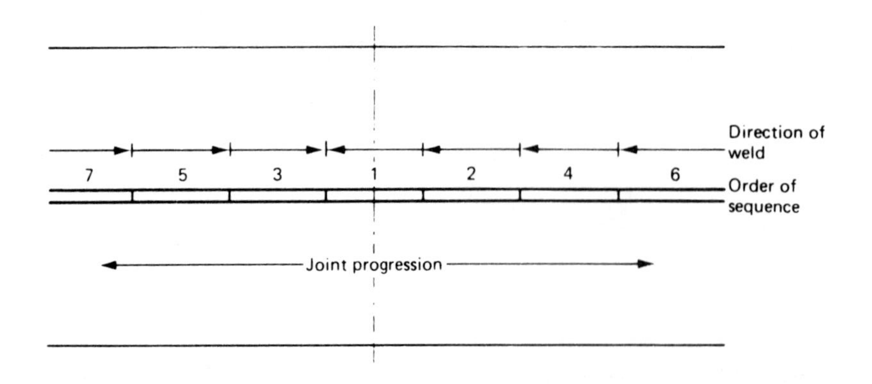

Figure 4.18 Back-step welding technique

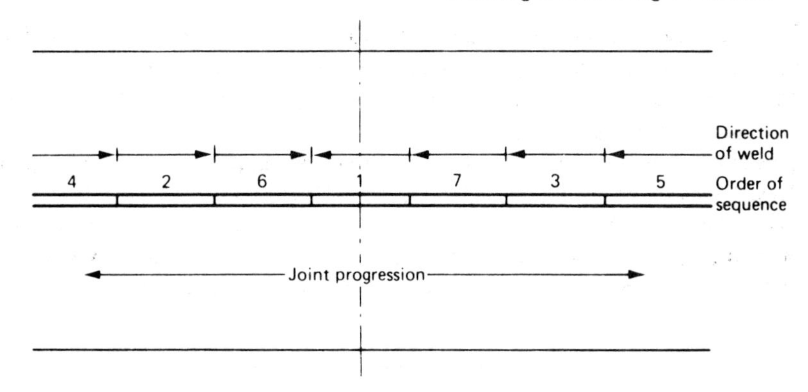

Figure 4.19 *Skip or wandering welding technique*

the numerical order and direction shown. A variation of this is 'skip' welding, which is shown in *Figure 4.19*, and likewise progresses in the numerical order and direction shown. Distortion may then be controlled by balancing the welding as much as possible and allowing the weld shrinkage to occur freely. Welding sequences taking this into account should be well thought out before welding commences.

Distortion correction

Despite the most stringent methods to eliminate it, distortion can still occur. Where the distortion in a joint is considered unacceptable the joint must be gouged, grooved or completely split, and then re-welded. Strongbacks may be placed across the joint to restrain distortion during re-welding.

Straightforward mechanical means may be used, such as hydraulic jacks or hammering on localised areas of distortion or buckling. Where such methods involve straining the welds, they should be examined for cracks after correction. Every effort should be made to avoid mechanically straightening structures for this reason.

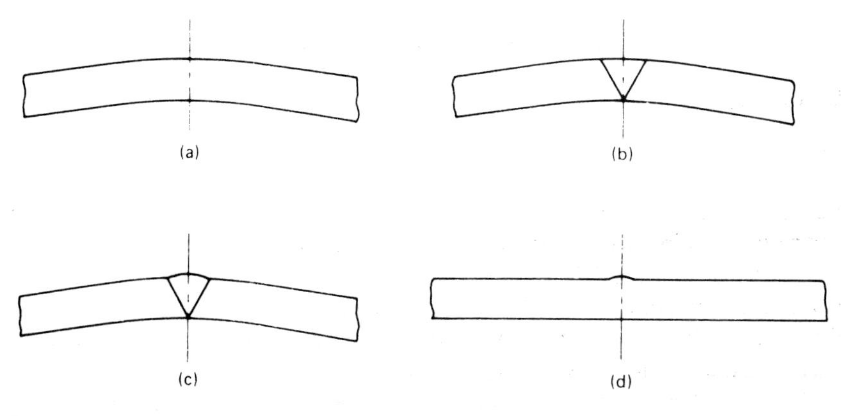

Figure 4.20 *Spot heating: (a) curved plate; (b) heated; (c) expansion; (d) levelled plate*

The application of concentrated heat from a gas-burning torch may be used for correcting distortion in steels other than the higher tensile, quenched and tempered types. The process is shown in *Figure 4.20*. A small area is heated on the side where the contraction would bring about an improvement. The steel is heated to a 'red heat' and the torch slowly moved along a previously drawn line, at such a speed that the 'red heat' does not pass right through the material. The area heated wants to expand, but is resisted by the surrounding material. The recrystallisation absorbs the expansion and, on cooling, contraction occurs which brings about a favourable distortion, thus correcting the original distortion structure (*Figure 4.21*).

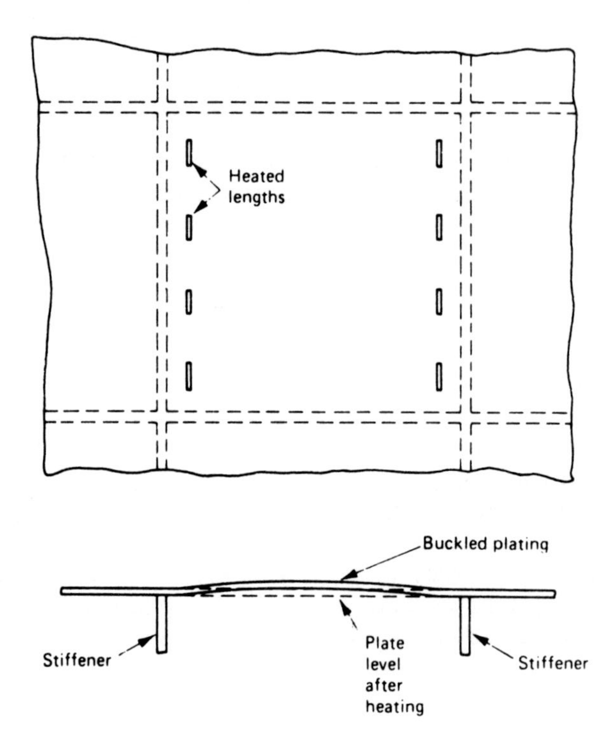

Figure 4.21 Distortion correction

Weld faults

The weld

Faults may occur in welding as in any other process. These faults may arise from bad workmanship, incorrect procedures, wrong materials used, etc. A good weld is illustrated in *Figure 4.22(a)*. In such a weld a degree of fusion should have taken place at the sides of the weld. There should be no overlap or undercut at the toe of the weld. A slight reinforcement or build-up of material should be present at the top surface and there should be root penetration along the bottom surface.

A bad weld is shown in *Figure 4.22(b)*. The absence of reinforcement and root penetration are the result of incorrect procedure or bad workmanship. Overlap is

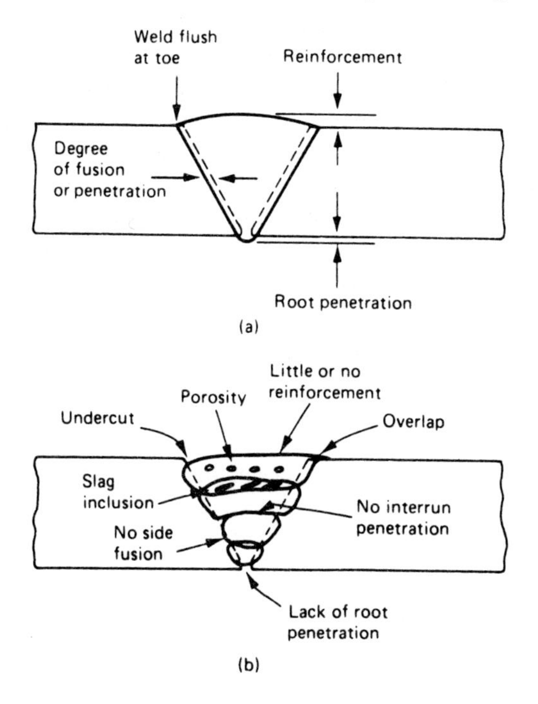

Figure 4.22 Examples of welds: (a) a good weld; (b) a bad weld

infused metal lying over the parent metal. Undercut is the wastage of parent metal, probably caused by too high a welding current. Porosity is caused by gases trapped in the weld. Slag inclusion is the result of inadequate cleaning between weld runs. Poor fusion or penetration between runs may be due to poor cleaning or incorrect voltage or current settings. The result of a bad weld is a weak or faulty joint. A bad weld can also be the starting point for a crack.

Lamellar tearing

Lamellar tearing around welded joints has become a problem as plate thicknesses have increased and structures have become more rigid. Lamellar tearing is a brittle cracking

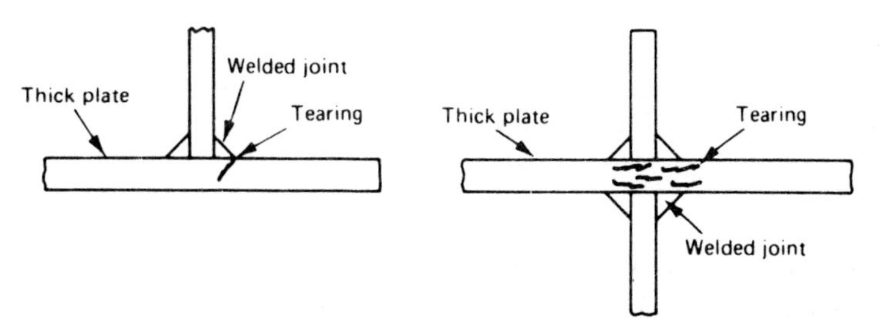

Figure 4.23 Examples of lamellar tearing

in steel plate as a result of tensile stresses at right-angles to the plate. It is caused by the contraction of weld metal when cooling. Lamellar tearing is most likely to occur when thick plates, large weldments and high internal connection restraint are all present. The characteristic 'tear' occurs in the cross-plate of a T-configuration and may begin at the toe or root of a weld or at some point below the weld (*Figure 4.23*).

One method of reducing the problem of lamellar tearing is the use of 'clean' steels such as those produced by the vacuum degassed process. Other measures include the use of joint configurations which avoid right angle tensile stressing of the plate, or preheating the plate before welding.

Weld testing

Several non-destructive techniques are used in the examination of welded joints. These include visual examination, dye penetrants, magnetic particles, radiography and ultrasonic methods. Destructive testing of special test plates and their welded joints is required for certain classes of work but most shipbuilding weld testing is non-destructive.

The trained experienced inspector and surveyor can detect surface defects and flaws in welds by visual examination. He may also request more detailed examination of known problem areas or regions of high stress. His constant vigilance and attendance during the welding up of a ship ensures good work and satisfactory standards of welding.

Magnetic particle testing is a surface examination technique. A mixture of iron filings in thin white paint is spread over a welded joint. The joint is then magnetised by attaching a large permanent magnet to it. Discontinuities then show up as concentrations of iron filings, resulting from the distorted magnetic field.

Dye penetrants are spread over the surface of a joint and then wiped or washed off. The weld surface is then examined using an ultraviolet light. Any crack will contain the luminous dye and will be readily visible.

Radiographic inspection is a means of 'photographing' welded joints. A photographic plate is exposed to radiations from X-ray or gamma ray devices on the far side of the joint. Any inclusions or gas holes will then show up on the photographic plate.

Ultrasonic inspection uses pulses of ultrasonic energy which are reflected at any surface they meet. For the ultrasonic waves to initially enter the metal a coupling medium is necessary. Cellulose paste has been found to be effective and peels off easily after use. A cathode ray tube is used to 'read' the reflection patterns and very minor flaws may be detected with this method of testing. It is particularly effective for detecting plate laminations and the degree of root penetration in welds.

Classification society weld testing

The classification societies require various tests, some of them destructive, in order to approve weld materials and electrodes. Joints made between the materials and the electrodes are then subjected to various strength, metallurgical and other tests.

Welding aluminium to steel

The bimetallic joint where, for example, an aluminium superstructure joins a steel hull, used to be bolted with appropriate insulation to prevent galvanic corrosion. A welded joint is now generally used with a transition bar fitted between the two materials. The transition bar is an explosively bonded laminate of steel and aluminium alloy with pure aluminium used at the interface. Examples of these materials are Kelocouple, Nitro Metal and Tri-Clad.

Taking Tri-Clad as an example, this is initially a 'sandwich' of aluminium alloy, pure aluminium and steel with polystyrene spacers between and a layer of dynamite on top. When the dynamite is detonated the plates are forced together and, in effect, welded into a single transition plate. After welding, or cladding as this process is often called, the plates are flattened and 100% ultrasonically tested.

The Tri-Clad transition plate is 35 mm thick and made up of 19 mm of A516gr55 steel, 9.5 mm of pure aluminium and 6.5 mm of sea water resistant Al/Mg alloy 5086. The ultimate tensile strength of the transition plate is about 100 N/mm^2. This material has been accepted for marine use by most classification societies.

In use the transition plate should be at least four times the thickness of the aluminium plate which is to be welded to it. This is because of the low strength of the plate and also to avoid problems at the interface when welding. The alloy plate should always be positioned in the centre of the transition plate and preferably welded first.

MIG equipment and techniques are preferred using argon shielding with a current of 300 A and a potential difference of 27 to 29 V. Standard welding techniques are acceptable for the steel side of the joint using low hydrogen, mild steel coated electrodes. Typical joint arrangements using bolts with insulating materials and the alternative transition plate are shown in *Figure 4.24*.

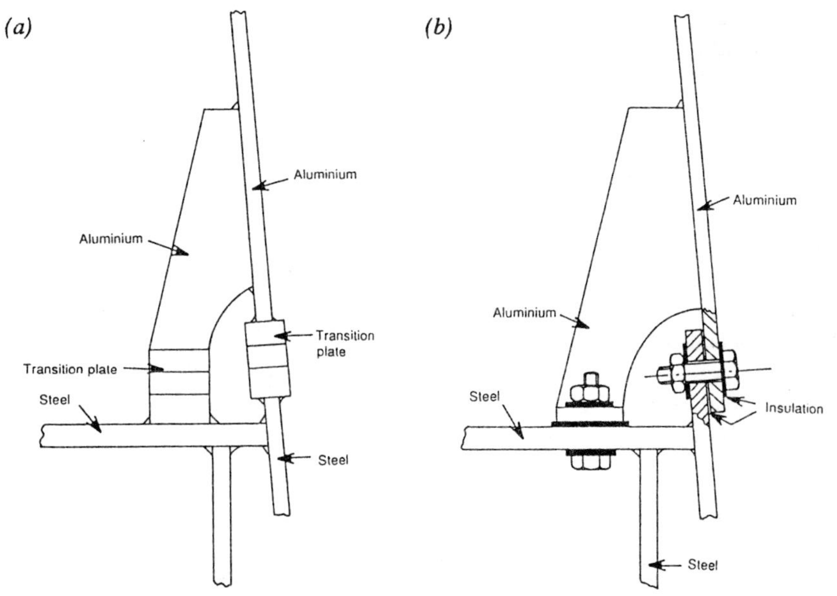

Figure 4.24 Joining aluminium to steel: (a) welding; (b) bolting

Corrosion is not a problem with transition plates since they form an extremely hard and inert corrosion product; aluminium oxide hydrate. This acts as a seal at any unpainted or exposed part of the plate and renders the system passive. Differential expansion is not a problem, since only a relatively small force will be built up even for a significant change in temperature.

Cutting processes

The majority of metal cutting in shipyards utilises gas cutting techniques. Plasma arc and gouging cutting techniques are also being increasingly used.

Gas cutting

During gas cutting the metal is, in effect, 'cut' by oxidising and blowing away a narrow band of material. The metal is heated by the preheat section of the flame and then oxidised by a stream of high pressure oxygen which carries away the oxidised metal. A narrow gap with parallel sides remains along the line of the cutting process, but large amounts of elements such as chromium may prevent this problem, particularly with stainless steel.

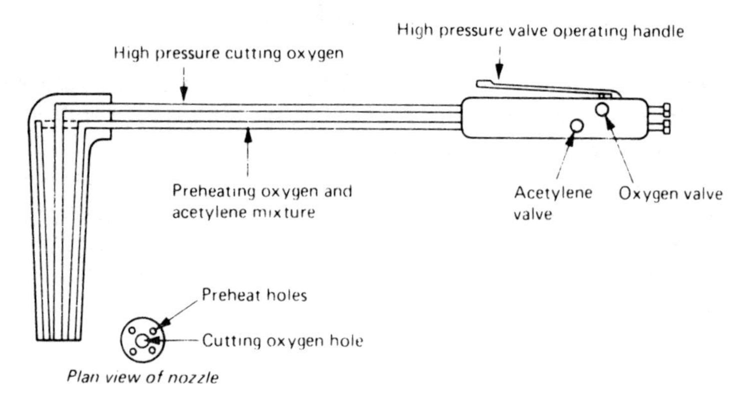

Figure 4.25 Oxy-acetylene cutting torch

Acetylene or propane is usually used as the preheating gas, in conjunction with oxygen. A typical cutting torch is shown in *Figure 4.25*. Automated arrangements of cutting torches are used in various machines for edge preparation, flame planing, etc., as mentioned in Chapter 3. An edge preparation arrangement of torches is shown in *Figure 4.26*.

Plasma arc cutting

The cutting torch consists of a tungsten electrode located in a water-cooled nozzle which acts as one electrode in the circuit (*Figure 4.27*). The material to be cut is the

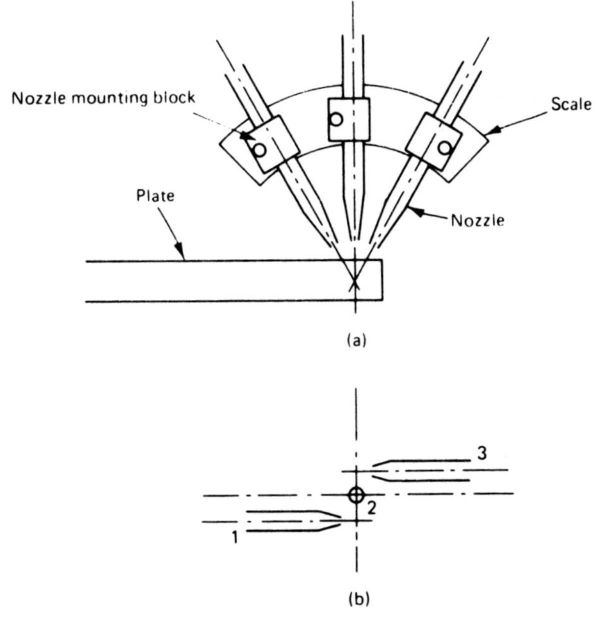

Figure 4.26 Edge preparation: (a) triple-nozzle head; (b) plan view of nozzles showing order of operation

other electrode and the circuit is completed by a stream of ionised gas which will conduct electricity. This 'plasma gas' is supplied around the tungsten electrode and constricts the arc formed between it and the metal plate.

A very high temperature region is created at the arc which melts the metal and cuts through it. The gas is initially ionised by a short electrical discharge between the electrode and the nozzle. Inert gases such as argon have been used but modern developments have enabled air or oxygen to be used. This is an automated cutting process which is much faster than other methods.

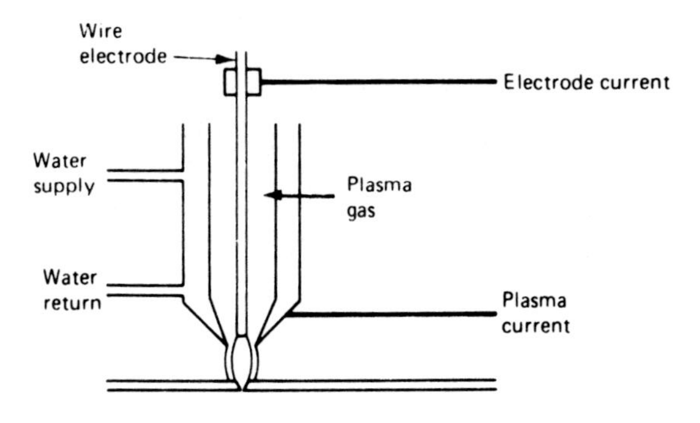

Figure 4.27 Plasma arc cutting torch

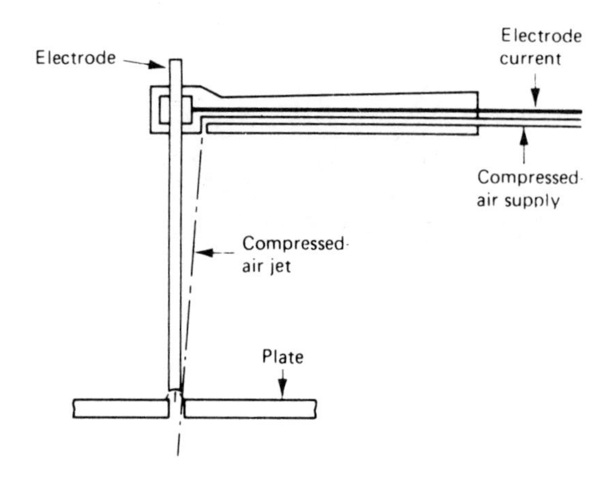

Figure 4.28 Arc-air gouging

Water jetting

Traditional metal cutting techniques using flame torches create edge distortions and stresses in the plate. Thin plates in particular, are affected. The use of high pressure water jets has been found to give excellent plate edge quality, although the process is a little slow.

The water jet process uses a very fine jet of water into which an abrasive medium has been introduced. Water pressures as high as 2 000 to 4 000 bar are used, with the lower pressure being for transportable equipment and the higher value for fixed production line equipment.

Gouging

Gouging steel plate by 'arc-air' or by a special cutter fitted to a gas torch is a way of removing metal for the 'back-runs' of a butt weld. Gas or arc welding processes may be modified for gouging purposes. Arc-air gouging consists of a solid copper-clad carbon graphite electrode in a special holder which has a compressed air pipe attached. A stream of compressed air is blown from a jet on to the workpiece to oxidise and remove the molten metal at the point of cutting. Another arrangement uses tubular electrodes to provide the high temperature arc. The air is blown down the inside of the electrode. The electrodes are consumed in both these processes. The solid electrode arrangement is shown in *Figure 4.28*.

5

Major Structural Items

SECTION A KEEL AND BOTTOM CONSTRUCTION

The bottom shell construction consists of the central keel of the ship, with the flooring structure and side shell plating on either side. Almost all vessels built today are fitted with a double bottom. This is an internal skin fitted about 1 m above the outer shell plating and supported by the flooring structure.

Keel

The keel runs along the centreline of the bottom plating of the ship and for the majority of merchant ships is of a flat plate construction. At right-angles to the flat plate keel, running along the ship's centreline from the fore peak to the aft peak bulkhead, is a watertight longitudinal division known as the centre girder or vertical keel. Where a double-bottom construction is employed, the centreline strake of tank top plating results in the formation of an I-section keel (*Figure 5.1*). This provides considerable strength to the structure and resistance to bending. The flat plate keel or 'middle line strake of plating' is increased in thickness for strength purposes and for a corrosion allowance, because of the difficulty in maintaining paint protection , stems in way of the docking blocks during the vessel's life.

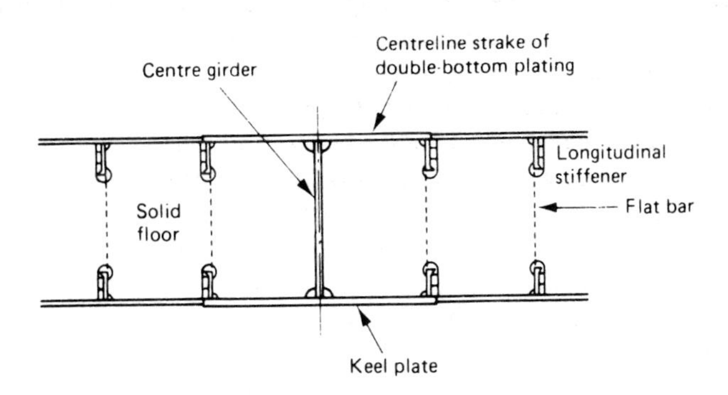

Figure 5.1 Flat plate keel

Some double bottoms have a duct keel fitted along the centreline. This is an internal passage of watertight construction running some distance along the length of the ship, often from the forepeak to the forward machinery space bulkhead. Use is made of this passage to carry the pipework along the length of the ship to the various holds or tanks. An entrance is usually provided at the forward end of the machinery space via a watertight manhole. No duct keel is necessary in the machinery space or aft of it, since pipework will run above the engine room double bottom and along the shaft tunnel, where one is fitted.

The construction of the duct keel uses two longitudinal girders spaced not more than 2.0 m apart. This restriction is to ensure that the longitudinal girders rest on the docking blocks when the ship is in drydock. Stiffeners are fitted to shell and bottom plating at alternate frame spaces and are bracketed to the longitudinal girders (*Figure 5.2*). The keel plate and the tank top above the duct keel must have their scantlings increased to compensate for the reduced strength of the transverse floors.

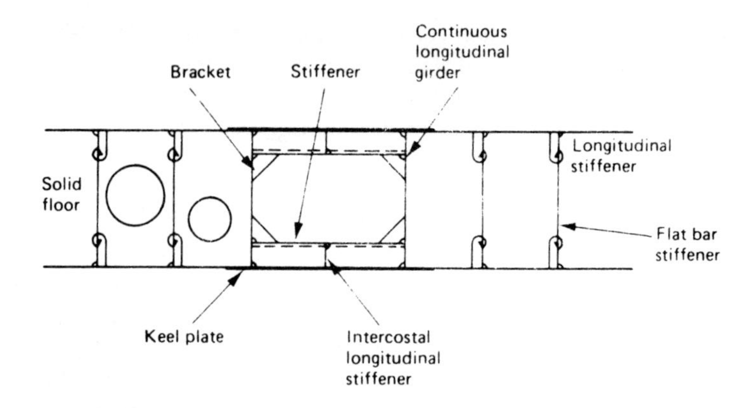

Figure 5.2 Duct keel

Double-bottom structure

Where a double bottom or inner shell is fitted it is watertight up to the bilges, thus providing complete watertight integrity should the outer shell be pierced in way of the double bottom. The minimum depth is determined by rule requirements for the size of vessel but the actual depth is sometimes increased in places to suit double-bottom tank capacities. The double bottom may have a sloping margin leading to the bilge radiused plating or a continuous double bottom extending to the side shell. The sloping margin construction requires the use of margin plates to connect up with the side framing and provides a collecting bay or well for bilge water (*Figure 5.3*). The continuous tank top or flat margin must have bilge water collecting points or drain 'hats' fitted into it (*Figure 5.4*). The flat margin is connected to the side framing by a flanged bracket. The flat margin type of construction is much used in modern construction.

The structure is made up of vertical floors which may be watertight, solid or of bracket construction. The floor structure is continuous from the centre girder to the

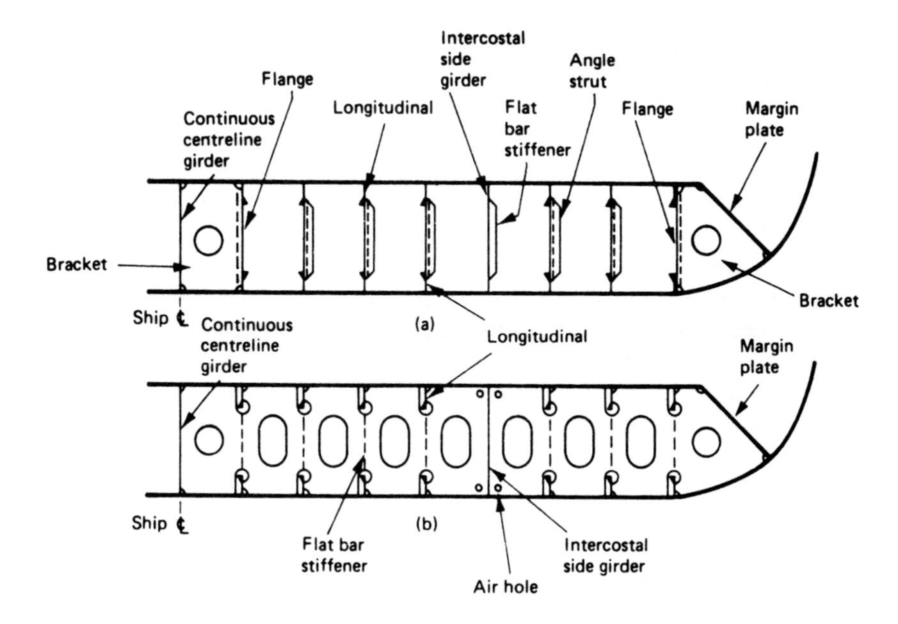

Figure 5.3 Longitudinally framed double bottom: (a) bracket floor; (b) solid floor

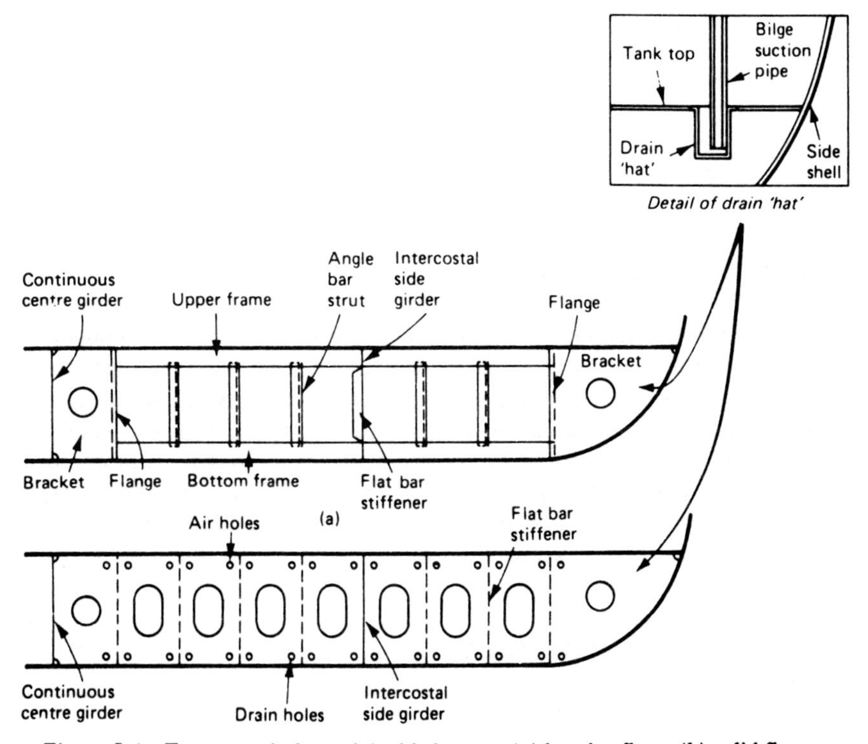

Figure 5.4 Transversely framed double bottom: (a) bracket floor; (b) solid floor

side shell and supports the inner bottom shell. Side girders are fitted in the longitudinal direction, their number depending on the width of the ship. These side girders are broken either side of the floors and are therefore called intercostal girders.

Watertight or oiltight floors are fitted beneath the main bulkheads and are also used to subdivide the double-bottom space into tanks for various liquids. Solid plate floors of non-watertight construction, usually lightened by manholes, are positioned in other places as required to stiffen the structure. Between solid plate floors, bracket floors are fitted. Bracket floors consist of plate brackets attached to the centre girder and the side shell with bulb plate stiffeners running between. The stiffeners are supported by angle bar struts at intervals and any side girders which are present in the structure.

The arrangement of flooring will be determined by the type of framing system adopted, which may be either transverse or longitudinal.

Transversely framed double bottom

When transversely framed, the double-bottom structure consists of solid plate floors and bracket floors with transverse frames. The bracket floor is fitted between the widely spaced solid floors. It consists of transverse bulb angle sections stiffening the shell and inner bottom plating. Vertical support is provided by brackets at the side shell and centre girder, any side girders and intermediate struts. The number of intercostal side girders fitted is determined by classification society rules. Solid and bracket floors for a transversely framed vessel are shown in *Figure 5.4*.

Longitudinally framed double bottom

This is the system favoured as a result of tests and it provides adequate resistance to distortion on ships of 120 m in length or greater. Offset bulb plates are used as longitudinal stiffeners on the shell and inner bottom plating, at intervals of about 1 m. Solid floors provide support at transverse bulkheads and at intervals not exceeding 3.8 m along the length of the ship. Brackets are fitted at the centre girder and side shell at intermediate frame spaces between solid floors. These brackets are flanged at the free edge and extend to the first longitudinal. Channel bar or angle bar struts are provided to give support at intervals of not more than 2.5 m where solid floors are widely spaced. Intercostal side girders are again fitted, their number depending upon classification society rules. Solid and bracket floors for a longitudinally framed vessel are shown in *Figure 5.3*.

Machinery space double bottom

The construction of the double bottom in the machinery space regardless of framing system has solid plate floors at every frame space under the main engine. Additional side girders are fitted outboard of the main engine seating, as required. The double-bottom height is usually increased to provide fuel oil, lubricating oil and fresh water tanks of suitable capacities. Shaft alignment also requires an increase in the double-bottom height or a raised seating, the former method usually being adopted. Continuity of strength is ensured and maintained by gradually sloping the tank top height and internal structure to the required position. Additional support and stiffening is necessary for the main engines, boilers, etc., to provide a vibration-resistant solid platform capable of supporting the concentrated loads. On slow-speed diesel-engined ships the tank top plating is increased to 40 mm thickness or thereabouts in way of the engine bedplate. This is achieved by using a special insert plate which is the length of the engine including the thrust block in size (*Figure 5.5*). Additional heavy girders are also fitted under this plate and in other positions under heavy machinery as required. Plating and girder material in the machinery spaces is of increased scantlings in the order of 10%.

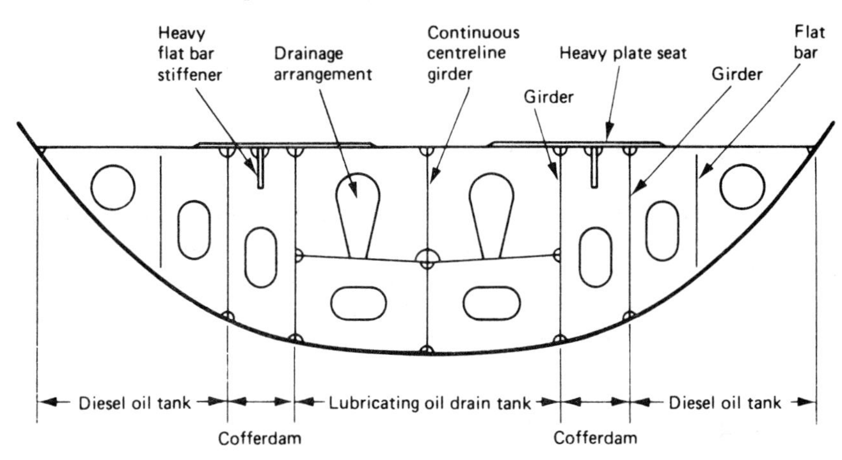

Figure 5.5 Machinery space double bottom

Double-bottom tanks

Access to the double-bottom tanks is usually by manholes cut in the tank top. These manholes are suitably jointed and bolted to be completely watertight when not in use. Docking plugs are fitted in all double-bottom tanks and are a means of completely draining these tanks for inspection in drydock (*Figure 5.6*). Air pipes are

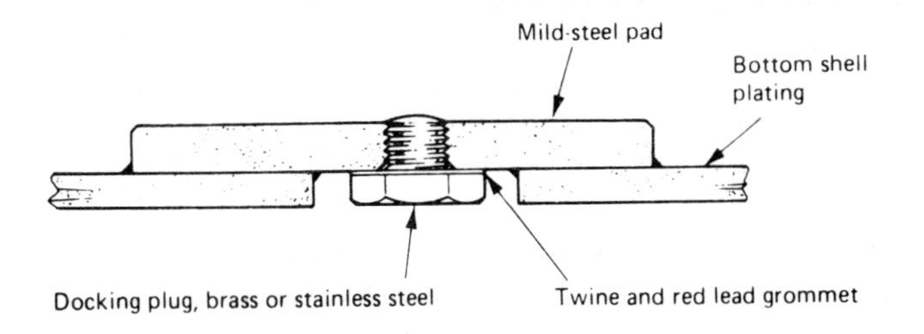

Figure 5.6 Docking plug and pad

fitted to all double-bottom tanks to release the air when filling. Sounding pipes are also fitted to enable the tanks to be sounded and their capacity determined. All double-bottom tanks are tested on completion by the maximum service pressure head of water or an equivalent air test.

Structure to resist pounding

Pounding or slamming results from the ship heaving or pitching, thus causing the forward region to 'slam' down on to the water. Additional structural strength must be provided from the forward perpendicular aft for 25–30% of the ship's length. The shell plating either side of the keel is increased in thickness, depending upon the ship's minimum draught. The frame spacing is reduced, full- and half height intercostal side girders are fitted and solid floors are installed at every frame space. With longitudinal framing the longitudinal spacing is reduced, intercostal side girders are fitted and transverse floors are installed at alternate frames.

Single-bottom construction

In older oil tankers particularly, and in some smaller vessels, a single-bottom construction is employed. The oil tanker bottom structure is detailed in Chapter 8. The construction of the single bottom in smaller ships is similar to double-bottom construction but without the inner skin of plating. The upper edge of all plate floors must therefore be stiffened to improve their rigidity.

SECTION B SHELL PLATING, FRAMING SYSTEMS AND DECKS

Shell plating

The side and bottom shell plating provides the watertight skin of the ship. The shell plating also makes the greatest contribution to the longitudinal strength of the ship's structure. As a result of its huge area the shell plating is composed of many strakes or plates arranged in a fore and aft direction and welded together. The horizontal welds are termed 'seams' and the vertical welds are termed 'butts'. Several strakes of plating are usually joined together as part of a unit. A shell expansion by units was shown in *Figure 3.2*. The thickness of shell plating is largely dependent upon ship length and frame spacing. The final structure must be capable of withstanding the many dynamic and static loads upon the hull, as discussed in Chapter 2. Some tapering off of shell plate thickness towards the ends of the ship is usual, since the bending moments are reduced in this region.

The strake of side plating nearest to the deck is known as the 'sheerstrake'. The sheerstrake is increased in thickness or a high tensile steel is used. This is because this section of plating is furthest from the neutral axis and subject to the greatest bending stress, as discussed in Chapter 2. The region where the sheerstrake meets

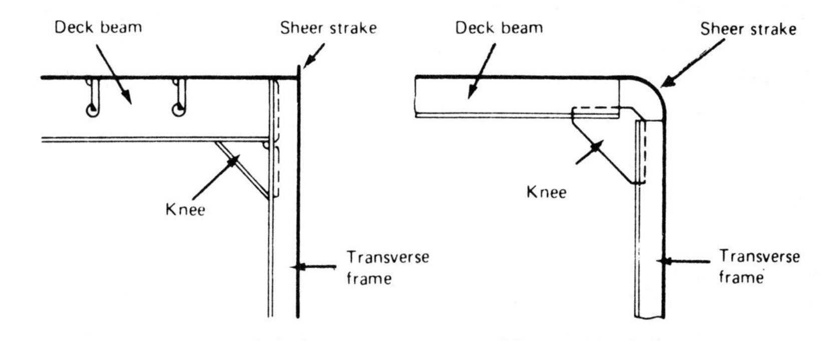

Figure 5.7 Gunwale arrangments

the deck plating is known as the gunwale. Two particular arrangements in this region are used and are shown in *Figure 5.7*. With the rounded gunwale arrangement no welding is permitted on the sheerstrake because of the high stressing which could result in cracks emanating from the 'toes' of fillet welds. Such welds reduce the resistance of components to cracking. Where such structure is butt welded the welding must blend into the parent plate. Towards the ends of the ship, as the cross-section reduces, the various strakes of plating will taper in width. Where these plate widths become small, a stealer plate or strake is fitted (*Figure 5.8*).

All openings in shell plating must have rounded edges to avoid stress concentrations and usually some form of compensation to avoid a discontinuity of strength.

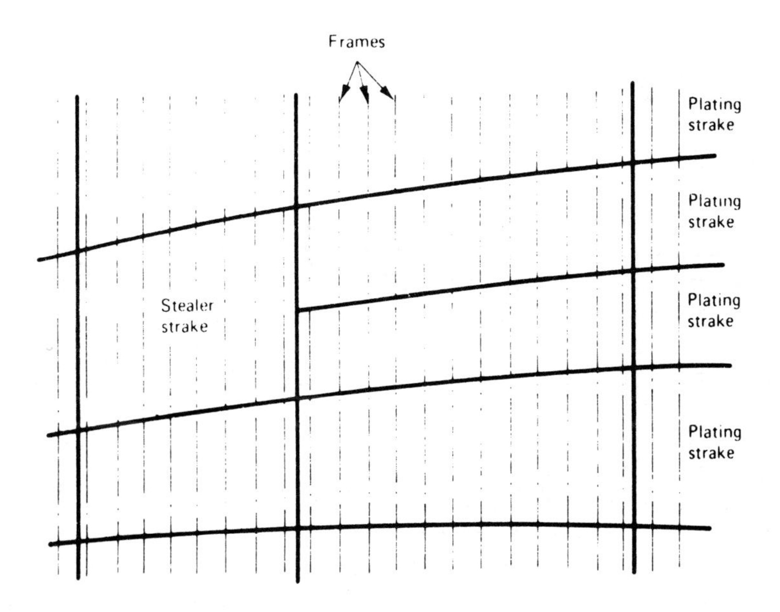

Figure 5.8 Stealer strake arrangement

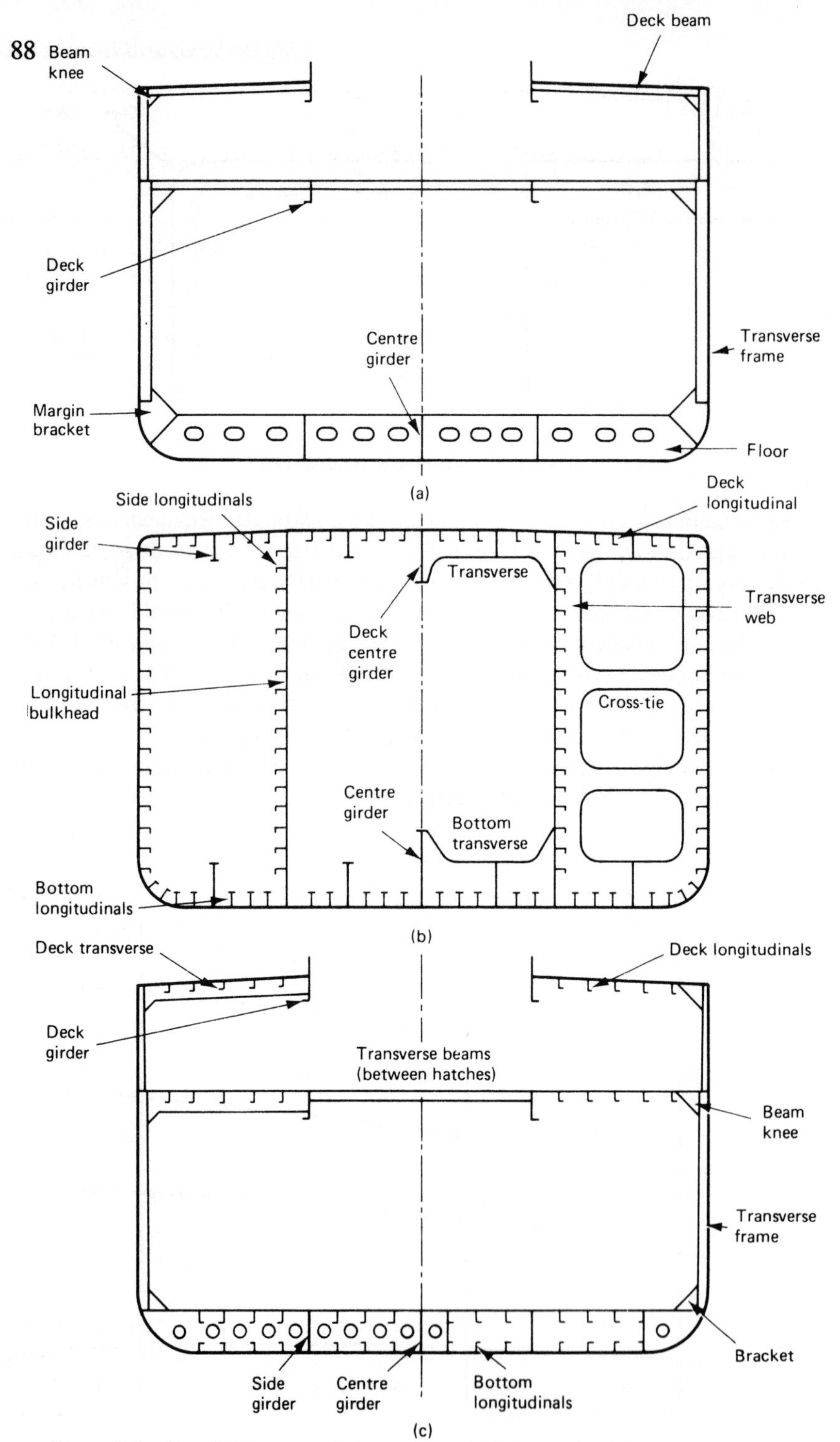

Figure 5.9 Framing systems: (a) transverse framing; (b) longitudinal framing; (c) combined framing

Framing systems

The bottom shell and side plating are framed, i.e. stiffened along their length, against the compressing forces of the sea. Two different types of framing, or a combination of the two, are employed. These are known, respectively, as transverse, longitudinal and combined framing and are shown in *Figure 5.9*. Cargo arrangements may influence the choice of framing systems but, generally, considerations of longitudinal strength are the deciding factor.

Transverse framing

Transverse framing of the shell plating consists of vertical stiffeners, either of bulb plate or deep-flanged web frames, which are attached by brackets to the deck beams and the flooring structure. The scantlings of the frames are to some extent dependent upon their depth and also on the nature of their end connections. Particular locations, such as at the ends of hatches, require frames of increased scantlings. Very deep web frames are often fitted in the machinery space.

Frame spacing is generally not more than 1000 mm but is always reduced in the pounding region and at the fore and aft ends in the peak tank regions.

Longitudinal framing

Longitudinal framing of the side shell employs horizontal offset bulb plates with increased scantlings towards the lower side shell. Transverse webs are used to support the longitudinal frames, their spacing being dependent upon the type of ship and the section modulus of the longitudinals. This construction is described and illustrated in Chapter 8 with reference to oil tanker construction.

Bilge keel

With a flat keel construction there is little resistance to rolling of the ship. A bilge keel is fitted along the bilge radius either side of the ship to damp any tendency the ship has to roll (*Figure 5.10*). Some improvement in longitudinal strength at the bilge radius is also provided. The bilge keel must be arranged to penetrate the boundary layer of water along the hull but not too deep to have large forces acting on it.

The bilge keel is fitted at right-angles to the bilge radiused plating but does not extend beyond the extreme breadth line. It runs the extent of the midship section of the ship and is positioned, after model tests, to ensure the minimum resistance to forward motion of the ship. Construction is of steel plate with a stiffened free edge or a section such as a bulb plate. A means of fastening to the hull is employed which will break off the bilge keel without damage to the hull in the event of fouling or collision. The ends are fastened to a doubling plate on the shell, since the bilge plating is in a highly stressed region of the ship.

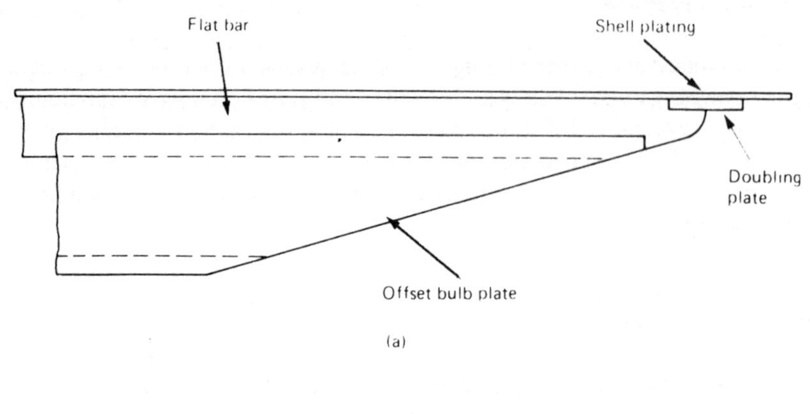

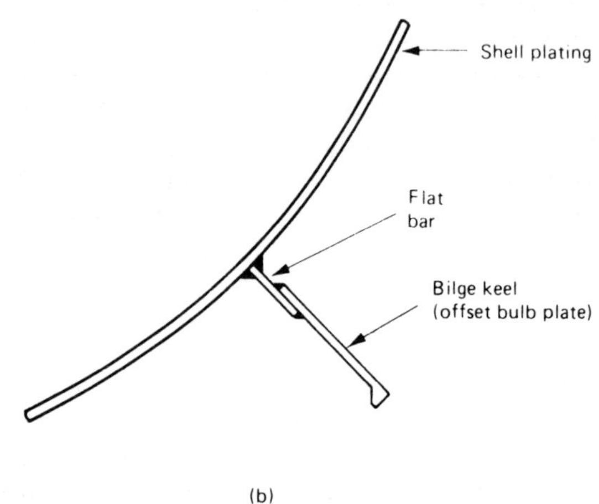

Figure 5.10 Bilge keel: (a) plan view showing arrangement at ends: (b) section through bilge keel

Ice navigation strengthening

Ice class notations 1*, 1, 2 or 3 are assigned to ships which have additional strengthening as required by classification society rules. Various means of additional stiffening by increased frame scantlings, reduced frame spacing and increased plate thickness are required. The extent and nature of the stiffening reduces from 1*, which is the highest classification, to 3, which is the lowest. Some modifications to the stem and stern regions may also be required.

Decks

The deck of a ship is the horizontal platform which completes the enclosure of the hull. It must provide a solid working platform capable of supporting any loads resting upon it, and also a watertight top cover to the hull structure. The deck with its various forms of stiffening and its plating provides a considerable contribution to the strength of the ship. Where the deck is pierced by hatches, special coamings or surrounds to the openings must be provided. These large openings require special compensation to offset their effect on the structural strength of the ship.

Deck plating

The deck plating is made up of longitudinal strakes of plating across its width. The plates or strakes nearest to the deck edges are termed 'stringer plates'. They are of thicker material than the remaining deck plating since they form the important join between the side shell and deck plating. Towards the ends of the ship the deck plating, like the shell plating, is reduced in thickness.

The large openings in the deck for hatchways, engine casing, pump room entrances, etc., require compensation to maintain the section modulus of the material. The deck plating abreast of such openings is therefore increased in thickness. The plating between the hatches of a cargo ship is thinner than the rest of the deck plating and contributes little to longitudinal strength.

The plating of the weather decks is cambered towards the ship's side to assist drainage of any water falling on the deck. This camber is usually of the order of one-fiftieth of the breadth of the ship at midships.

Deck stiffening

The deck plating is supported from below in a manner determined by the framing system of the ship. With longitudinal framing, a series of closely spaced longitudinals are used in addition to deep web transverses. With transverse framing, transverse deck beams are used at every frame space. Where hatches are fitted to a ship, continuous longitudinal girders are fitted over the length of the ship running alongside the hatches.

Deck beams and transverses

Deck beams are fitted across the width of the ship and are joined to the side frames by brackets known as 'beam knees'. Continuous longitudinal girders which run alongside the hatchways are fitted on the ship, and the beams are bracketed to these girders. In this way the unsupported span is reduced. Deck beams are usually offset bulb plates. For the length of the open hatch space the beams are broken and bracketed to the longitudinal girder or hatch side coaming. The beams are likewise broken and bracketed to the longitudinal girders in way of the engine casing. A beam broken in this manner is known as a 'half-beam'.

Deck transverses support the longitudinally framed deck. These are deep plate webs with a facing flat or a flanged edge. They are bracketed to the side frames by

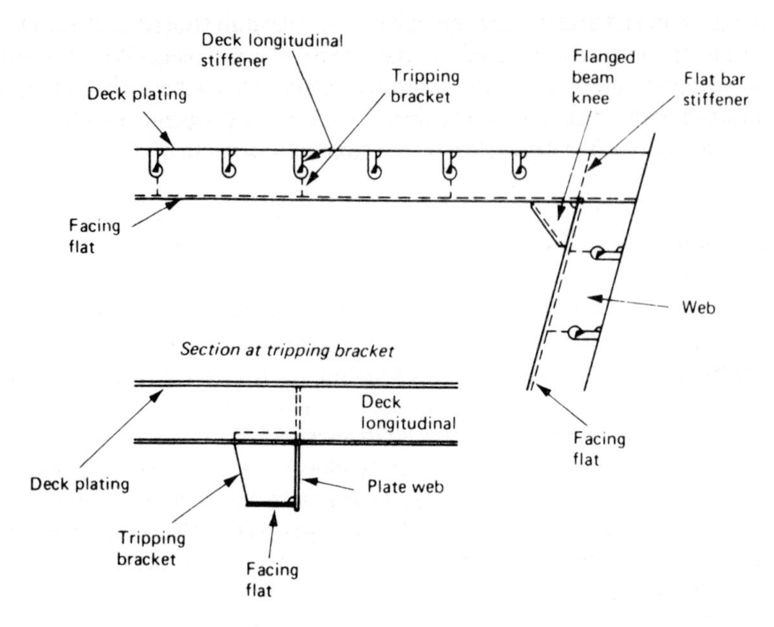

Figure 5.11 Deck beam

beam knees. Small tripping brackets are fitted between alternate longitudinals and the transverse (*Figure 5.11*).

Deck girders

Deck girders exist in a number of forms, depending upon their location. A flanged girder with tripping brackets will often be used as part of a hatch coaming. Such a flanged girder is referred to as unsymmetrical and must have tripping brackets fitted at alternate frame spaces. The symmetrical girder is often used, particularly as a centreline girder. Brackets join the girder to the deck beams and are fitted at every fourth frame space. At hatch corners these girders must be additionally supported

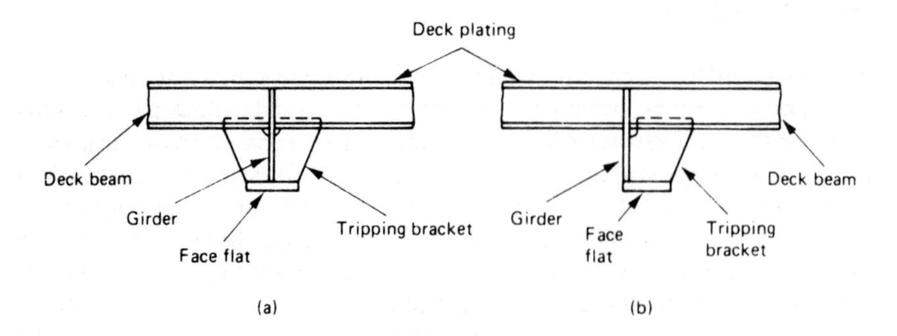

Figure 5.12 Girder arrangements: (a) symmetrical; (b) unsymmetrical

either by pillars or transverse girders. The symmetrical and unsymmetrical types of girder are shown in *Figure 5.12*. The combination of longitudinal girders with transverse beams is much in use in modern ships. The deck longitudinal girders extend as far as possible along the full length of the ship on the outside of the hatches. This continuous longitudinal material permits a reduction in deck plate thickness, in terms of classification society requirements.

The deck between the hatches must be supported by longitudinal or transverse beams. Where side girders join transverse beams, particularly beneath hatch openings, gusset plates are fitted (*Figures 5.13* and *5.14*).

Local loading

On the deck, where concentrated loads are situated or likely, additional stiffening must be provided. Machinery such as winches, windlasses, etc., will also require seatings which are discussed in detail in Chapter 6. Also, any beams fitted in way of deep tanks, bunker tanks, etc., must have increased scantlings and perhaps reduced spans to be at least equal in strength to the boundary bulkheads.

Discontinuities

A discontinuity, as discussed here, refers to any break or change in section, thickness or amount of plating material. Great care must be taken to compensate for any discontinuities in shell or deck plating resulting from doors, hatchways, etc. Where the loss of longitudinal material results, this compensation is of particular importance. Where changes in the amount of plating material occur, such as at bulwarks, the change should be gradual and well radiused.

Well-radiused corners must be used and sometimes the fitting of doubling plates or thicker insert plates, at the corners of all openings. Any sharp corner can produce a notch which, after stressing, could result in a crack. *Figure 5.15* shows an insert plate fitted at the corner of a hatch opening.

Hatch coamings

The edges of all hatch openings are framed by hatch coamings. On the weather deck the coamings must be at a minimum height of 600 mm according to the load line regulations. This is to reduce the risk of water entry to the holds. Internal coamings, e.g. those within the superstructure or holds, have no height specified and in tween-deck holds particularly are often made flush with the deck for uninterrupted cargo stowage. The weather deck coaming must be a minimum of 9 mm thick, and where the height is in excess of 600 mm it must be stiffened by a horizontal stiffener and vertical brackets must be fitted not more than 3 m apart. An edge stiffener must also be provided which may be a preformed section where wooden hatch covers are fitted (see *Figure 7.1*, later) or a half-round steel bar as in *Figure 5.16*.

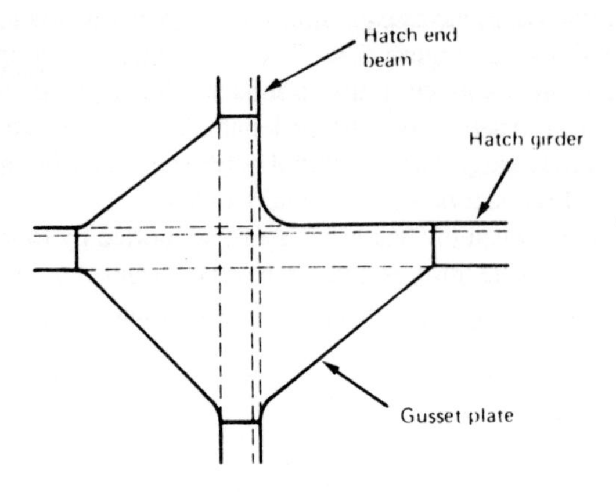

Figure 5.13 Hatch corner gusset plate, viewed from below

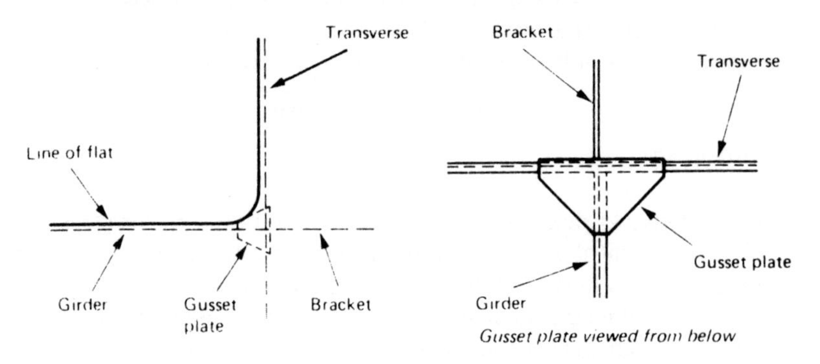

Figure 5.14 Gusset plate used in machinery space construction

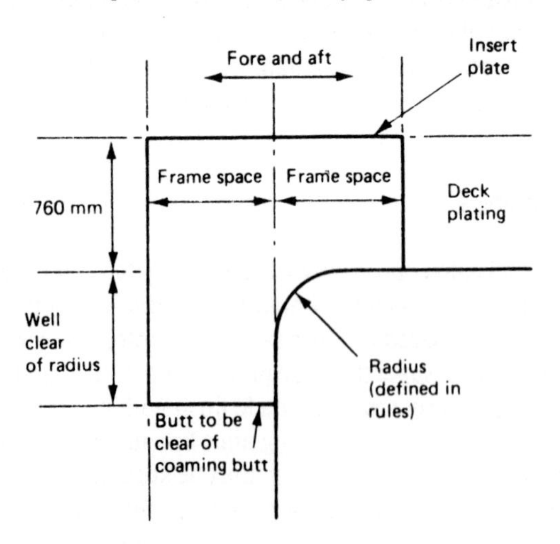

Figure 5.15 Insert plate fitted at hatch corner

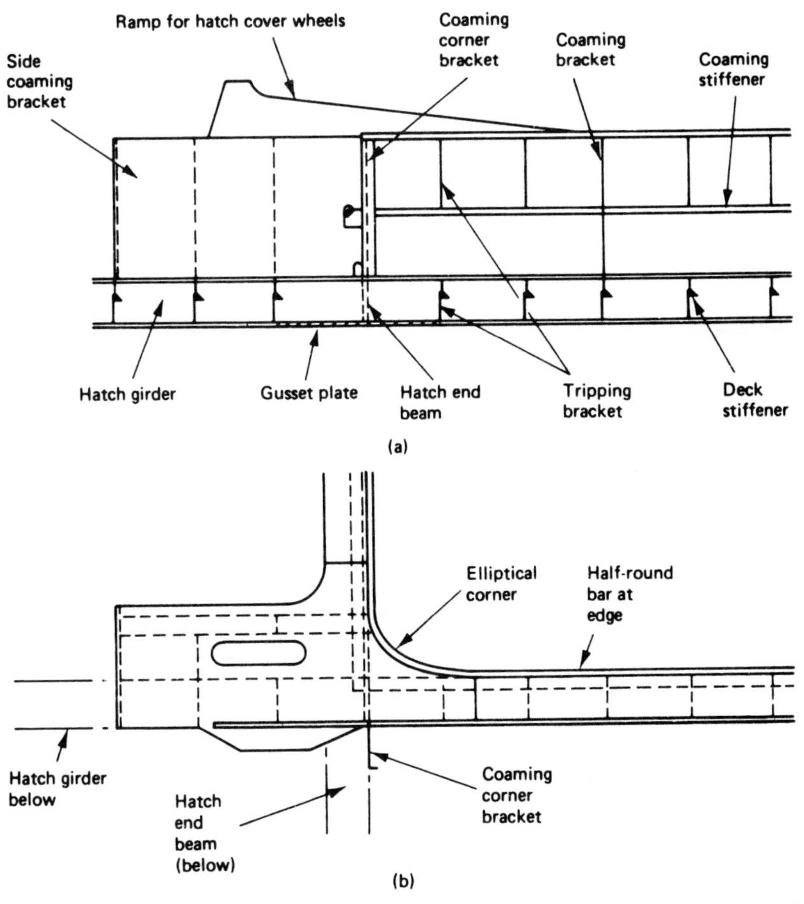

Figure 5.16 Hatch coaming: (a) elevation of hatch coaming (steel hatch covers); (b) plan view of hatch coaming (steel hatch covers)

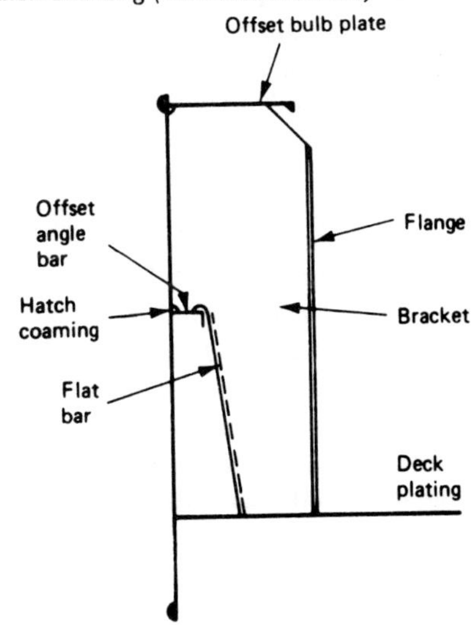

Figure 5.17 Coaming bracket

The side coaming plates, as an extension of the longitudinal girder, are of greater thickness than the end coaming plates and are extended beyond the hatch opening in the form of brackets (*Figure 5.16*). These brackets also serve to support the platforms used for the hatch operating equipment. Smaller vertical brackets are fitted around the remainder of the coaming structure to stiffen it (*Figure 5.17*).

SECTION C BULKHEADS AND PILLARS

Bulkheads

The vertical divisions arranged in the ship's structure are known as bulkheads. Three basic types are found, namely watertight, non-watertight and oiltight or tank bulkheads. Oiltight or tank bulkheads are watertight in their construction but are subjected to more rigorous testing than a simply watertight bulkhead.

The transverse watertight bulkheads subdivide the ship into a number of watertight compartments and their number is dictated by classification society regulations. Oiltight bulkheads form the boundaries of tanks used for the carriage of liquid cargoes or fuels. Non-watertight bulkheads are any other bulkheads such as engine casing, accommodation partitions or stores compartments.

Watertight bulkheads

In addition to subdividing the ship, transverse bulkheads also provide considerable structural strength as support for the decks and to resist deformation caused by broadside waves (racking). The spacing of watertight bulkheads, which is known as the watertight subdivision of the ship, is governed by rules dependent upon ship type, size, etc. All ships must have:

(1) A collision or fore peak bulkhead, which is to be positioned not less than $0.05 \times$ length of the ship, nor more than $0.08 \times$ length of the ship, from the forward end of the load waterline.
(2) An after peak bulkhead which encloses the sterntube(s) and rudder trunk in a watertight compartment.
(3) A bulkhead at each end of the machinery space; the after bulkhead may, for an aft engine room, be the after peak bulkhead.

Additional bulkheads are to be fitted according to the vessel's length, e.g. a ship between 145 m and 165 m long must have 8 bulkheads with machinery midships and 7 bulkheads with machinery aft.

Fitting less than the standard number of bulkheads is permitted in approved circumstances where additional structural compensation is provided. Watertight bulkheads must extend to the freeboard deck but may rise to the uppermost continuous deck. The aft peak bulkhead may extend only to the next deck above the load waterline, where the construction aft of this deck is fully watertight to the shell.

The purpose of watertight subdivision and the spacing of the bulkheads is to provide an arrangement such that if one compartment is flooded between bulkheads the ship's waterline will not rise above the margin line. The margin line is a line drawn parallel to and 76 mm below the upper surface of the bulkhead deck at the ship's side. The subdivision of passenger ships is regulated by statutory requirements which are in excess of classification society rules for cargo ships, but the objects of confining flooding and avoiding sinking are the same.

Construction of watertight bulkheads

Watertight bulkheads, because of their large area, are formed of several strakes of plating. They are welded to the shell, deck and tank top. The plating strakes are horizontal and the stiffening is vertical. Since water pressure in a tank increases with depth and the watertight bulkhead must withstand such loading, the bulkhead must have increasingly greater strength towards the base. This is achieved by increasing the thickness of the horizontal strakes of plating towards the bottom. The collision bulkhead must have plating some 12% thicker than other watertight bulkheads. Also, plating in the aft peak bulkhead around the sterntube must be doubled or increased in thickness to reduce vibration. The bulkhead is stiffened by vertical bulb plates or toe-welded angle bar stiffeners spaced about 760 mm apart. This spacing is reduced to 610 mm for collision and oiltight bulkheads. The ends of the stiffeners are bracketed to the tanktop and the deck beams. In tween decks, where the loading is less, the stiffeners may have no end connections. A watertight bulkhead arrangement is shown in *Figure 5.18*.

Corrugated watertight bulkheads

The use of corrugations or swedges in a plate instead of welded stiffeners produces as strong a structure with a reduction in weight. The troughs are vertical on transverse bulkheads but on longitudinal bulkheads they must be horizontal in order to add to the longitudinal strength of the ship.

The corrugations or swedges are made in the plating strakes prior to fabrication of the complete bulkhead. As a consequence, the strakes run vertically and the plating must be of uniform thickness and adequate to support the greater loads at the bottom of the bulkhead. This greater thickness of plate offsets to some extent the saving in weight through not adding stiffeners to the bulkhead. The edges of the corrugated bulkhead which join to the shell plating may have stiffened flat plate fitted to increase transverse strength and simplify fitting the bulkhead to the shell. On high bulkheads with vertical corrugations, diaphragm plates are fitted across the troughs. This prevents any possible collapse of the corrugations. A corrugated bulkhead arrangement is shown in *Figure 5.19*.

A watertight floor is fitted in the double bottom directly below every main transverse bulkhead. Where a watertight bulkhead is penetrated, e.g. by pipework, a watertight closure around the penetration must be ensured by a collar fully welded to the pipe and the bulkhead.

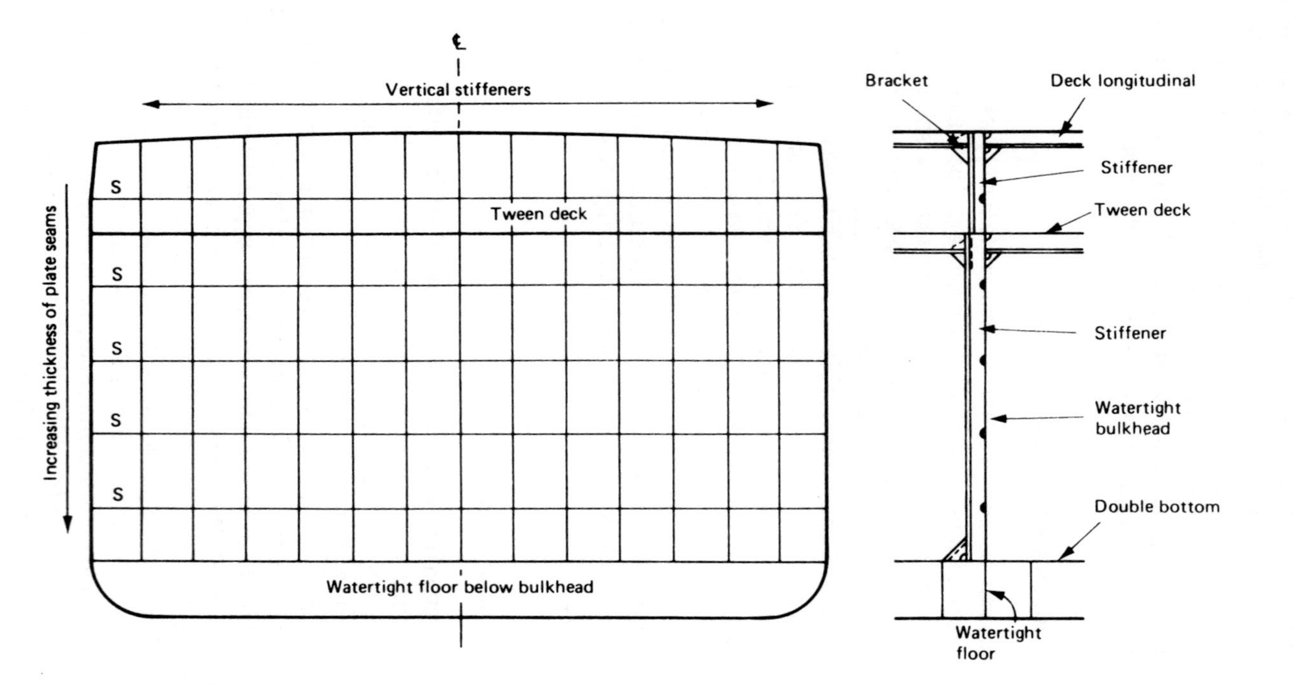

Figure 5.18 ***Plain watertight bulkheads (S, plate seam)***

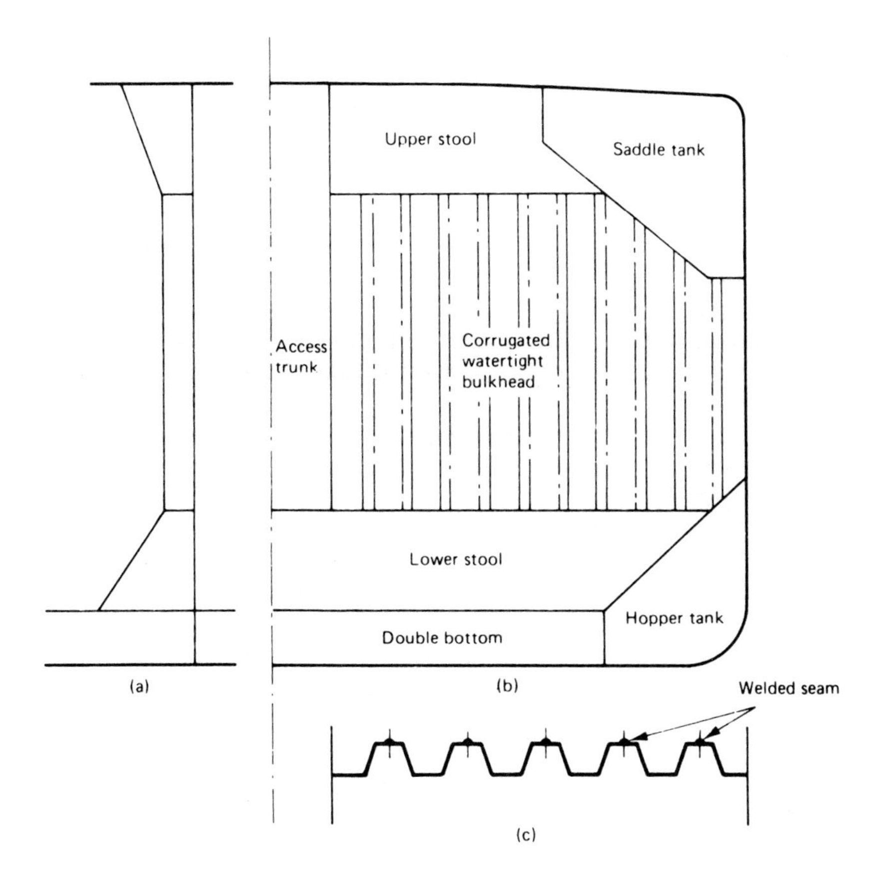

Figure 5.19 Corrugated watertight bulkhead: (a) section through corrugation; (b) elevation of bulkhead; (c) plan view of corrugations

Testing of watertight bulkheads

The main fore and aft peak bulkheads must be tested by filling with water to the load waterline. Subdividing watertight bulkheads are tested by hosing down. Oiltight and tank bulkheads must be tested by a head of water not less than 2.45 m above the highest point of the tank.

Non-watertight bulkheads

Any bulkheads other than those used as main subdivisions and tank boundaries may be non-watertight. Examples of these are engine room casing bulkheads, accommodation partitions, store room division, etc. Wash bulkheads fitted in deep tanks or in the fore end of a ship are also examples of non-watertight bulkheads. Where a non-watertight bulkhead performs the supporting function similar to a pillar, its stiffeners must be adequate for the load carried. In all other situations the non-watertight bulkhead is stiffened by bulb plates or simply flat plates welded edge on. Corrugated and swedged bulkheads can also be used for non-watertight bulkheads.

Pillars

Pillars provide a means of transferring loads between decks and fastening together the structure in a vertical direction. The pillars which transfer loads, as in the cargo holds or beneath items of machinery, are largely in compression and require little or no bracketing to the surrounding structure. Pillars which tie structure together and are subjected to tensile forces are adequately bracketed at the head or top and the heel or bottom.

Hold pillars are usually large in section and few in number to reduce interference with cargo stowage to a minimum. Pillars are provided to reduce the need for heavy webs to support the hatch girders or end beams. The use of pillars also enables a reduction in size of the hatch girders and beams, since their unsupported span is reduced. Where pillars are fitted between a number of vertical decks they should be in line below one another to efficiently transfer the loads.

Hold pillar sections are usually a hollow fabricated shape manufactured from steel plate. Typical sections are round, square and sometimes octagonal. Machinery space pillars are usually fabricated from sections and, while smaller in dimensions than hold pillars, a greater number are fitted (*Figure 5.20*). Additional structural material must be provided at the head and heel of pillars to evenly distribute the load. At the head a plate is used, often with tripping brackets to the surrounding structure.

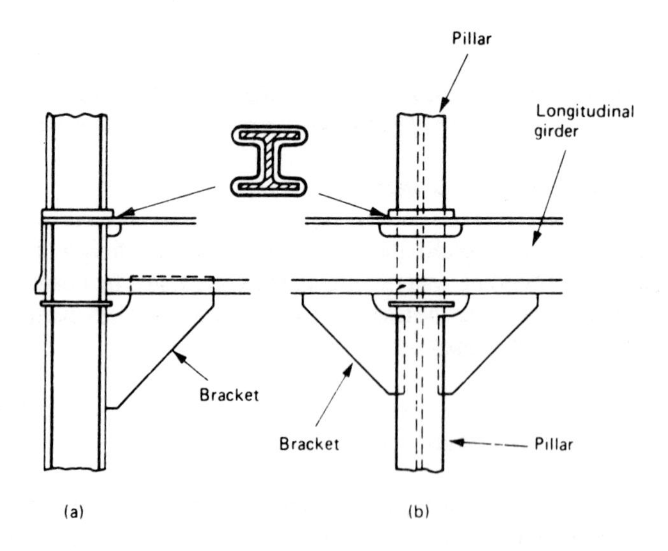

Figure 5.20 Machinery space pillar arrangements: (a) sectional elevation looking aft; (b) elevation looking outboard

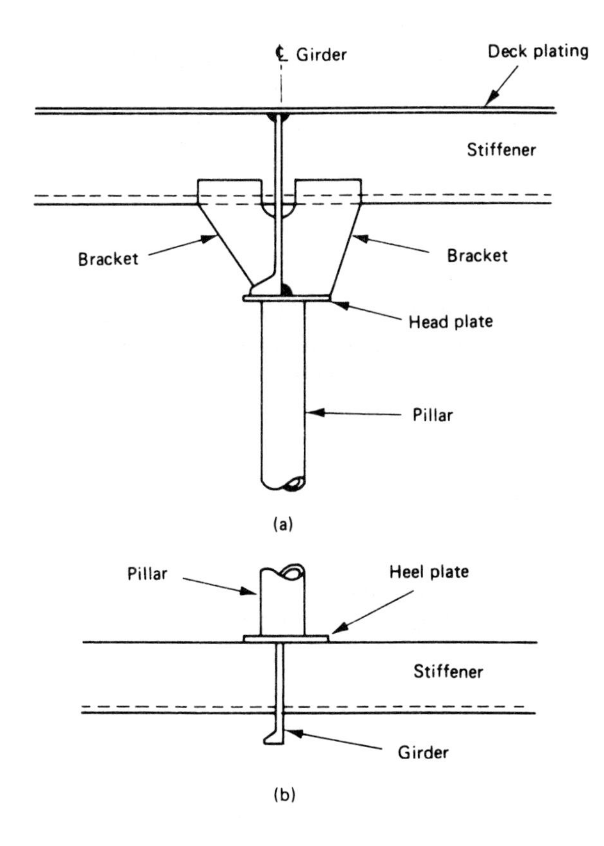

Figure 5.21 Tubular pillar arrangements: (a) pillar head connection; (b) pillar heel connection

At the heel an insert plate or doubling plate is used, with or without brackets depending upon the type of loading (*Figure 5.21*).

Solid pillars may be fitted in accommodation spaces or under points of concentrated loading. Solid round bar up to about 100 mm diameter is fitted, again with head and heel plates to spread the load.

SECTION D FORE END CONSTRUCTION

The forward end of a ship refers to the structure forward of the collision bulkhead. The forward end is designed to provide a smooth entry to the water and a streamlined flow along the ship. As a result, resistance to motion is reduced to a minimum. The stem is the most forward part of the ship and runs down to the keel. It is constructed in two parts—a bar stem from the keel to the load waterline and a plate stem up to the deck. The plate stem usually rakes well forward providing pleasing lines to the ship, an increased deck area and a readily collapsible region in the event of a collision. The side shell plating is flared out to further increase the deck area. This arrangement also serves to deflect sea water and spray away from the ship in heavy weather. The forward deck area or forecastle houses the windlasses and winches required for anchor and mooring duties. The anchor chain is housed in a chain locker beneath the forecastle. A bulbous bow may be fitted, i.e. a protrusion below the waterline designed to reduce the ship's resistance to motion.

Stem

The stem is the terminating point of the forward shell plating. It is made up of a stem bar from the keel to the load waterline and a stiffened plate structure up to the forecastle deck (*Figure 5.22*). The stem bar is a solid round bar which is welded to the inside of the keep plate at the lower end. At its upper end the bar joins the stem plate. The shell plating is welded to either side of the stem bar.

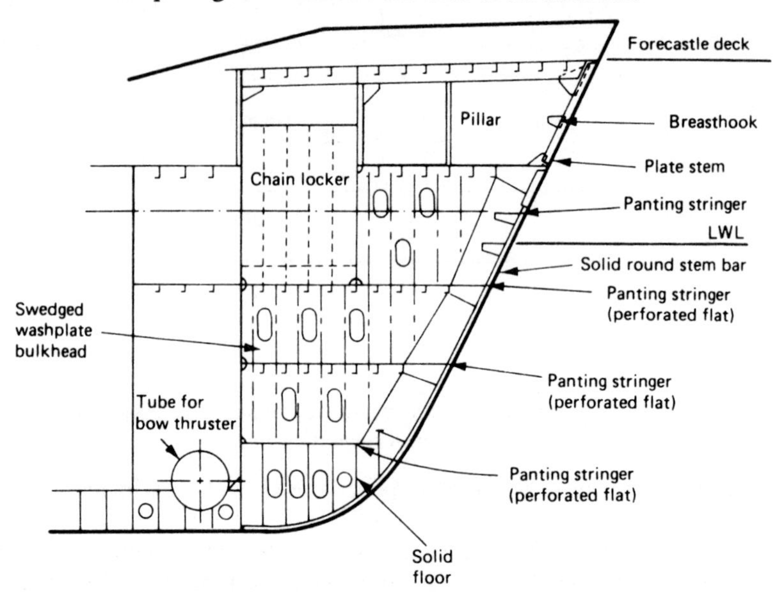

Figure 5.22 Fore end construction

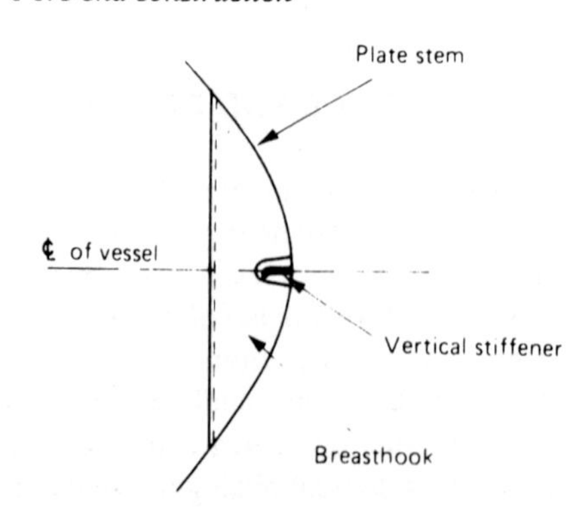

Figure 5.23 Section through plate stem showing breasthook

The stem plate construction of curved plates is stiffened at intervals by breasthooks which are small flange plates fitted horizontally (*Figure 5.23*). A continuous bulb or flat bar stiffener may be fitted where the stem plate radius is considerable. Heavier than usual shell plating may be fitted at the stem plate region.

Panting structure

Panting is an in-and-out movement of the shell plating resulting from the variations of water pressure as waves pass along the hull and when the vessel pitches. Special structural arrangements are necessary in the forward region of the ship to strengthen the ship's plating against this action. The structure must be strengthened for 15–20% of the ship's length from forward to the stem. This stiffening is made up of horizontal side stringers, known as 'panting stringers', fitted at about 2 m intervals below the lowest deck. Panting beams are fitted across the ship at alternate frame spaces and are bracketed to the panting stringer. The intermediate frames are connected to the panting stringer by brackets (*Figures 5.24* and *5.25*). A partial wash bulkhead or a series of pillars is fitted on the centreline to further support the structure. Perforated flats may be fitted instead of beams but these must not be more than 2.5 m apart. Perforations of at least 10% of the plate area are required in order to reduce water pressure on the flats.

Bulbous bow

The bulbous bow is fitted in an attempt to reduce the ship's resistance. Arrangements vary from a casting plated into the forward end to a fully radiused plated structure, or in some cases a cylindrical shape plated into the forward end. The effectiveness of the arrangement is the subject of much discussion but improved buoyancy forward is provided which will reduce the pitching of the ship.

The construction shown in *Figure 5.26* consists of a vertical plate web which stiffens the free edge of the breasthooks fitted right forward in the bulb. Deep frames with panting beams are fitted at every frame space with a wash bulkhead on the centreline. The panting stringers consist of perforated plates running the full width and length of the bulb. Another vertical plate web joins the bulb to the fore end structure. A small stem casting connects the top of the bulb to the plate stem above the load waterline. The numerous manholes cut into the structure permit access to all parts of the bulb. The anchor and cable arrangements must ensure that the bulb is not fouled during any part of the operation.

Anchors and cables

The forecastle deck houses the windlass or windlasses which raise and lower the anchor and cable. Various items of mooring equipment, such as bollards, fairleads, etc., are also arranged around the deck edge. The anchors are housed against the

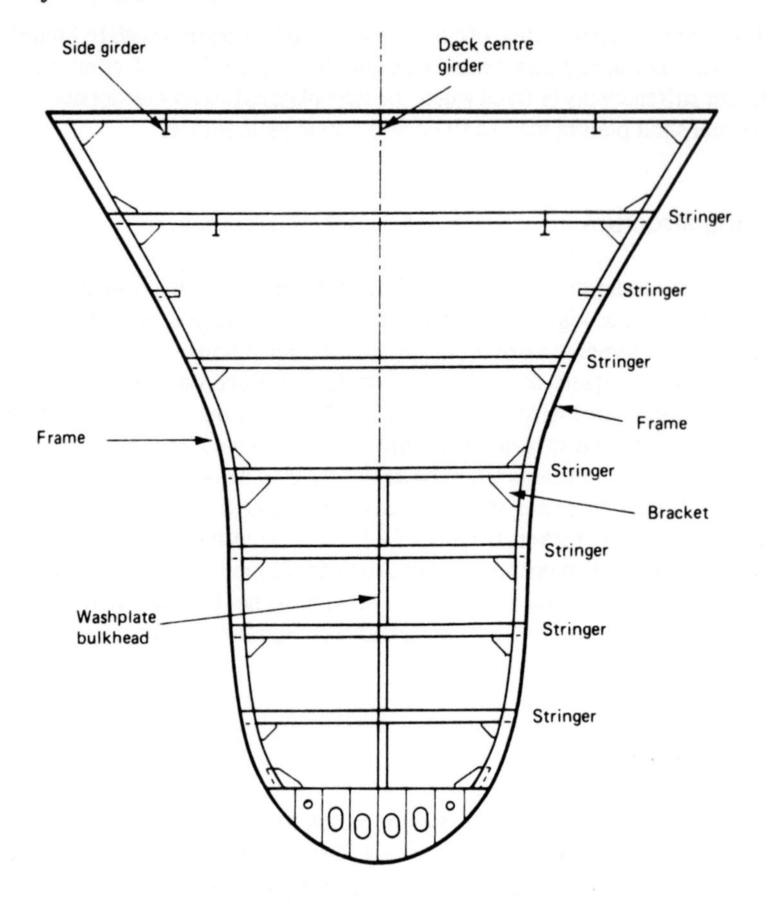

Figure 5.24 Transverse fore end section showing panting structure

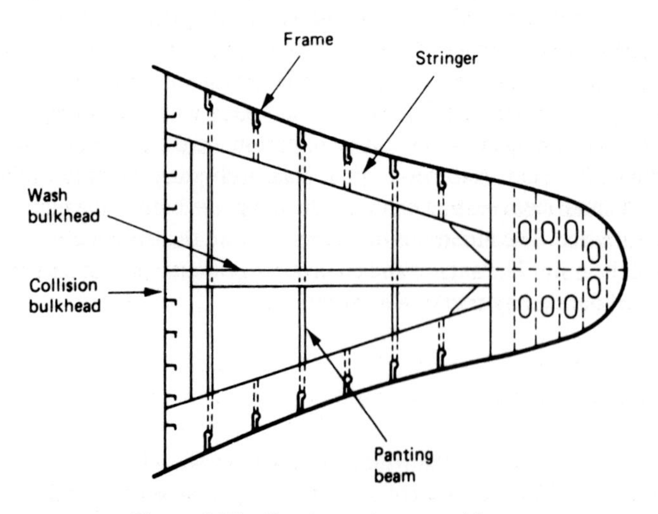

Figure 5.25 Panting stringers and beams

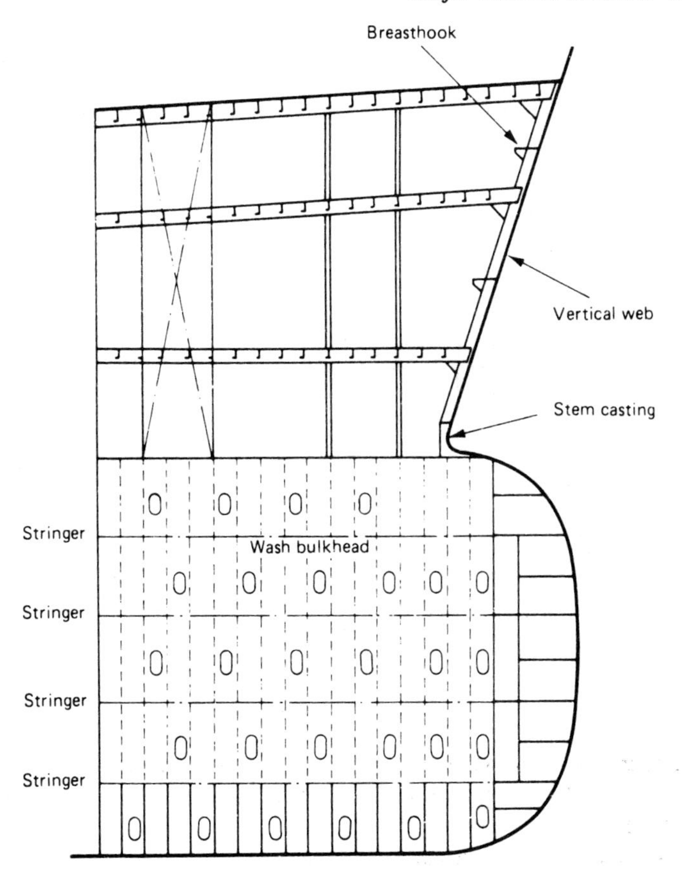

Figure 5.26 Bulbous bow construction

forward side shell, sometimes in specially recessed pockets. The anchor cable passes through the shell via the hawse pipe on to the forecastle deck. It travels over the cable stopper and on to the windlass cable lifter drum. From the cable lifter it drops vertically down into the chain locker below.

The main or bower anchors are usually of the stockless design in order to enable the shank to be drawn fully into the hawse pipe. A typical stockless anchor is shown in *Figure 5.27*. The entire head is able to pivot about the end of the shank. Thus when the anchor strikes the sea bed the tripping palm chafes and causes the arms to rotate and the flukes to dig in. If the recess in the head becomes choked with sea bed material, the anchor may fail to trip and grip. It should, therefore, be washed and checked after use.

The chain cable is made up of links of either forged mild steel or special quality forged steel. The cable size is measured by the diameter of bar used for the links. Studs are fitted across the centre of the links to prevent longitudinal stretching and also prevent kinking of the chain. Cable is manufactured in lengths of 27.5 metres called shackles and the various lengths are normally joined by a lugless shackle.

The lugless shackle is manufactured of nickel steel and is in four parts as shown

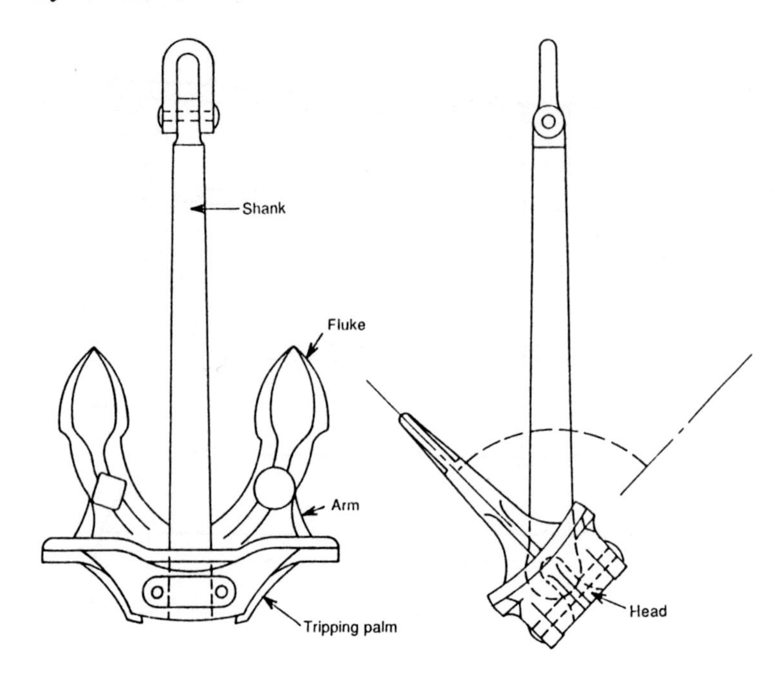

Figure 5.27 Stockless anchor

in *Figure 5.28*. The assembly is secured by a spile pin driven through the sides of the link and the centre stud. The minimum diameter of the bar used is 1.25*D* where *D* is the size of the chain cable.

Anchors and cables are subjected to material tests determined by their weight and size respectively.

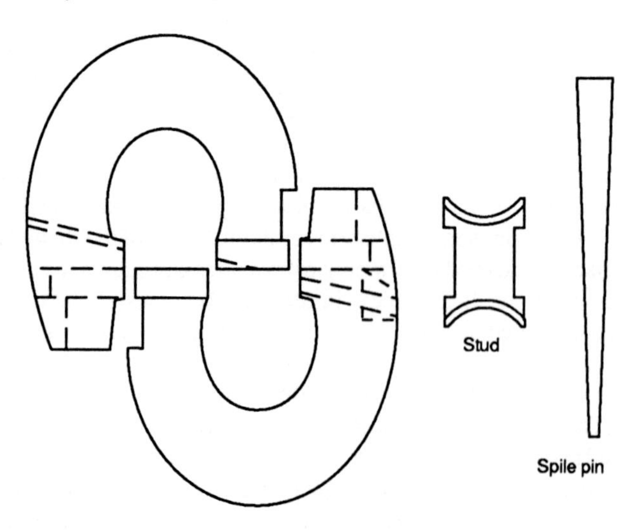

Figure 5.28 Lugless joining shackle

Hawse pipe

The hawse pipe is fitted to enable a smooth run of the anchor cable to the windlass and to maintain the watertight integrity of the forecastle (*Figure 5.29*). It should be of ample size to pass the cable without snagging when raising or lowering the anchor. Construction is usually of thick plating which is attached to a doubling plate at the forecastle deck and a reinforced strake of plating at the side shell. A rubbing or chafing ring is also fitted at the outside shell. A sliding plate cover is shaped to fit over the cable and close the opening when the ship is at sea.

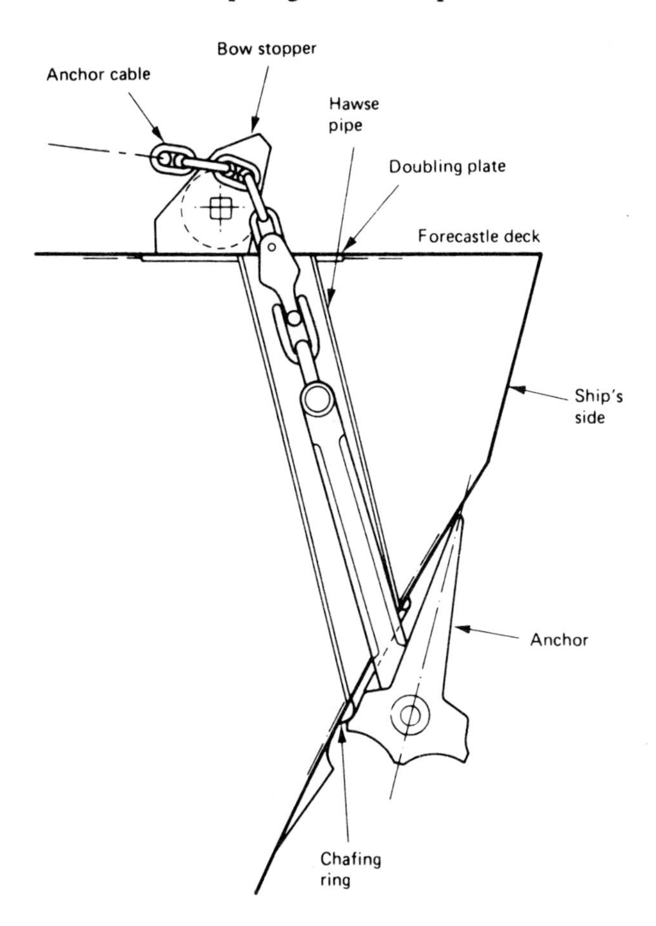

Figure 5.29 Hawse pipe

Cable stopper

The chain, cable or bow stopper is fitted on the forecastle deck in line with the run of the anchor cable. It is used to hold the anchor cable in place while the ship is riding at anchor or the anchor is fully housed. In this way the windlass is freed and isolated

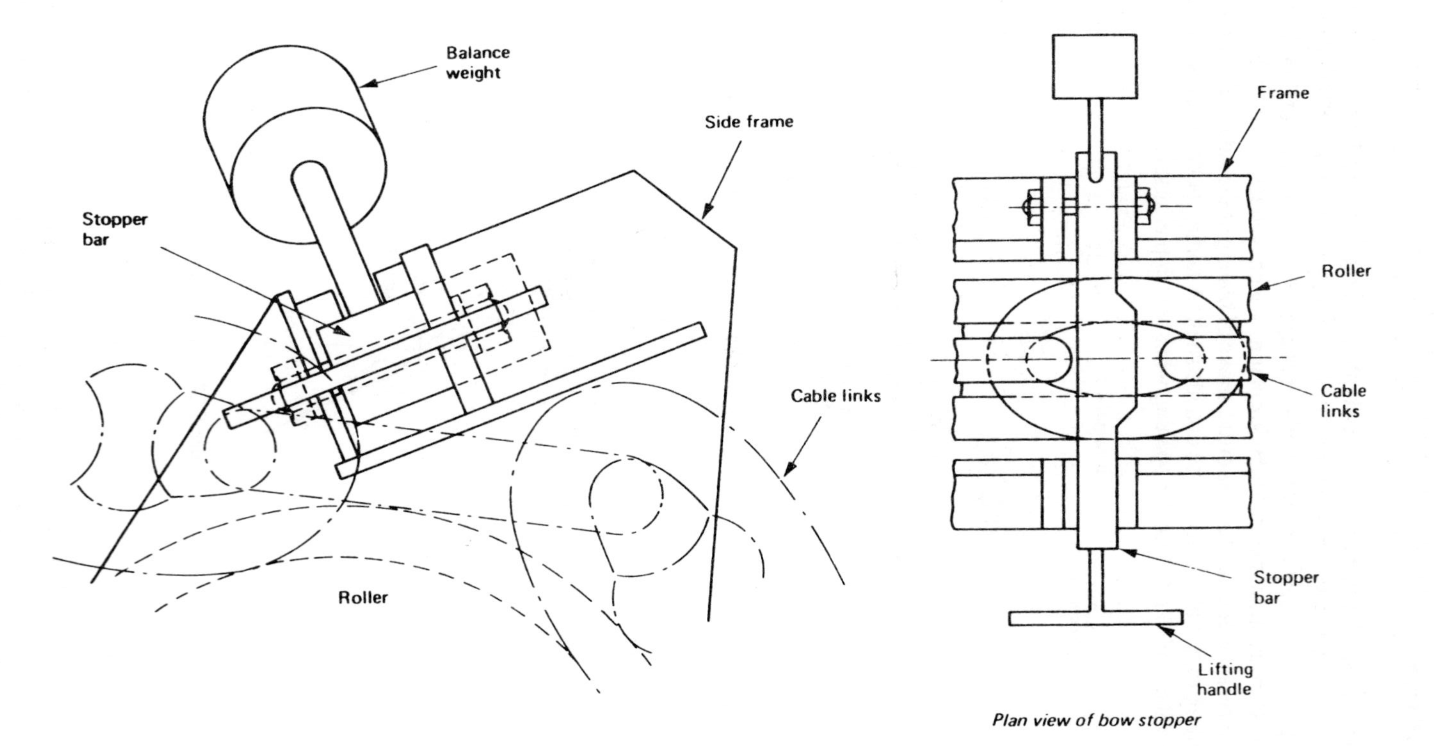

Figure 5.30 Roller bow stopper

from any shocks or vibrations from the cable. The chain stopper is not designed to stop the moving cable, but only hold it in place. One type is shown in *Figure 5.30* and consists of a fabricated structure of heavy plate with a roller which the cable passes over. A hinged bar is designed to fall between two vertical links and hold the cable in place. The chain stopper is welded or bolted on to a heavy insert plate in the deck and is additionally stiffened by brackets.

Windlass

The windlass is the lifting device for the anchor cables or chains and is also used for mooring and winching duties. Various drums or barrels can be 'clutched in' to perform the different duties. For raising the anchor, the cable lifting drum is engaged.

This is a barrel with specially shaped 'snugs' which the cable links fit into and pass round before dropping into the chain locker via the spurling pipe. The anchor cable is allowed to lower under its own weight with the lifting drum declutched, while the brake band around it is used to control the speed of descent.

Chain locker

The chain locker is normally fitted forward of the collision bulkhead. It is of dimensions adequate to house all the anchor cable and still leave a considerable empty space above. Two lockers or a centrally divided single locker will be fitted for the port and starboard anchor cables. The chain locker should be as low as practicable to reduce the height of the centre of gravity of the considerable mass of the cables. A perforated false floor or grating is fitted at the bottom to provide a drainage well and keep the cable out of mud and water.

Figure 5.31 shows an arrangement of a chain locker. It consists of a plate structure with vertical stiffeners around the outside. Plate webs which form part of

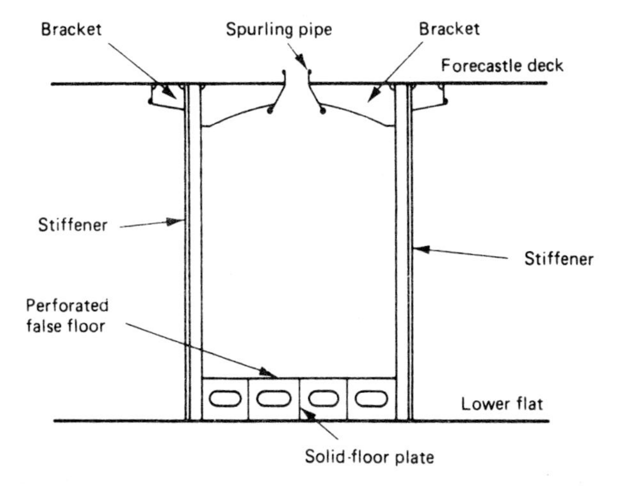

Figure 5.31 Chain locker

the ship's internal structure are also utilised for stiffening. A raised perforated false floor is fitted and supported by solid floors. The well thus formed is connected to the bilge system and should be emptied every time the anchor is raised. The forecastle deck forms the top of the locker with the spurling pipe at the centre. The spurling pipe is manufactured of heavy plate with a solid round bar as a chaffing ring on the lower edge. Brackets radiate from the spurling pipe to the chain locker sides to strengthen the forecastle deck and the spurling pipe. A U-section plate welded to the side with footholes cut in provides access to the bottom of the chain locker from a watertight door at the upper deck. Provision is also made for securing the final link of the anchor cable. The chain locker illustrated is one of a pair fitted port and starboard beneath their respective windlasses.

Clench cable assembly

The final link of the anchor cable is secured to the ship's structure by a clench pin. On most modern ships this pin is positioned on the outside of the chain locker and can be released easily and quickly. A situation may arise where the safety of the ship does not allow time to raise the anchor. By releasing the clench pin all the cable can quickly pass out of the chain locker, leaving the ship free to proceed out of danger. An arrangement is shown in *Figure 5.32*, where an insert heavy plate pocket is fitted into the chain locker side with a vertical pin holding the final link of anchor cable. A hand-wheel assembly on deck is used to raise the pin and release the link.

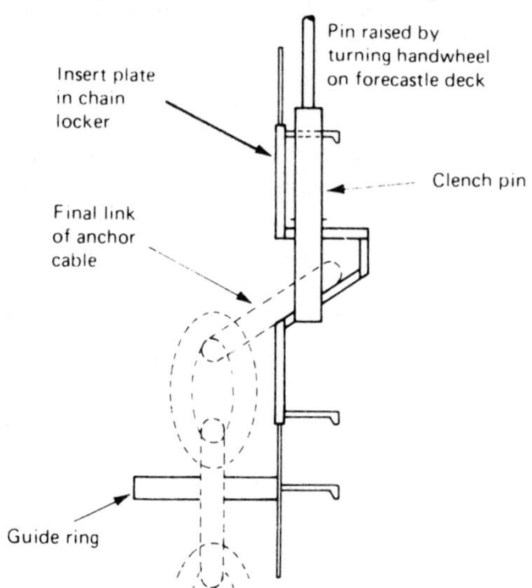

Figure 5.32 Cable clench arrangement

Thrusters

A thruster is usually considered to be a device which assists in docking, manœuvring, or positioning of a vessel which is moving at a low speed. Some form of

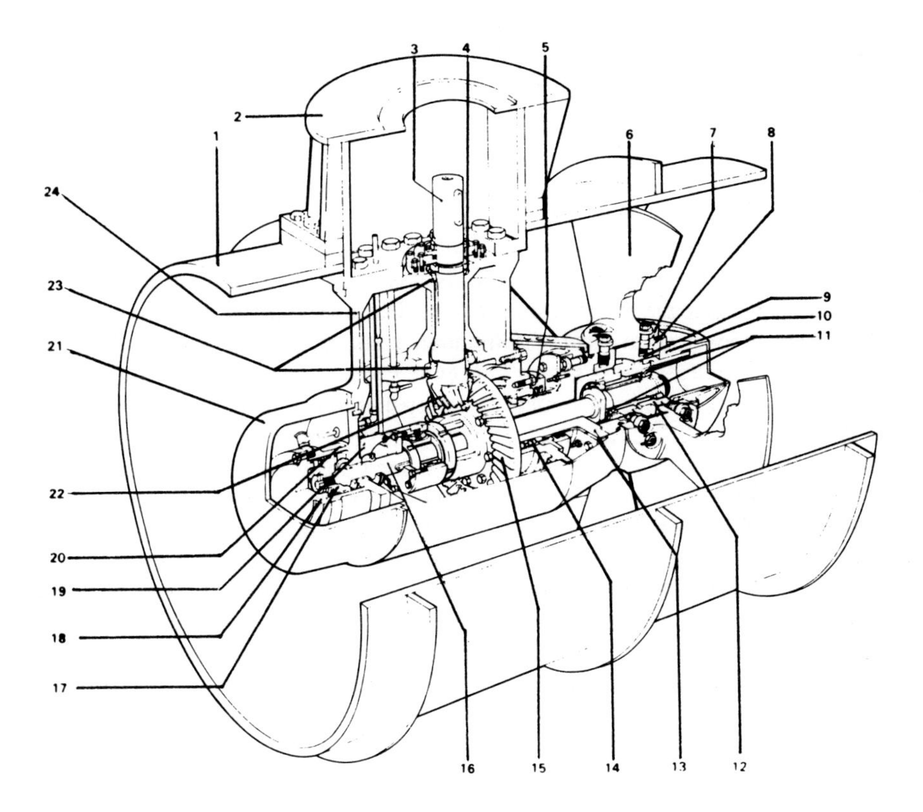

1. *Tunnel section*
2. *Motor mounting stool*
3. *Input drive shaft*
4. *Input drive shaft cartridge*
5. *Propeller shaft seal*
6. *Propeller blade*
7. *Blade palm seal*
8. *Hub body*
9. *Crank pin ring*
10. *Crosshead bearing housing*
11. *Taper roller thrust bearing*
12. *Crosshead*
13. *Propeller shaft*
14. *Propeller shaft thrust bearing*
15. *Spiral bevel wheel*
16. *Piston rod*
17. *Servo motor piston*
18. *Servo motor cylinder head*
19. *Feed back linkage*
20. *Servo motor cylinder*
21. *Servo motor end cover*
22. *Spiral bevel pinion*
23. *Drive shaft taper roller bearing*
24. *Gear housing*

Figure 5.33 Tunnel thruster unit

propeller-type device is used to move water either freely or in a duct. The propeller may be fixed or controllable pitch and complete unit may be retractable or exposed, fixed in position or able to rotate (azimuth).

Probably the most common unit fitted on merchant vessels is the tunnel thruster using either a fixed pitch or a controllable pitch propeller. The fixed pitch unit would require a reversible drive. A controllable pitch type thruster is shown in *Figure 5.33*. A non-rotating servo motor located in the gear housing is used to change the pitch of the propeller blades. The force on the servomotor piston is transmitted by a piston rod inside the propeller shaft to the crosshead and crank mechanism in the hub. Water flow can thus be provided in either direction simply by changing the blade pitch angle. Any non-reversing prime mover can therefore be used, e.g. a single speed electric motor. The prime mover need not be stopped during manœuvring operations since the blades can be placed at zero pitch when no thrust is desired. The drive is obtained through a flexible drive shaft, couplings and bevel gears. Special seals prevent any sea water leakage into the unit.

The complete assembly includes part of the athwartships tunnel through which water is directed to provide the thrust. Grids must be fitted at either end of the tunnel and this can reduce the thrust to some extent. The actual tunnel location is usually decided by model tests to ensure the minimum resistance when not in use. A tunnel construction arrangement is shown in *Figure 5.34*.

Gill jet thrusters utilise a vertical axis propeller in a T-shaped tunnel. Water is drawn in from both sides and leaves through the bottom of the hull. Rotatable gill fins direct the water in one of a number of fixed positions around a circle. The hydrojet thruster has a similar arrangement but draws water in from below and discharges it at the sides with vanes directing the thrust. Steering vanes in the diverging liquid path can also be used to maximise the thrust to one side or the other. Ducted jet thrusters operate somewhat similarly to a tunnel thruster except that the duct is usually curved. This duct may be located either on the ship's side or the bottom shell and usually requires large openings.

An azimuth or rotating thruster usually consists of a ducted propeller which can rotate through 360°. The propeller may be fixed or controllable pitch. This unit is particularly suited for dynamic positioning and some propulsion duties. When fitted to ships, an azimuth thruster is usually retractable.

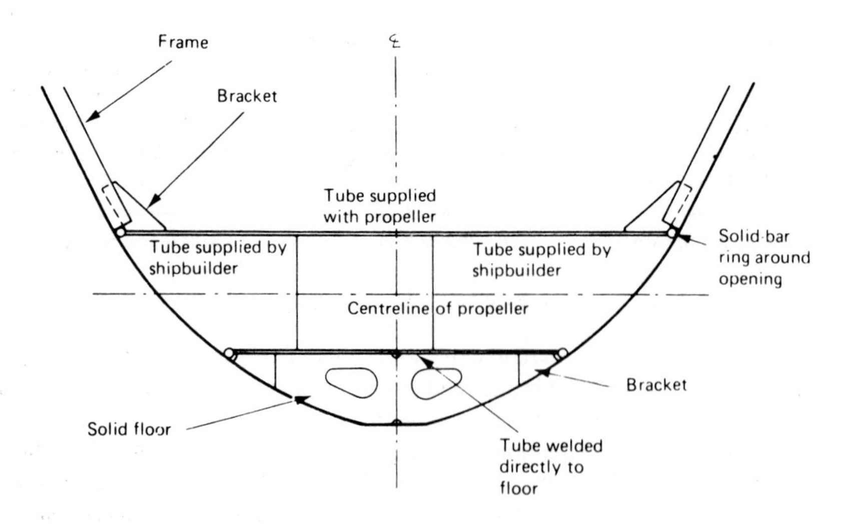

Figure 5.34 Bow thruster tunnel

SECTION E AFT END CONSTRUCTION

The aft end of a ship terminates the structure and is designed to provide a smooth water flow into and away from the propeller. The propeller and rudder are also positioned and supported at the after end and require certain structural arrangements in order to operate satisfactorily. The after end construction involves an amount of overhanging structure to accept the steering gear below deck and mooring equipment higher up on the weather deck. This arrangement leads to large slamming forces in this after region, and an adequately stiffened structure is therefore required.

Two main types of stern construction have been used to date—the cruiser stern and the transom stern. The cruiser stern is rarely used in modern construction but it is still to be seen in a large proportion of the ships at sea. The transom stern, with its straight line form, lends itself well to current manufacturing techniques. It also provides a greater deck area aft and is currently much used for a variety of ship types.

Cruiser stern

The construction of the cruiser stern (*Figure 5.35*) ensures adequate resistance to any pounding stresses which may occur. Solid plate floors are fitted at every frame space and a heavy centreline girder is fitted below each of the decks in the stern. A centreline web as a continuation of the centreline girder is fitted at the after end shell plate and runs down to the centreline girder in the flooring region. Special frames are radiused around the after end and are known as 'cant frames', since they are set at an angle to the centreline of the ship. These cant frames join cant beams which support the deck at the radiused after end. Horizontal stringers may also be fitted to stiffen up the structure by connecting it to the transverse frames further forward.

Transom stern

Deep solid-plate floors are also a feature of the transom stern construction, together with a centreline girder (*Figure 5.36*). The flat plate of the transom stern construction, however, allows use of vertical stiffeners around the shell plating. The vertical stiffeners are bracketed to the floor and to the deck beams which run transversely across the stern. A deep horizontal stringer can provide additional stiffening to the shell plating if required. A deep centre girder runs beneath each of the decks at the stern and is bracketed to the deep web at the centreline of the after shell plating. This web is likewise bracketed to the various floors in the stern and finally to the solid-plate floor construction below.

Rudder trunk

The rudder trunk is an open section which is left in the stern for the entry of the rudder stock into the steering flat (*Figure 5.36*). A horizontal platform is sometimes fitted midway up the trunk to fit a watertight gland. The trunking above is then

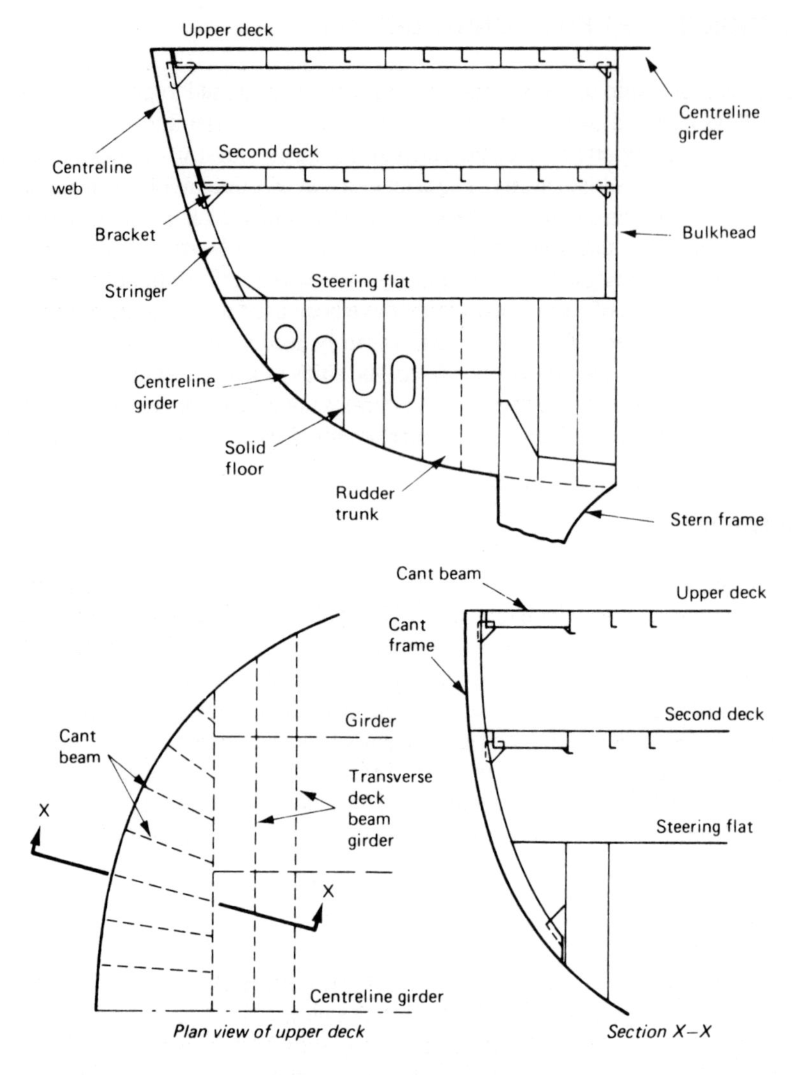

Figure 5.35 Cruiser stern

constructed to be watertight and access to this upper section and the gland is provided by a manhole.

Sternframe

The shell plating at the after end is terminated by the sternframe (*Figure 5.36*). This is usually a casting, but fabrications and forgings are sometimes used. In single-screw ships the sternframe has a boss on the centreline for the tailshaft to pass through and an adequate aperture is provided for the propeller to operate in. If sufficient clearance at the blade tips were not allowed then serious vibrations would

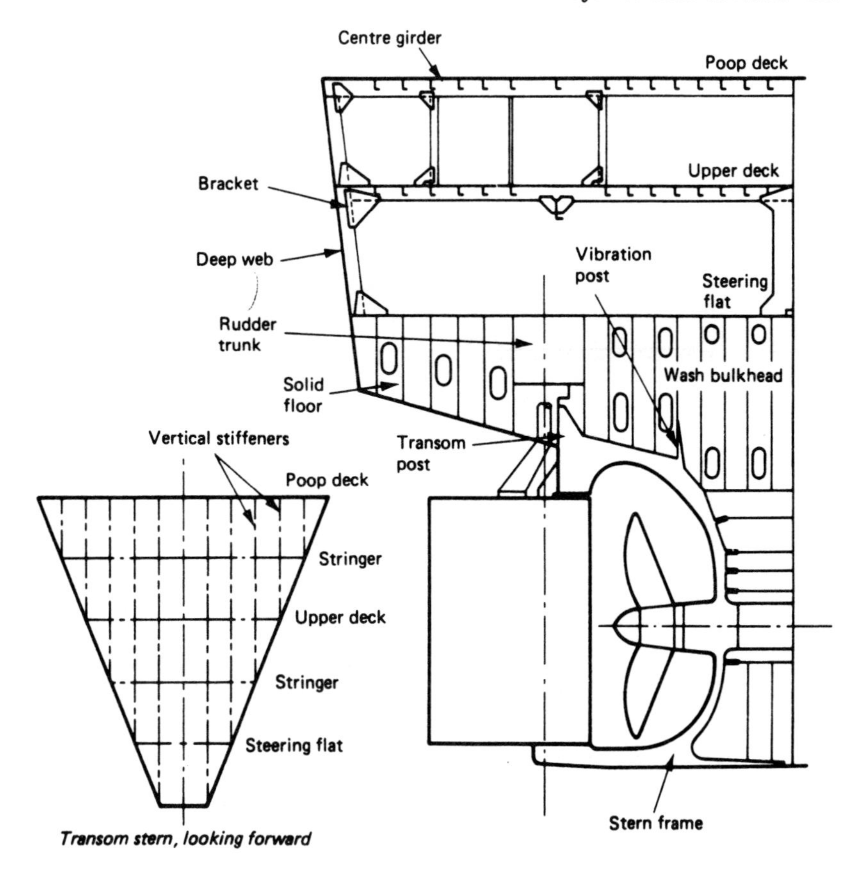

Figure 5.36 Transom stern

be set up in the after end of the ship. The lower part of the sternframe may provide a support for the rudder post or an overhanging section may provide gudgeons for the rudder pintles. *Figures 5.43*, *5.44* and *5.45* show different arrangements. Various sections of the sternframe, particularly above the arch, provide connecting points to the individual floors of the after end construction. The transom post and vibration post are two particular connections (*Figure 5.36*). Sound connections at these points ensure that propeller-induced vibrations are kept to a minimum. Twin-screw ships have a sternframe which is only required to support the rudder pintles and is thus much reduced in size. Larger sternframes, particularly those of cast construction, are manufactured in two parts with provision made for bolting together and, after careful alignment, welding at the suitably prepared joint.

A-brackets and bossings

Twin-screw vessels with their shafts set away from the centreline require support for the shaft overhang as it leaves the shell. Bossings are often used to increase the

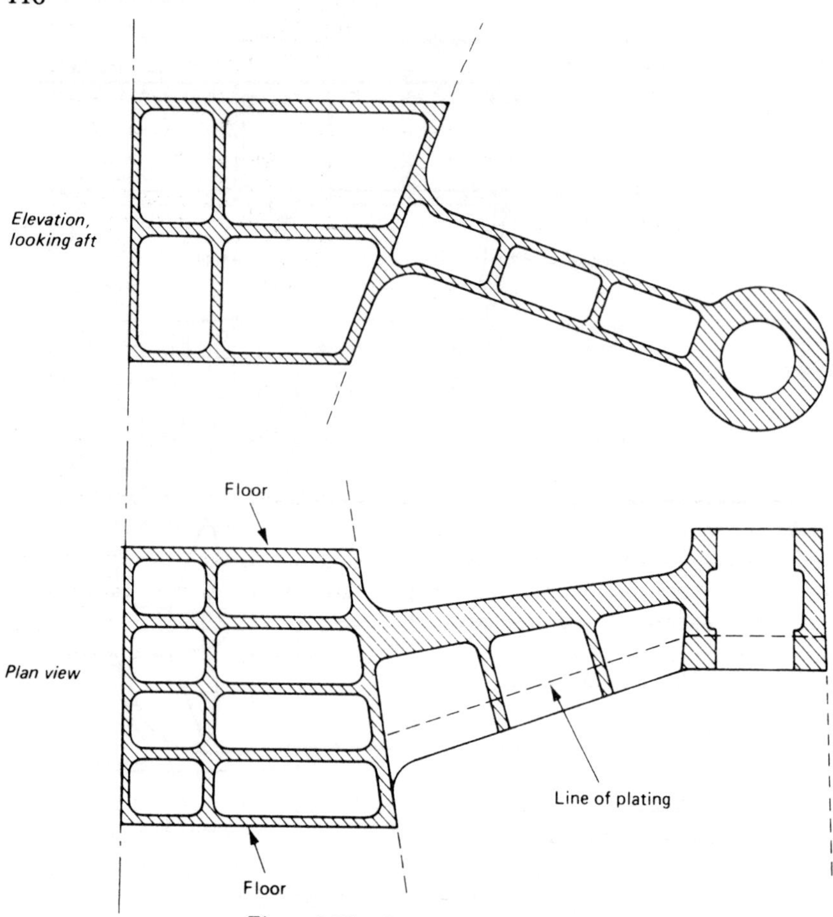

Figure 5.37 Cast spectacle frame

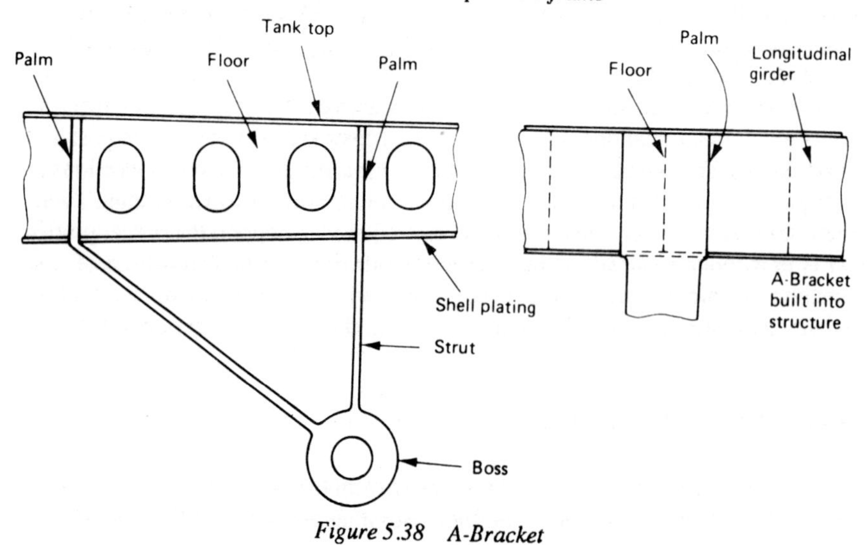

Figure 5.38 A-Bracket

vessel's width and allow the shafts to remain within the hull while still retaining a streamlined flow of water to the propellers. The shafting is protected and internal inspection is possible with this arrangement. These bossings are symmetrical about the ship's centreline and give rise to the term 'spectacle frame' because of their appearance from aft of the vessel (*Figure 5.37*). Some modern constructions make use of A-brackets set out from the hull to support the shafts (*Figure 5.38*). The final A-bracket in addition to acting as a bearing, must support the weight of the propeller.

Both bossings and A-frames are led into the stern and solidly built into the structure with additional local stiffening where required.

Sterntubes

The propeller shaft enters the ship through the sterntube which acts as the final bearing and a watertight seal to the sea. Traditional practice saw the use of lignum vitæ and certain synthetic materials as bearing surfaces within the sterntube and these were lubricated by sea water. The increased loadings, as a result of slow speed shafts and heavier propellers on more modern ships, has led to the widespread use of oil-lubricated whitemetal bearings. With this arrangement wear down in service is much reduced but there is a need for more accurate alignment and for seals at each end of the sterntube. An oil-lubricated sterntube arrangement is shown in *Figure 5.39*.

Propellers

A propeller consists of a boss which has several helicoidal form blades. When rotated it 'screws' or thrusts its way through the water by giving momentum to the column of water passing through it. The thrust is transmitted along the shafting to the thrust block and finally to the ship's structure. The thrust block must therefore have a rigid seating or framework which is integrated into the ship's structure to absorb the thrust. The propeller will usually be either of the fixed pitch or controllable pitch type. In addition some special designs and arrangements are in use which offer particular advantages.

Fixed pitch propeller

Although described as fixed pitch, a solid single-piece cast propeller has a pitch which varies with increasing radius from the boss. The pitch at any particular point on a blade is however fixed and an average value for the complete propeller is used in all calculations. A fixed pitch propeller is shown in *Figure 5.40*, where most of the terms used in describing the geometrical features are also given. It should be noted that the face is the surface farthest from the stern and is the 'working' surface. A cone is fitted to the boss to provide a smooth flow of water away from the propeller. A propeller which rotates clockwise, when viewed from aft, is considered to be right-handed. Most single-screw ships have right-handed propellers. A twin-screw ship will usually have a right-handed starboard propeller and a left-handed port propeller.

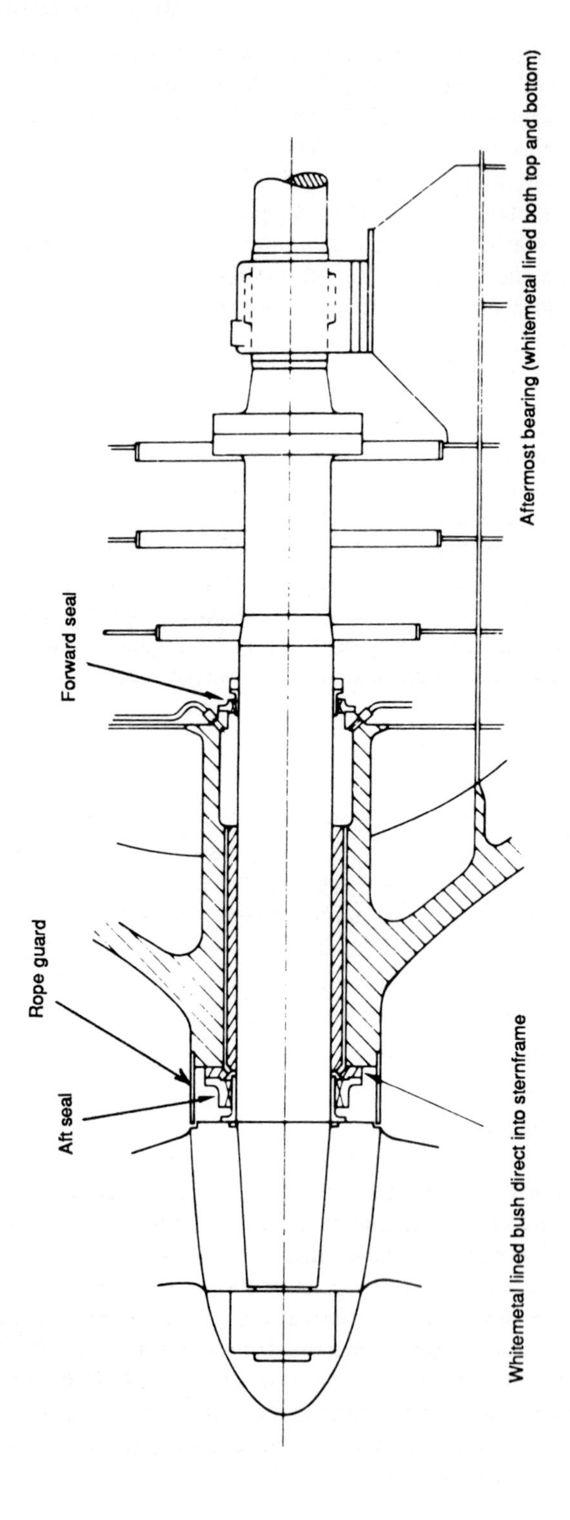

Figure 5.39 Oil-lubricated sterntube

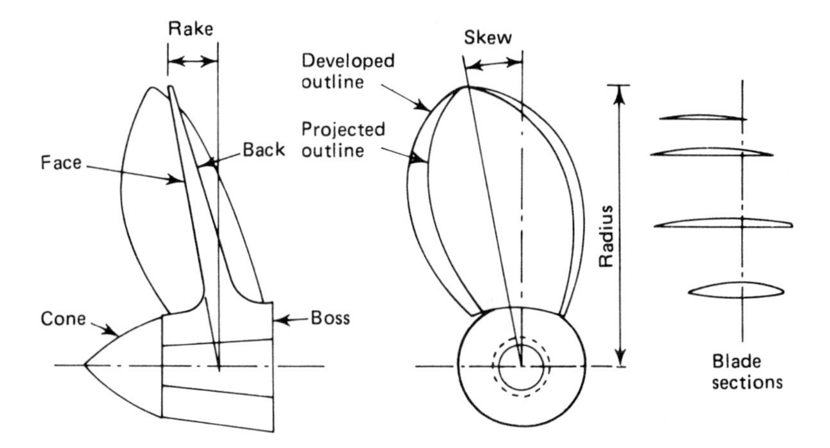

Figure 5.40 Fixed pitch propeller

Cavitation is the forming and bursting of vapour filled cavities or bubbles and occurs as a result of certain pressure variations on the back of a propeller blade. The results of this phenomenon are a loss of thrust, erosion of the blade surface, vibrations in the afterbody of the ship and noise. It is usually limited to high-speed, heavily loaded propellers and is not a problem under normal operating conditions with a well-designed propeller.

The propeller, when turning in the ship's wake, is a potential source of vibration excitation. To some extent this can be minimised by having the leading edges skewed back. Skew back is an advantage when the propeller is working in a varying wake as not all the blade is affected at the same time. Variations in the thrust and torque are therefore smoothed out. Since the vibrations are blade excited, then the number of blades is significant and determines the vibration frequency. Where severe vibration problems exist it may ultimately be necessary to change the propeller for one with a different number of blades.

Propeller mounting

The propeller is fitted onto a taper on the tailshaft and a key may be inserted between the two; alternatively a keyless arrangement may be used. A large nut is fastened and locked in place on the end of the tailshaft. A cone is then bolted over the end of the tailshaft to provide a smooth flow of water from the propeller.

One method of keyless propeller fitting is the oil injection system. The propeller bore is machined with a series of axial and circumferential grooves. High-pressure oil is injected between the tapered section of the tailshaft and the propeller. This reduces the friction between the two parts and the propeller is pushed up the shaft taper by a hydraulic jacking ring. Once the propeller is positioned, the oil pressure is released and the oil runs back leaving the shaft and propeller securely fastened together.

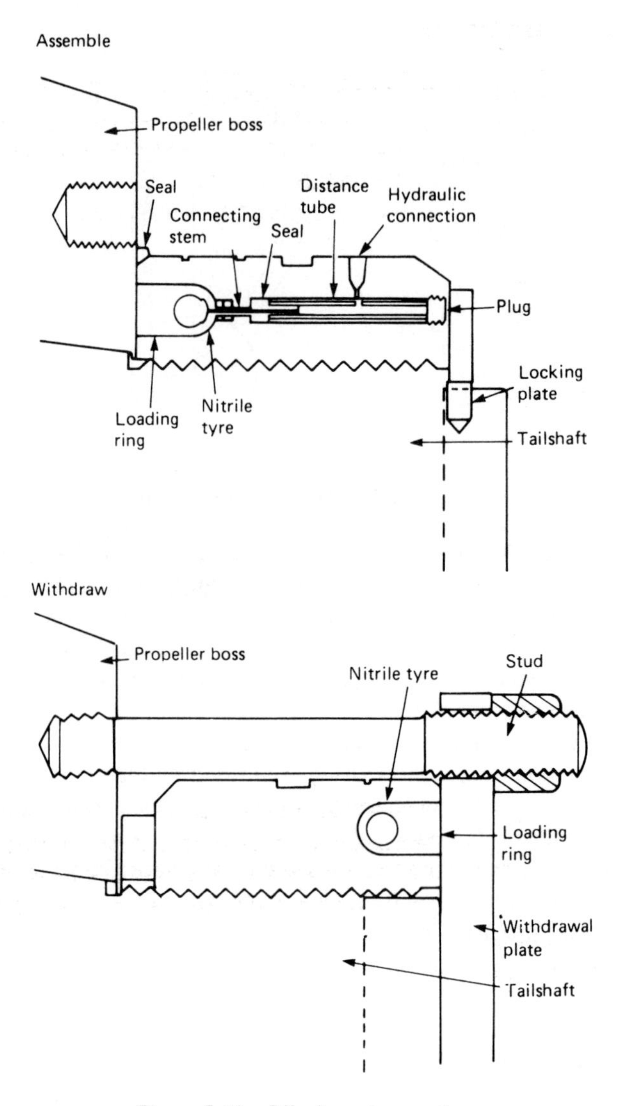

Figure 5.41 Pilgrim nut operation

The pilgrim nut is a patented device which provides a predetermined frictional grip between the propeller and its shaft. With this arrangement the engine torque may be transmitted without loading the key (where fitted). The pilgrim nut is, in effect, a threaded hydraulic jack which is screwed onto the tailshaft (see *Figure 5.41*). A steel ring receives thrust from a hydraulically pressurised nitrile rubber tyre. This thrust is applied to the propeller to force it onto the tapered tailshaft. Propeller removal is achieved by reversing the Pilgrim Nut and using a withdrawal plate which is fastened to the propeller boss by studs. When the tyre is pressured the propeller is drawn off the taper. Assembly and withdrawal are shown in *Figure 5.41*.

Controllable-pitch propellers

A controllable-pitch propeller is made up of a boss with separate blades mounted into it. An internal mechanism enables the blades to be moved simultaneously through an arc to change the pitch angle and therefore the pitch. A typical arrangement is shown in *Figure 5.42*.

When a pitch demand signal is received, a spool valve is operated which controls the supply of low pressure oil to the auxiliary servo-motor. This moves the sliding thrust block assembly to position the valve rod which extends into the propeller hub. The valve rod admits high pressure oil into one side or the other of the main servo-motor cylinder. The cylinder movement is transferred by a crankpin and ring to the propeller blades. The propeller blades rotate together until the feed-back signal balances the demand signal and the low pressure oil to the auxiliary servo-motor is cut off. To enable emergency control of propeller pitch in the event of loss of power, the spool valves can be operated by hand. The oil pumps are shaft driven.

The control mechanism, which is usually hydraulic, passes through the tailshaft and operation is from the bridge. Varying the pitch will vary the thrust provided and since a zero pitch position exists the engine shaft may turn continuously. The blades may rotate to provide astern thrust and therefore the engine does not require to be reversed.

Special types

A number of specialised arrangements or types of propeller exist and have particular advantages or applications. The Voith-Schneider propeller is a vertically-rotating device. The blades are vertically positioned around a disc and can be rotated by cams in order to change the blade angle at a particular point in each revolution. This results in a thrust whose magnitude and direction is determined by the cams. It is, therefore, in some respects similar to a controllable-pitch propeller in that the disc is driven and the blades can be positioned independently of the main drive. This unit can effectively thrust in any direction and will respond rapidly to the pitch control mechanism. The complete assembly is unfortunately complex, noisy in operation and considerable maintenance is necessary. It is often used for main propulsion in ferries and vessels requiring considerable manœuvrability. It may also be used as a thruster or propulsion device for drill ships or floating cranes which require accurate positioning.

The use of a duct or nozzle around the propeller can result in an improvement of the propeller performance. Furthermore the aerofoil shape of the duct can produce a forward thrust which will offset any drag it creates. The duct also protects the propeller from damage and reduces noise. It is usually fitted on ships with heavily loaded propellers, e.g. tugs, and has been used on larger vessels. One particular patented design of duct is known as the Kort Nozzle.

The CLT (Formerly TVF) propeller is a recent special design which results in much improved propeller efficiency. The blade tips are fitted with pieces at right angles to the plane of rotation. The initial impression is that the blade edges have

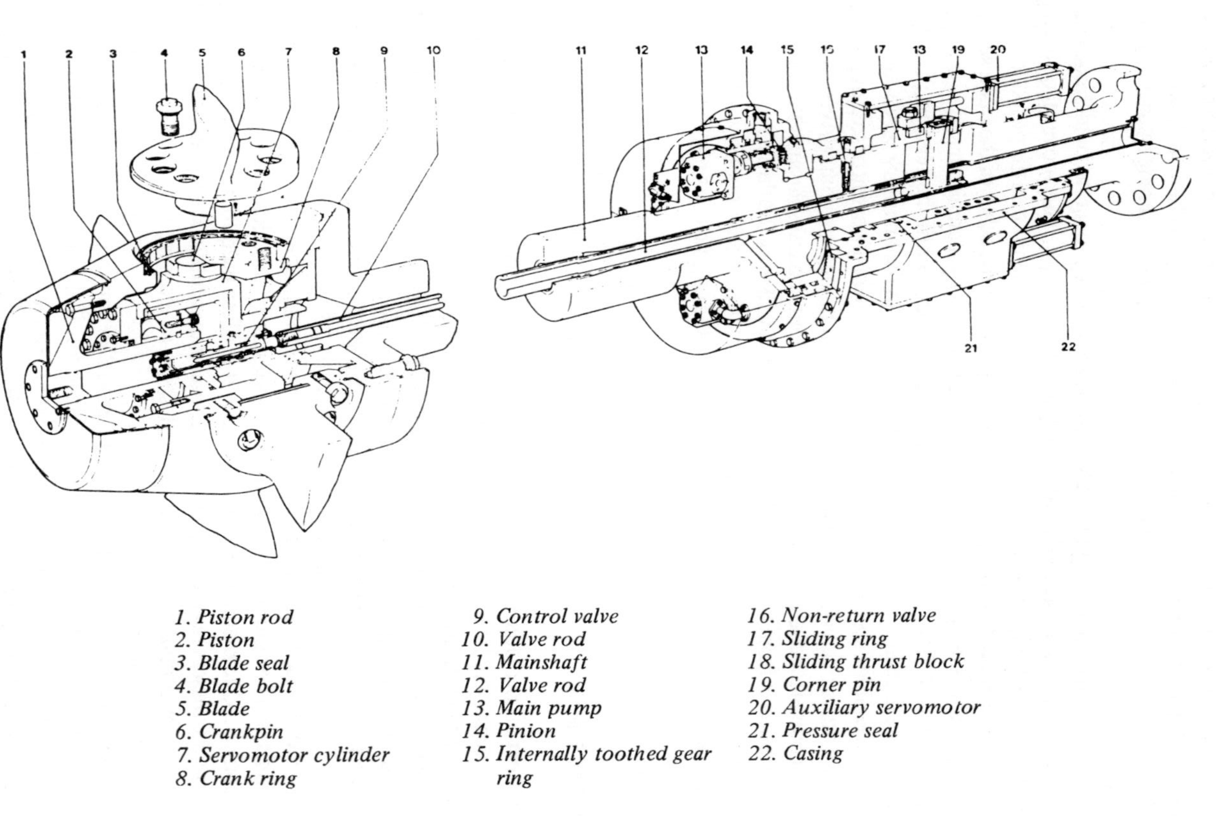

1. *Piston rod*
2. *Piston*
3. *Blade seal*
4. *Blade bolt*
5. *Blade*
6. *Crankpin*
7. *Servomotor cylinder*
8. *Crank ring*
9. *Control valve*
10. *Valve rod*
11. *Mainshaft*
12. *Valve rod*
13. *Main pump*
14. *Pinion*
15. *Internally toothed gear ring*
16. *Non-return valve*
17. *Sliding ring*
18. *Sliding thrust block*
19. *Corner pin*
20. *Auxiliary servomotor*
21. *Pressure seal*
22. *Casing*

Figure 5.42 Controllable pitch propeller

been bent over towards the face, i.e. away from the ship. The attachments at the blade tips serve to generate thrust across the whole propeller blade and thus improve the propeller efficiency. A nozzle surrounds the propeller and a tunnel structure under the stern on either side is used to direct the incoming flow of water.

The Grim Wheel or vane wheel is mounted aft of the main propeller and is larger in diameter. It is a freely rotating propeller with high aspect ratio blades which vary from a coarse pitch at the boss to a very fine pitch at the tip. The wheel is rotated by, and extracts energy from, the propeller slipstream and produces an additional thrust from the tip region of its blades.

The contra-rotating propeller uses two driven propellers which rotate in opposite directions. A special gearbox and shafting arrangement enables a single engine to drive the two propellers. Significant efficiency gains have been achieved by the first unit which was fitted to a bulk carrier.

Propeller boss cap fins convert the propeller hub vortex energy into additional torque and thrust which is transmitted back to the propeller shaft. The boss cap with its short blades is fixed to the main propeller boss.

Rudders

The rudder is used to steer the ship. The turning action is largely dependent on the area of the rudder, which is usually of the order of one-sixtieth to one-seventieth of the length × depth of the ship. The ratio of the depth to width of a rudder is known as the aspect ratio and is usually in the region of 2.

Streamlined rudders of a double-plate construction are fitted to all modern ships and are further described by the arrangement about their axis. A rudder with all of its area aft of the turning axis is known as 'unbalanced' (*Figure 5.43*). A rudder with a small part of its area forward of the turning axis is known as 'semi-balanced' (*Figure 5.44*). When more than 25% of the rudder area is forward of the turning axis there is no torque on the rudder stock at certain angles and such an arrangement is therefore known as a 'balanced rudder' (*Figure 5.45*).

Modern rudders are constructed with steel plate sides welded to an internal webbed framework. Integral with the internal framework may be heavy forgings which form the gudgeons or bearing housings of the rudder. The upper face of the rudder is formed into a, usually, horizontal flat palm which acts as the coupling point for the rudder stock. A lifting hole is provided in the rudder to enable a vertical in-line lift of the rudder when it is being fitted or removed. A special lifting bar with eye plates is used to lift the rudder. A fashion or eddy plate can be seen at the forward edge on the unbalanced and semi-balanced rudders shown in *Figures 5.43* and *5.44* respectively. This is welded in place after the rudder is fitted to provide a streamlined water flow into the rudder. After manufacture, every rudder is air tested to a pressure equivalent to a head of 2.45 m above the top of the rudder in order to ensure its watertight integrity. The internal surfaces are usually coated with bitumen, or some similar coating, to protect the metal should the plating leak. A drain hole is provided at the bottom of the rudder to check for water entry when the ship is examined in drydock.

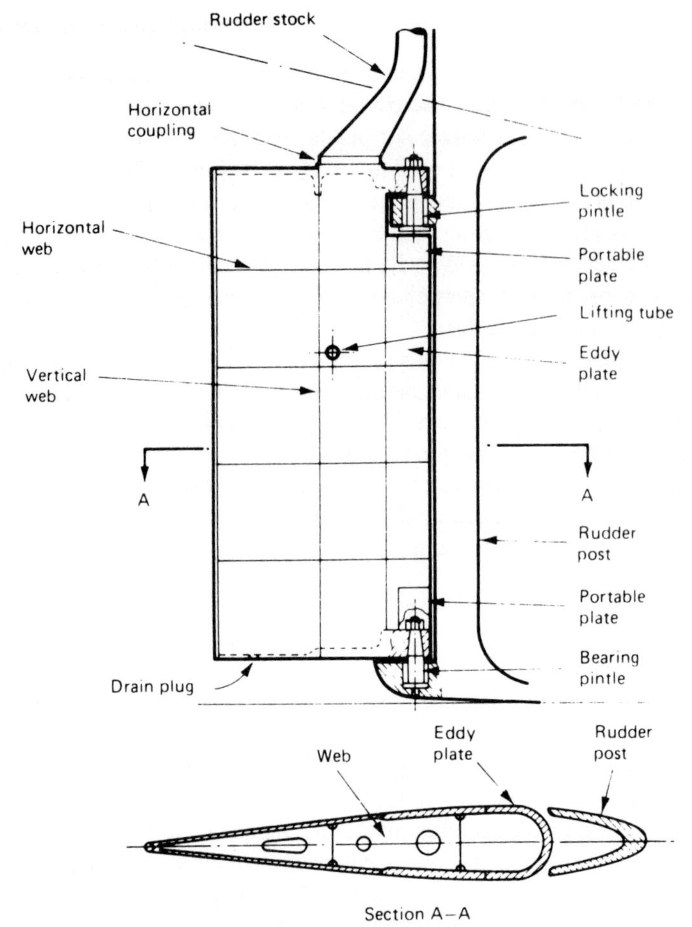

Figure 5.43 Unbalanced rudder

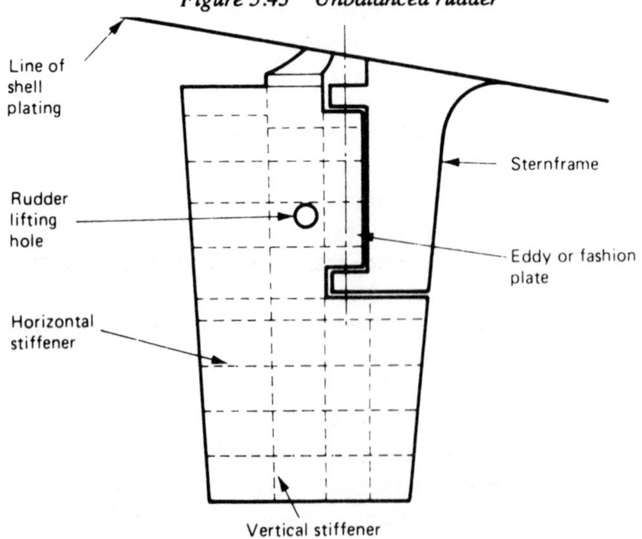

Figure 5.44 Semi-balanced rudder

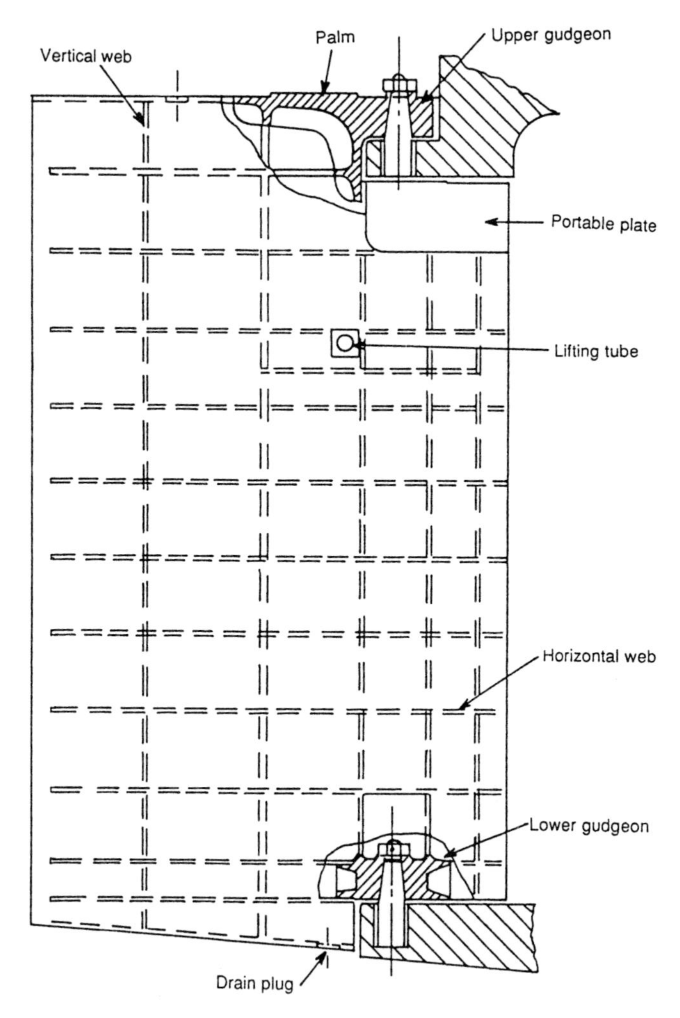

Figure 5.45 Balanced rudder

Rudder pintles and bearings

The rudder, depending on its type and arrangement, will turn on either pintles or bearings.

The balanced rudder in *Figure 5.36* has a rudder axle fitted at its turning axis. Upper and lower bearings are fitted in the rudder, as shown in *Figure 5.46*. The bearing consists of a stainless steel bush in the rudder and a stainless steel liner on the axle. The stainless steel bush is spirally grooved to permit lubrication. Other materials are in use, such as gunmetal for the liner and lignum vitæ or tufnol for the bush. The upper and lower pair of tapered bearing rings are fitted between the rudder and the sternframe. These are fitted with a small clearance but may support the weight of the rudder should the carrier fail.

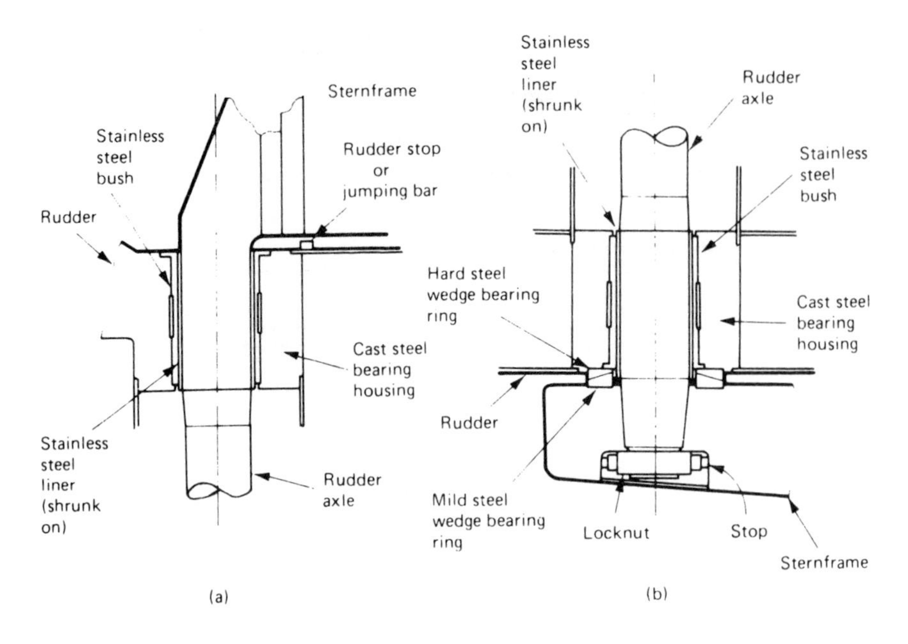

Figure 5.46 Axle-bearing arrangements: (a) upper bearing arrangement; (b) lower bearing arrangement

The semi-balanced rudder shown in *Figure 5.44* turns on pintles. Arrangements vary but the pintle consists of a bearing length of constant diameter and a tapered length which is drawn into a similarly tapered hole on the rudder or sternframe gudgeon. The pintle is drawn in by a large nut pulling on the threaded portion of the pintle. The pintle nut is securely locked in place after tightening. A locking pintle has a shoulder of increased diameter at its lower end which prevents excessive lift of the rudder. A bearing or heel pintle has a bearing surface at its lower edge which rests on a hard steel disc. This bearing pintle is only required to support the weight of the rudder in the event of the rudder carrier failing. Both types of pintle are shown in *Figure 5.43*. Liners of brass or sometimes stainless steel are fitted to the pintle bearing surface. The bearing material is held in a cage in the gudeon and is usually tufnol or some hard-wearing synthetic material. Lubrication is provided by sea water which is free to circulate around the bearing surfaces of both pintles.

Rudder stock and carrier

The stock passes through a gland and a rudder carrier before entering the steering compartment. The gland and carrier may be combined or separate items of equipment.

The rudder carrier consists of two halves which provide an upper and lower bearing surface (*Figure 5.47*). The upper part of the rudder carrier is keyed to the stock so that they turn together. The major part of the rudder's weight is transferred to the rudder carrier by either a shoulder, as part of the stock forging, or a collar fitted

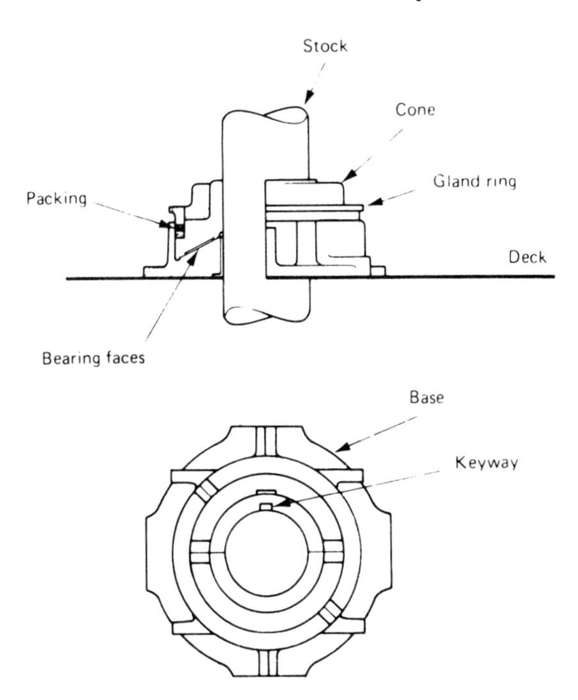

Figure 5.47 Rudder carrier

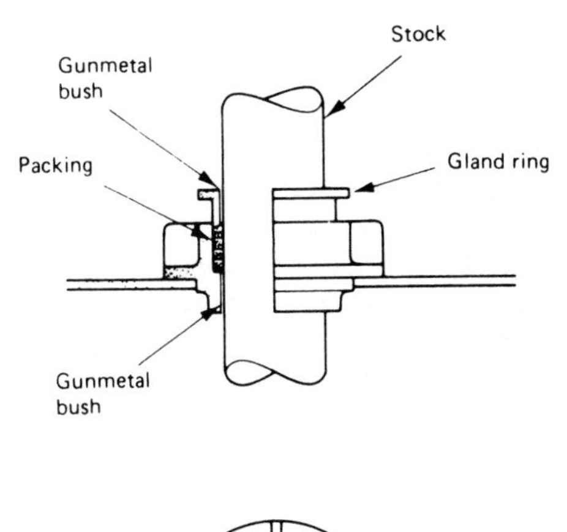

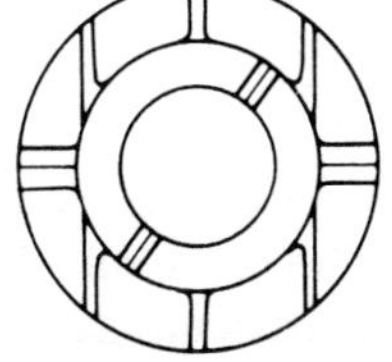

Figure 5.48 Watertight gland for rudder stock

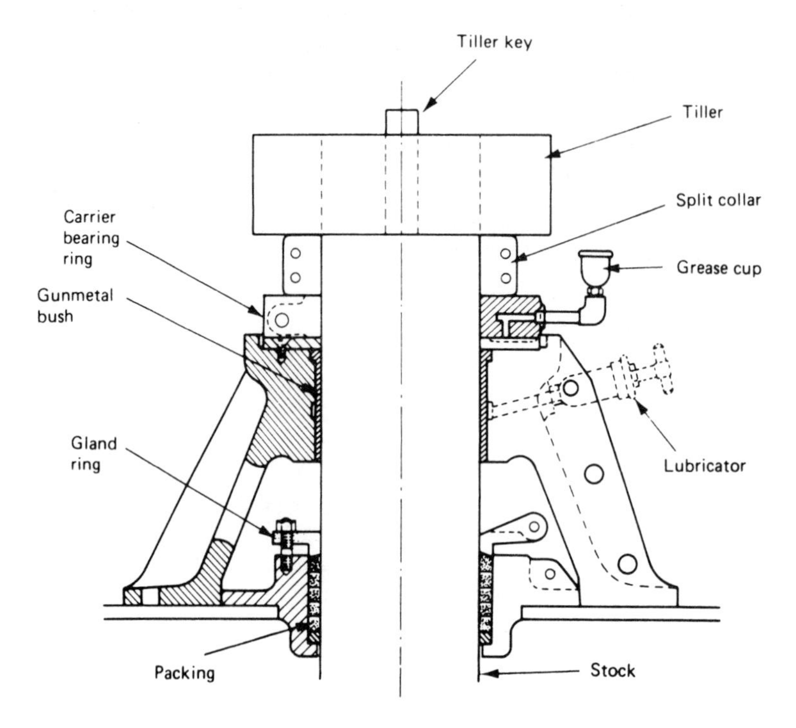

Figure 5.49 Combined rudder carrier and gland

between the tiller and the carrier. The rudder weight is thus transferred to the lower bearing surface of the carrier which is grease lubricated. A flat or conical bearing surface may be used depending on the particular design. The lower half of the carrier is bolted into a heavy insert plate in the deck of the steering flat and is chocked against fore and aft and athwartships movement.

A separate watertight gland is often fitted where the stock enters the rudder trunk. This arrangement provides access to a greater length of the rudder stock, removes the need for a watertight construction of the carrier bearing and reduces the unsupported length of the stock (*Figure 5.48*). A combined type of watertight gland and rudder carrier is shown in *Figure 5.49*. It is essential for ease of operation of the rudder that the pintles and rudder stock turning axes are in the same vertical line. Great care must be taken during installation to ensure this correct alignment.

SECTION F SUPERSTRUCTURES AND ACCOMMODATION

The superstructure is that part of the ship's structure built above the uppermost complete deck and is the full width of the ship. Deckhouses are smaller structures not extending the full width and one or more storeys high. They may be built on to the superstructure or at the base of masts, etc. The construction of superstructures and deckhouses uses frames, plating, girders and brackets in a similar manner to the hull, but of smaller scantlings. However, superstructures extending 15% of the ship's length are considered to contribute to the longitudinal strength of the ship. As such, they must have equivalent scantlings and strength to the main hull.

The most forward section of the superstructure is known as the 'forecastle'. Any section of the superstructure around the midships region of the ship is referred to as a 'bridge structure'. The deck area aft is known as the 'poop' and any superstructure located aft is likewise known. A raised quarter deck is a weather deck extending for some portion of the ship's length from aft and is positioned above the upper deck.

Most modern ships have most of the superstructure and accommodation situated aft above the machinery space. The superstructure and deckhouses usually total four or five storeys. Most of this space, excluding that lost to the machinery casing, is used for crew accommodation.

Forecastle

All ships must be fitted with a forecastle or an arrangement to provide a minimum bow height, as defined in classification society rules. It is usual to fit forecastles, and where this is done they must extend from the stem a distance 0.07 L aft (where L is the freeboard length). The side plating of the forecastle, being a continuation of the shell plating, is thicker than the end plating. Adequate arrangements for stiffening of the forecastle plating must be provided.

Bridge structure

Where a bridge structure exceeds 15% of the ship's length, the side plating thickness must be increased by 25% above that of other superstructures. A heavily plated bridge front is required with the after end plating somewhat lighter. Stiffener scantlings will likewise be increased at the forward end and reduced at the after end. Web frames or partial bulkheads must be fitted to support structure above, particularly at the corners of deckhouses above. House tops or decks in way of davits must be strengthened and supported from below.

Poop structure

The poop front must be adequately plated and stiffened as for the bridge front. The internal stiffening will include webs and partial bulkheads as required, particularly where deckhouses are located above. The after end of the poop, being exposed, requires a more substantial construction than that of the aft ends of other structures.

Raised quarter deck

The raised quarter deck results in a greater depth of ship over its length. Increased scantlings must therefore be provided for the frames, shell, deck plating and beams. Structures may be built on to the raised quarter deck as already described.

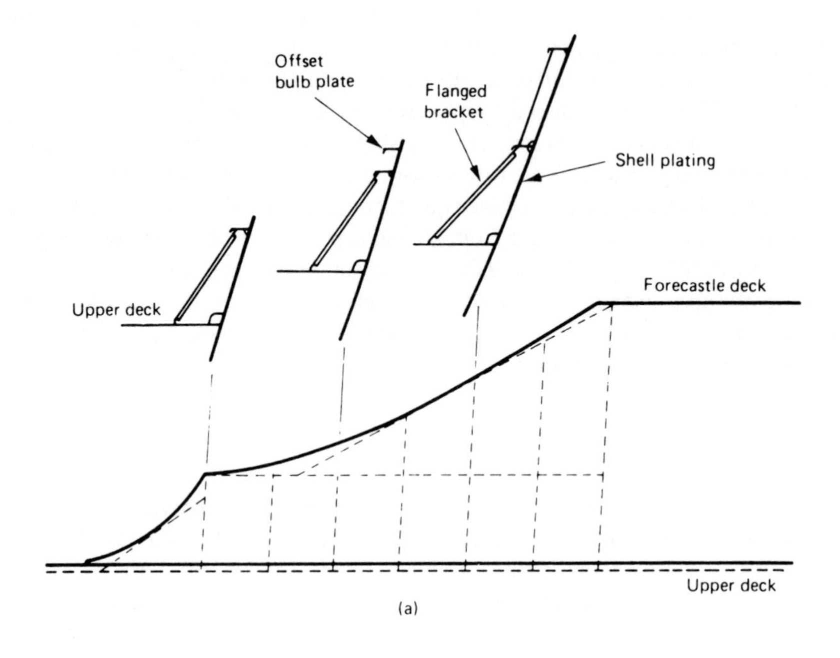

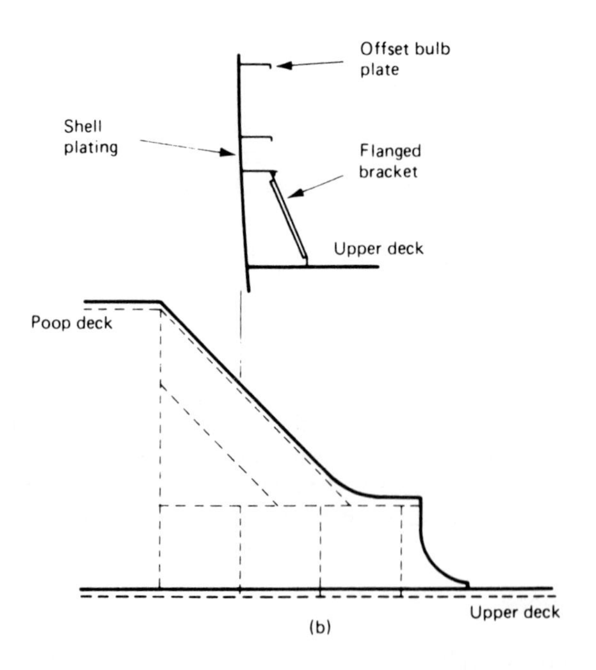

Figure 5.50 Discontinuities: (a) forecastle deck plating break; (b) poop deck plating break

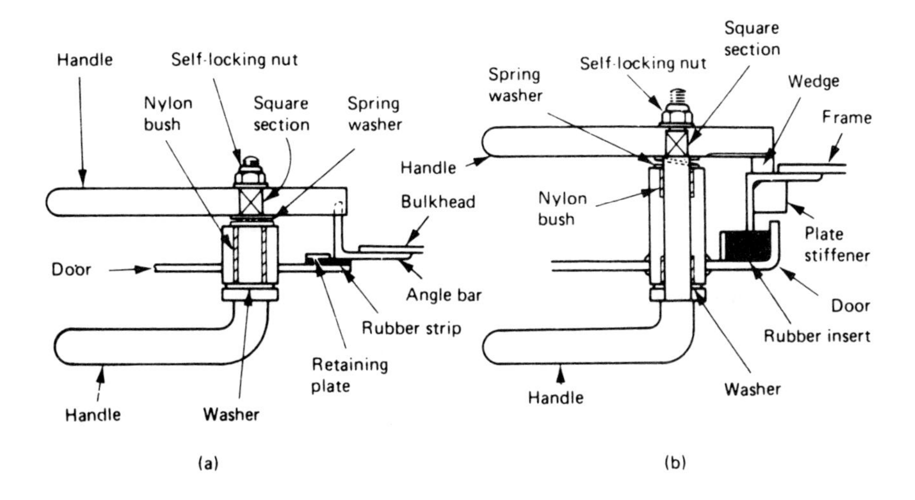

Figure 5.51 Door clamps: (a) gastight door clamp; (b) weathertight door clamp

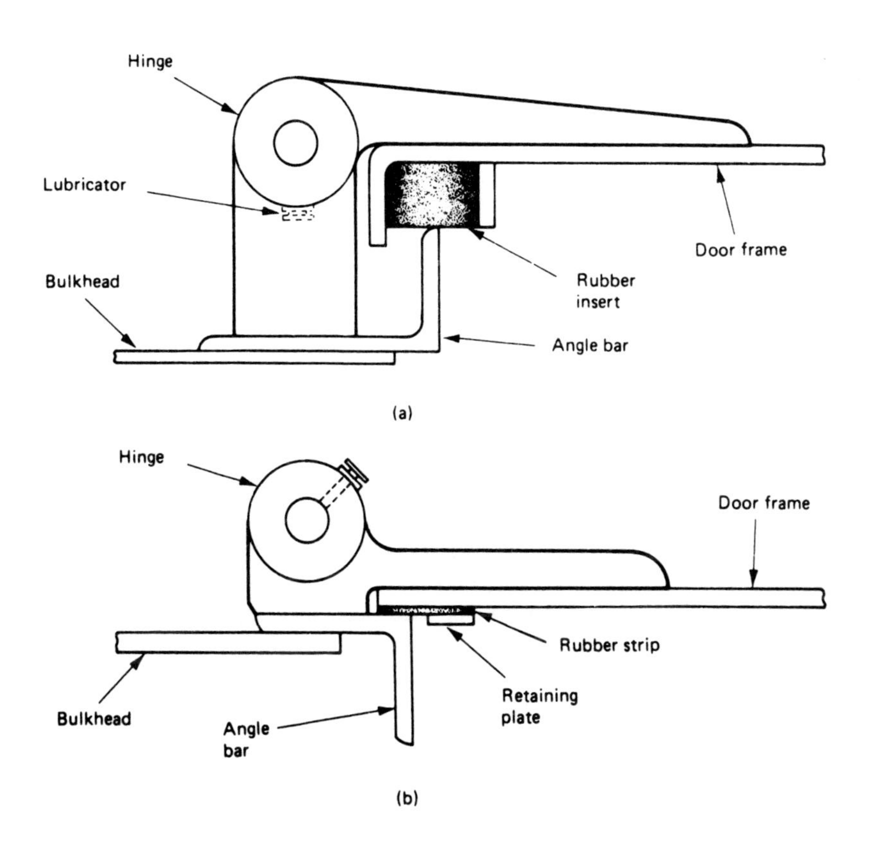

Figure 5.52 Door hinges: (a) weathertight hinge; (b) gastight hinge

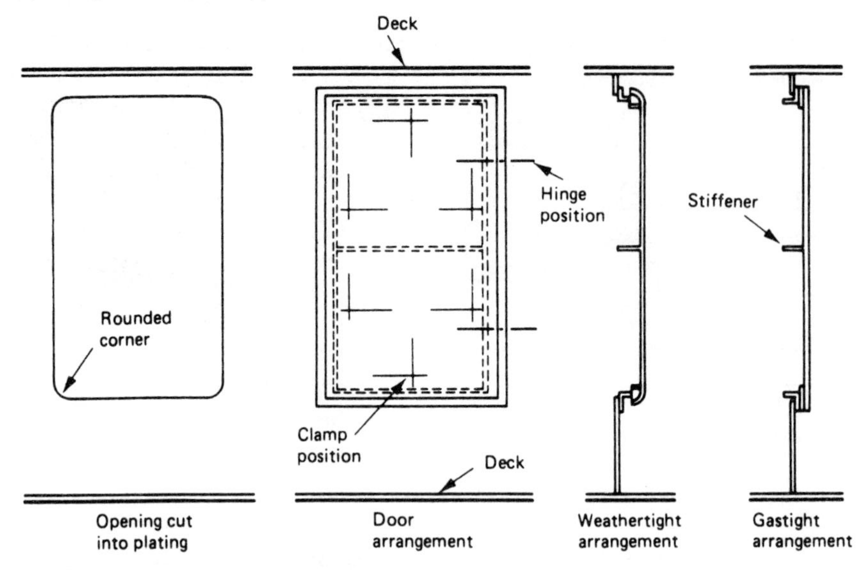

Figure 5.53 *Steel doors*

Discontinuities

The ends of superstructures represent major discontinuities in the structure of the ship. Longer structures such as bridges and forecastles require considerable strengthening at the ends. Classification society rules require the upper deck sheerstrake thickness to be increased by 20%, except where the structure does not extend to the side shell. Deck plating at superstructure ends is also increased in thickness. Side plating forming part of the superstructure is well radiused at the ends towards the side shell (*Figure 5.50*).

Watertight opening and doors

Where doors are fitted into structures above the freeboard deck they must be of adequate strength and able to maintain the watertight integrity of the structure. The openings have radiused corners to reduce the stress effects of the discontinuity. A substantial framing is also fitted or additional stiffening to retain the strength of the structure. Doors fitted to the openings are of steel suitably stiffened, with a rubber gasket fitted to effect watertightness. The doors have securing clips or 'dogs' which can be operated from either side. The dogs fasten on wedges which pull the frame edge into the gasket, sealing the door shut. Details of the door construction and closing arrangements are shown in *Figures 5.51–5.53*.

Accommodation

The superstructure will comprise several storeys of cabins, public rooms, offices, navigation areas and machinery rooms. A typical arrangement of cabins and rooms is shown in *Figure 5.54*. Stiffened steel bulkheads are used to support the structure above and provide subdivision for fire containment (see Chapter 11). Intermediate partitions are used to create individual cabins. Plastic laminates either side of a fire-resisting material core are used for the partitions. They are set into U-section light-plate channels at the deck and the ceilings, as shown in *Figure 5.55(a)* and *(b)*. Ceiling panels are fitted on to wood grounds or battens between the partitions. Typical floor coverings comprise a bituminous coating with vinyl tiles fitted to provide an easily cleaned hardwearing surface.

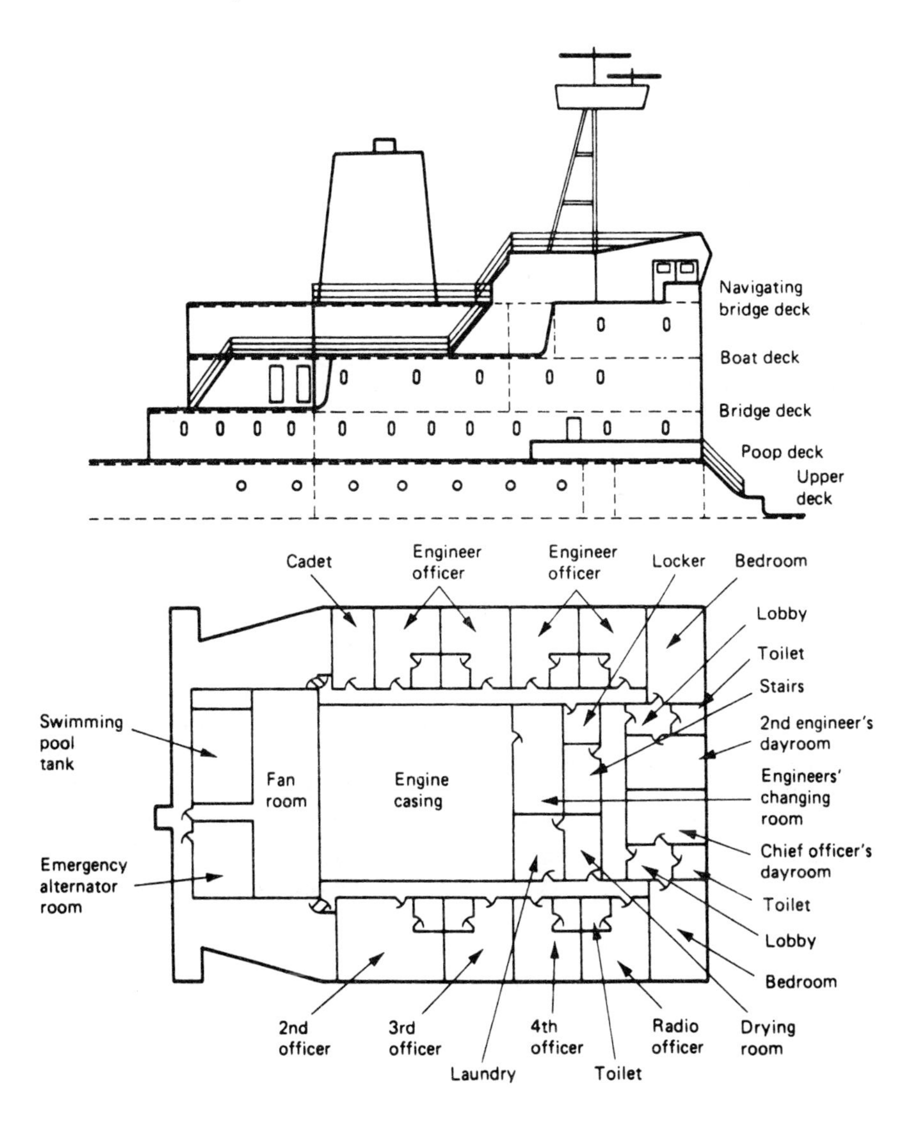

Figure 5.54 Accommodation arrangement

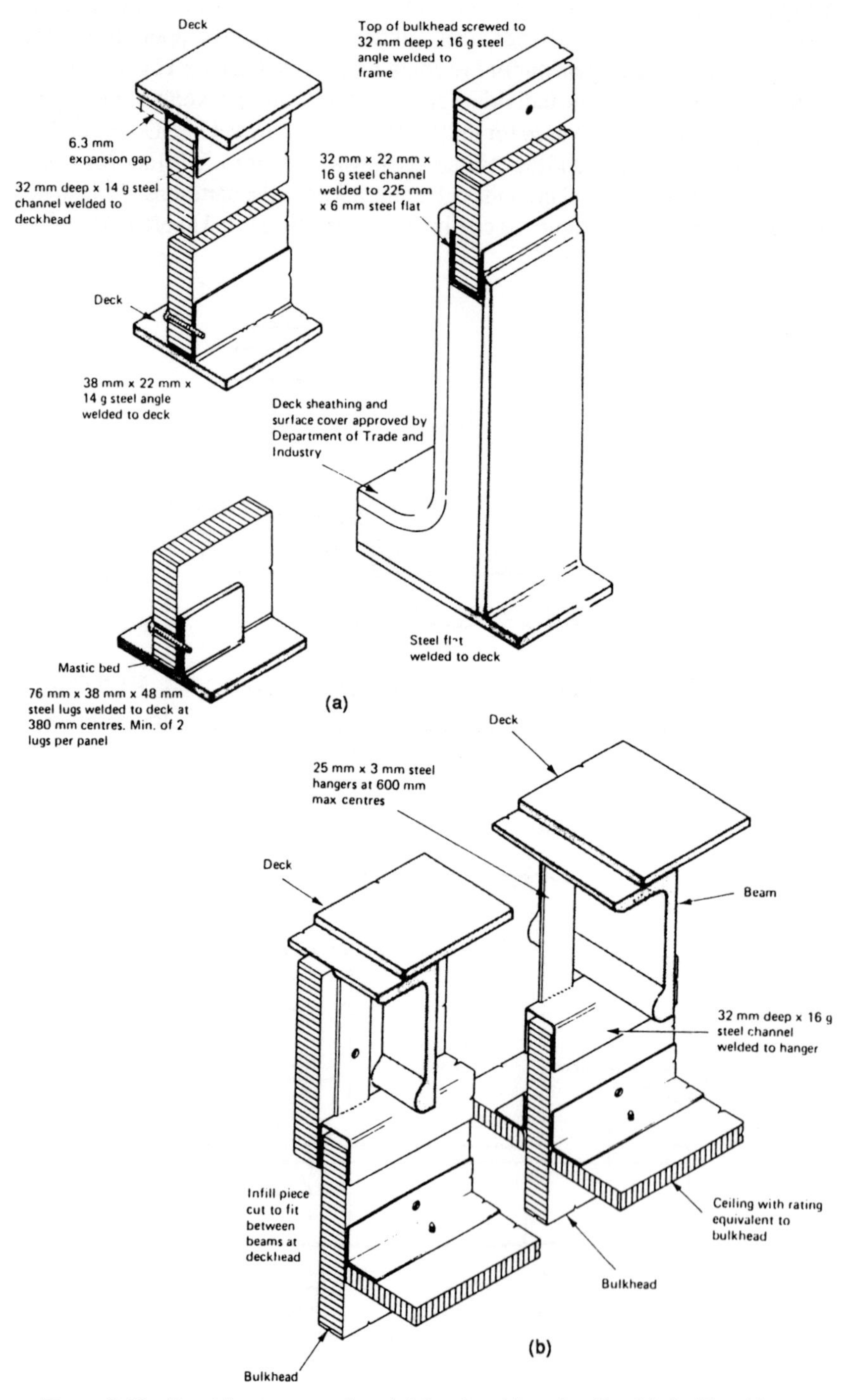

Figure 5.55 Partition construction: (a) head and foot details; (b) deckhead beams

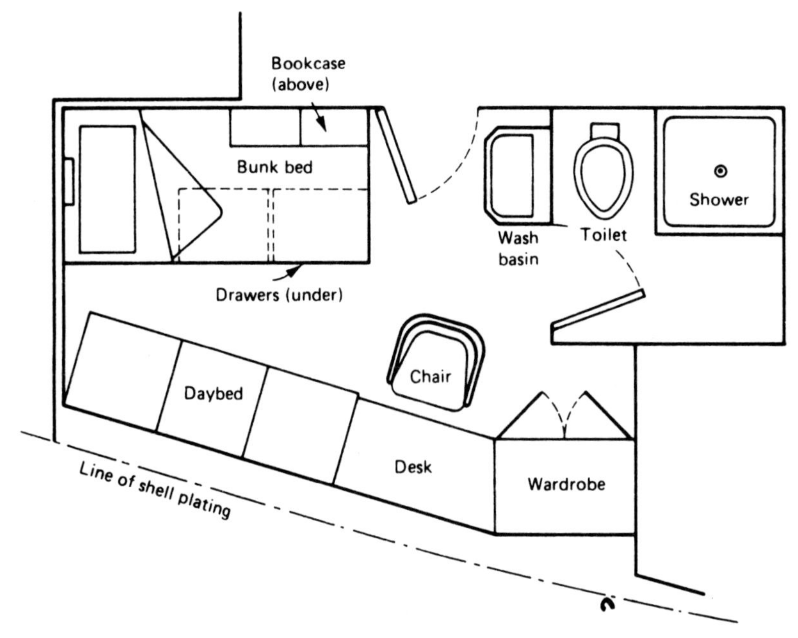

Figure 5.56 Crew cabin

Coaming strips are fitted at the edges to complete the arrangement. The cabins are provided with various arrangements of built-in furniture and fittings for crew comfort, as shown in *Figure 5.56*.

6

Minor Structural Items

Minor structural items are now considered which, while not contributing greatly to the strength of the vessel, can nevertheless be considerable in size and have requirements for strength in themselves.

Funnel

The funnel is a surround and support for the various uptakes which ensure the dispersion of exhaust gases into the atmosphere and away from the ship. The shape of the funnel is sometimes determined by the shipowner's requirements but more often by smoke-clearing arrangements and the need for streamlining to reduce resistance. The owner's housemark or trademark is often carried on the outside of the funnel structure.

The funnel is constructed of steel plating stiffened internally by angle bars of flat plates fitted end on (*Figure 6.1*). Brackets are fitted at the stiffener connections to the deck and the plating of the funnel is fully welded to the deck. A base plate may be fitted between the funnel plating and the deck. Internal flats are fitted to the funnel and are made watertight with scupper drains to collect any rainwater. The number of flats fitted is dependent upon the height of the funnel. The various main engine and auxiliary uptakes are fitted within the funnel casing, usually on sliding feet to permit expansion. Some uptakes are arranged to stand proud of the funnel casing.

In the funnel shown in *Figure 6.1* ventilation louvres are fitted on the after end below the upper rainflat. These louvres disperse the exhausts from the various ventilators led up the funnel. Fire flaps are fitted in the airtight flat beneath these ventilators and are used to shut off the air outlet from the engine room in the event of a fire. A hinged watertight door is fitted in the funnel leading out on to the deck upon which the funnel stands. Holes or grilles are cut into the forward face of the funnel towards the top, and the whistle is fitted on a small seat just aft of the opening.

Ladders and platforms are also provided inside the funnel for access purposes. Lugs are fitted around the outside top shell plating to permit painting of the funnel.

Engine casing

The accommodation or upper deck spaces are separated from the engine room or machinery spaces by the engine casing. Access doors are provided at suitable levels

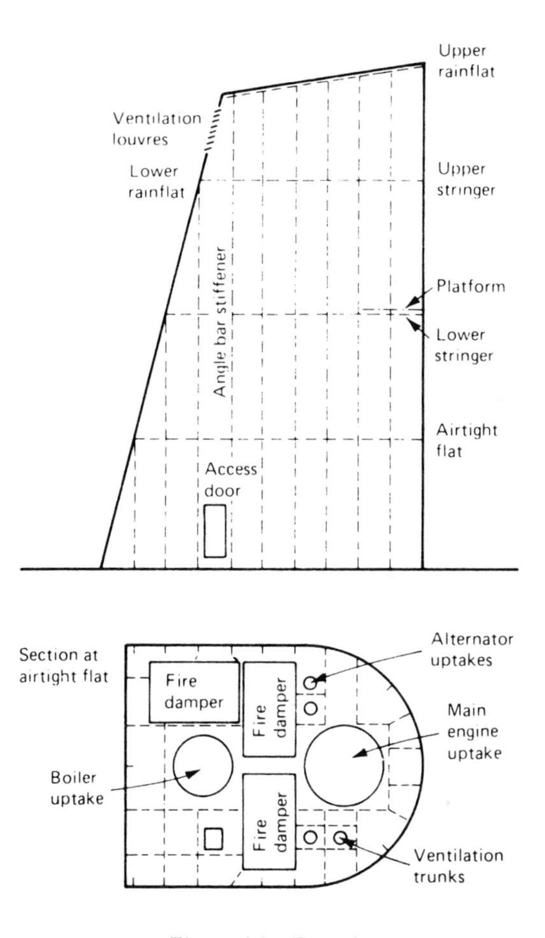

Figure 6.1 Funnel

between the engine casing and the accommodation. The volume enclosed by the casing is made as small as possible but of sufficient dimensions to allow maintenance and machinery removal from the engine room. The casing leads up to the upper decks, finishing below the funnel. Fresh air is drawn in through jalousies or louvres in small fan rooms off the casing and passes down trunking into the engine room. The hot air rises up the engine room into the casing and out of the funnel at the top.

The construction of a typical engine casing is shown in *Figure 6.2*. The casing is a lightly plated structure with closely spaced vertical stiffeners. These bulb plate or angle bar stiffeners are fitted on the machinery room side of the casing to ensure continuity. Swedged or corrugated bulkheads could also be used for the casing sides. Stringers and brackets are fitted at various heights, where no flats exist, to further strengthen the structure.

The casing sides are also used to support seats for certain auxiliaries and as securing points for pipe clips or hangars. The casing is supported on a deep girder

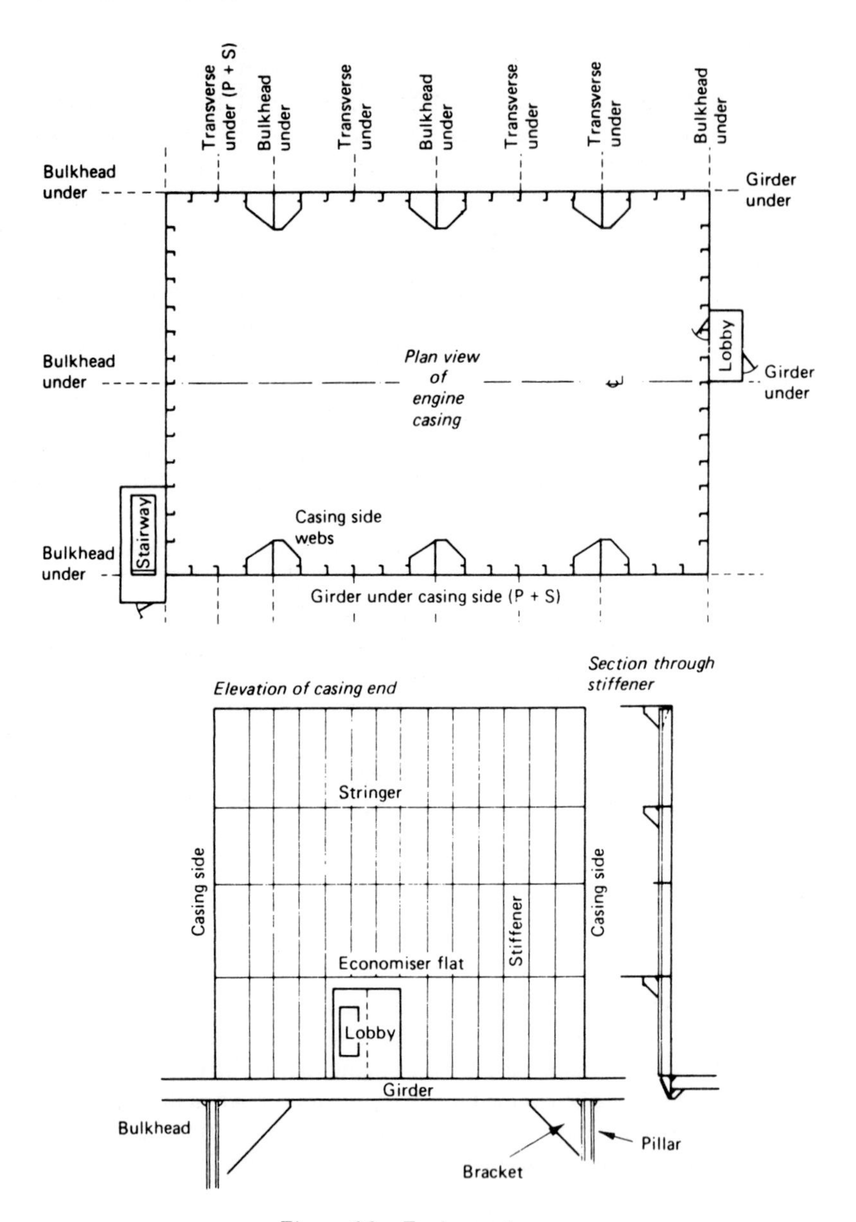

Figure 6.2 Engine casing

running around the engine room. This deep girder is in turn supported by the pillars, transverse and bulkheads of the engine room structure (see *Figure 6.2*).

The casing top is of stiffened plate construction, with deep girders and brackets around the openings for the uptakes. Heavy brackets connect the transverse beams to the vertical stiffeners. This arrangement ensures adequate support for the funnel, which sits on the casing top.

Shaft tunnel

Where a ship's machinery space is not right aft an enclosed area or tunnel is provided to lead the shafting to the after peak bulkhead. The tunnel must be of watertight construction to provide integrity should the shaft seal cease to operate correctly. The forward end of the tunnel is fitted with a sliding watertight door to seal off the tunnel if necessary. The tunnel is made of sufficient proportions to enable access for maintenance to the shafting, and an escape route is provided from the after end.

Two types of construction are used, either a curved top or roof, or a flat roof. The curved roof is stronger and can therefore be made of lighter plate than the flat-roof type. The flat-topped construction does, however, lend itself to more straightforward construction and provides a flat platform in the hold above. The plating is stiffened by bulb plates usually fitted in line with the frames. A continuous ring of stiffener bar is fitted with the curved-roof type of tunnel. The flat-roof type has brackets connecting the roof stiffeners to the vertical stiffeners. Examples of each are shown in *Figure 6.3*.

The structure must be capable of withstanding the water pressure should the tunnel become open to the sea. The scantlings must therefore be equivalent to those of a watertight bulkhead. The width of the tunnel is decided by access and maintenance considerations and will be reduced to the minimum necessary. A raised floor is usually fitted and pipework is run along beneath it. The shaft bearings which are positioned at intervals along the tunnel are carried on stools or seats. These stools are welded to the tank top and the tunnel structure to form a rigid platform. The tunnel is opened out into a larger area at the after end to provide an adequate working space for withdrawal of the tailshaft. The spare tailshaft is usually mounted on the shell in this open area or recess. Shaft tunnels must be hose tested on completion to ensure their watertightness.

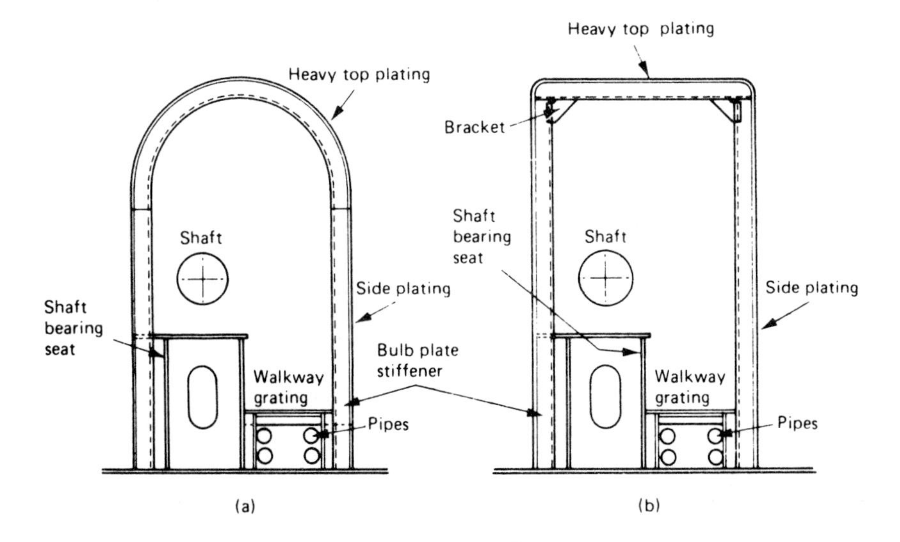

Figure 6.3 Shaft tunnels: (a) curved-roof type; (b) flat-roof type

Bulwarks

Bulwarks are barriers fitted to the deck edge to protect passengers and crew and avoid the loss of items overboard should the ship roll excessively. Bulwarks are considered solid or open—the solid type being constructed principally of plate, the open type being railings, *Figure 6.4(a)*.

The bulwark makes no contribution to longitudinal strength and as such, in the solid form, is of relatively thin plate supported by stays from the deck. The stays are set back from the deck edge and must not be welded to the sheerstrake. This avoids the high stresses, particularly at the midships section, being transmitted to the bulwarks and possible cracking occurring.

Where the solid bulwark meets the deck, freeing ports must be fitted to allow the rapid drainage of any water shipped, which could seriously affect the stability of the ship. sometimes a 'floating' type of construction is used to provide a continuous freeing port area, *Figure 6.4(b)*. The depth of the freeing port must be restricted to 230 mm.

Open bulwarks consist of rails and stanchions supported by stays which again are set back from the deck edge. The lower rail spacing must be a maximum of 230 mm, whereas the rails above may have a maximum spacing of 380 mm.

Bulwarks of both types are usually 1 m in height. Bulwark plating, particularly in the forecastle region, is increased in thickness where it is penetrated by mooring fittings.

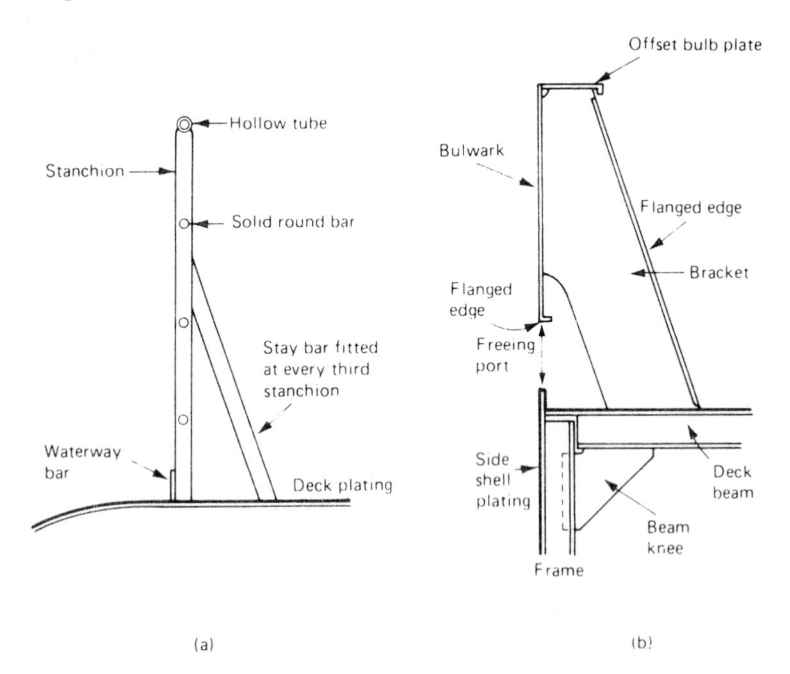

Figure 6.4 Bulwarks: (a) open bulwark or railing; (b) arrangement of 'floating' bulwark

Deep tanks

Deep tanks are fitted in some ships for the carriage of bunker oil, ballast water or liquid cargoes such as tallow. The entrance to the deep tank from the deck is often via a large oiltight hatch; this enables the loading of bulk or general cargoes if required. A deep tank is smaller than a cargo hold and of a much stronger construction. Hold bulkheads may distort under the head of water if flooded, say in a collision. However, deep tank bulkheads which may be subjected to a constant head of oil or water must not deflect at all. The deep tank construction therefore employs strong webs, stringer plates and girders, fitted as closely spaced horizontal and vertical frames. Wash bulkheads may be fitted in larger deep tanks to reduce surging of the liquid carried. Deep tanks used for bunker tanks must have wash bulkheads if they extend the width of the ship, to reduce free surface effects of the liquid.

The construction of a deep tank used for bunker oil is shown in *Figure 6.5*. The tank is one of two and extends for half the width of the ship. The strakes of plating which form the oiltight bulkheads of the tank increase in thickness towards the bottom of the tank where the loading is greatest. The after oiltight bulkhead is stiffened by closely spaced vertical bulb plates. The forward oiltight bulkhead is stiffened externally by a series of diaphragm plates. The diaphragm plates form a cofferdam between the bunker tank and the oiltight bulkhead of the cargo hold forward.

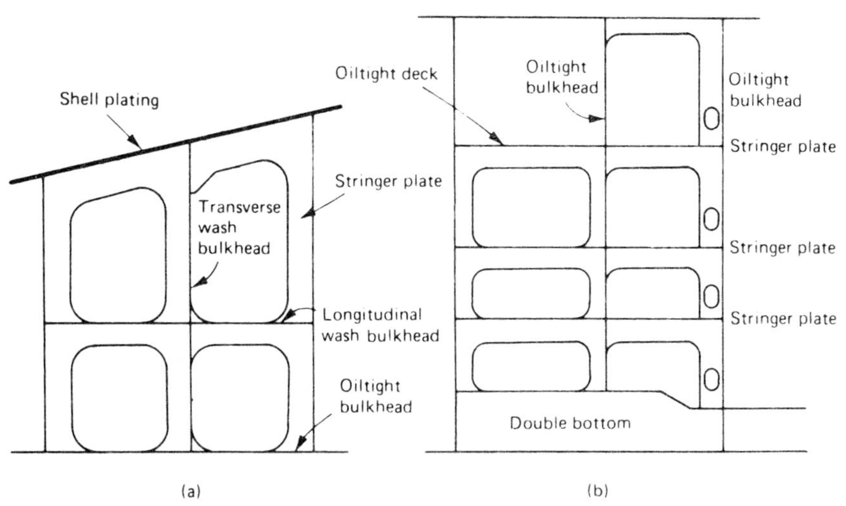

Figure 6.5 Deep tank: (a) plan view; (b) elevation looking outboard

Three horizontal stringers are fitted across the tank, a transverse wash bulkhead and a longitudinal wash bulkhead. The stringers are bracketed to the stiffeners at the tank sides and to the wash bulkheads which they join. The whole structure is therefore stiffened by a series of deep 'ring' girders in both a horizontal and vertical direction. A very strong structure is thus formed with considerable restrictions to liquid movement within the tank.

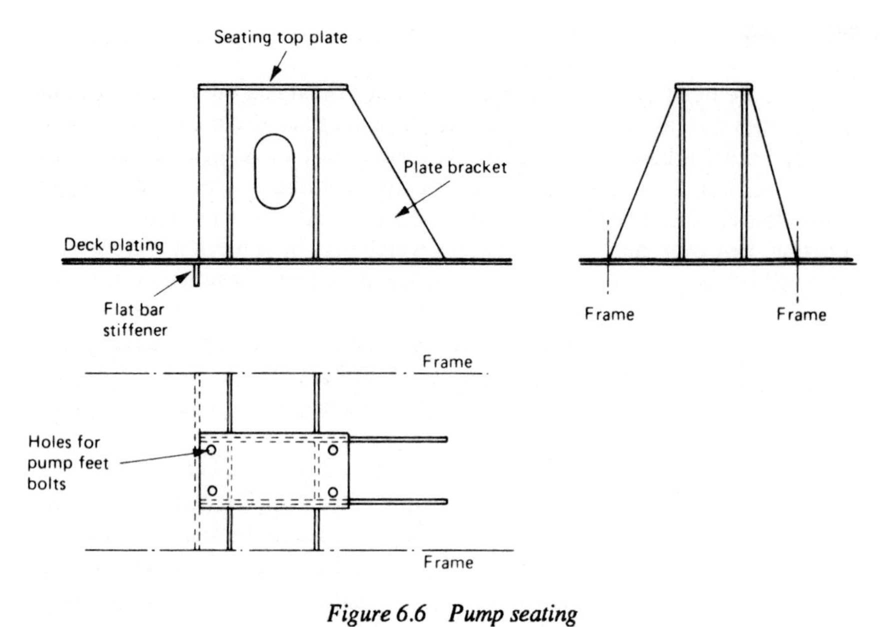

Figure 6.6 Pump seating

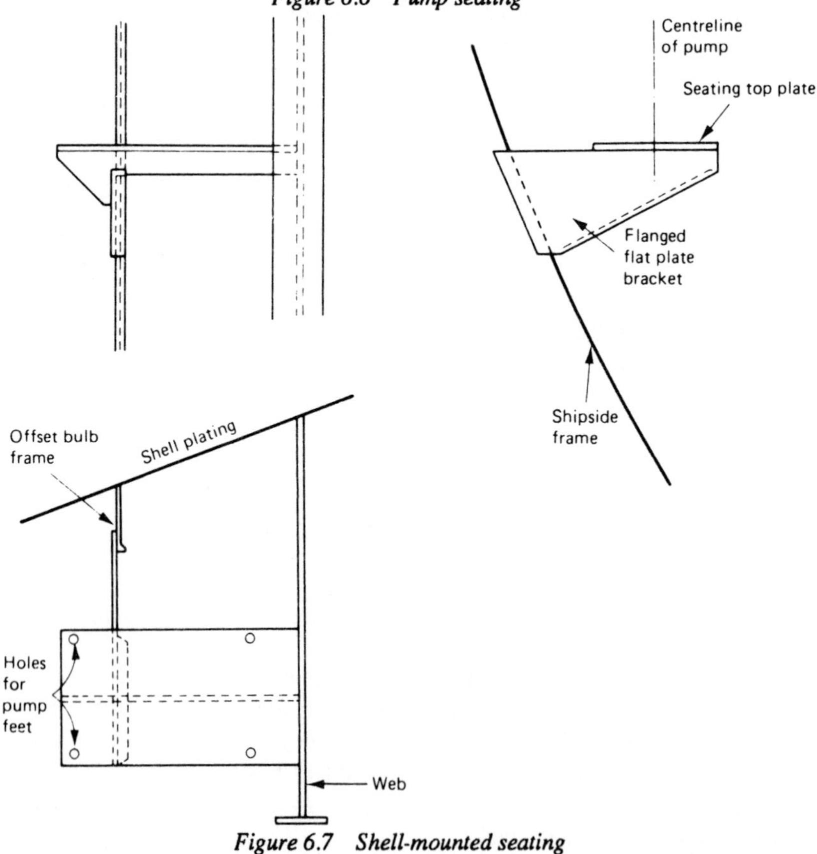

Figure 6.7 Shell-mounted seating

Corrugated or swedged bulkheads may be fitted to deep tanks, particularly those intended for liquid cargoes which require the tank to be cleaned. Conventional stiffening could be positioned on the outside of small deep tanks to similarly facilitate cleaning. Heating coils may be fitted in tanks intended for cargoes such as tallow. Deep tanks must be tested on completion by a head of water equivalent to their maximum service condition or not less than 2.44 m above the crown of the tank.

Machinery seats

Main engines, auxiliary machinery and associated items of equipment are fastened down on a rigid framework known as a seating or seat. These seats are of plate, angle and bulb construction and act as a rigid platform for the equipment. They are welded directly to the deck or structure beneath, usually in line with the stiffening. The seat is designed to spread the concentrated load over the supporting structure of the ship. It may be extended to the adjacent structure or additional stiffening may be supplied in way of the seat. Steel chocks are often fitted between the seat and the machinery item to enable a certain amount of fitting to take place and ensure a solid 'bed'. The item can then be bolted down to the seat without penetrating the double bottom or deck below.

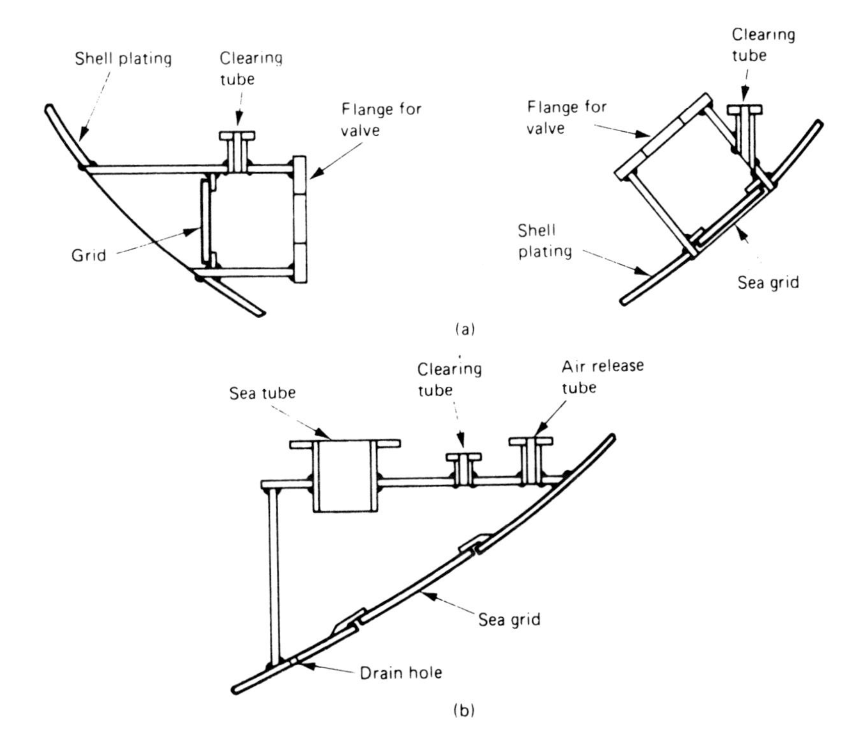

Figure 6.8 Sea water inlet arrangements: (a) sea tubes; (b) sea inlet box

Seats in the machinery space also serve as platforms to raise the pumps, coolers, etc., to the floorplate level for easier access and maintenance. A typical pump seating as used in an engine room is shown in *Figure 6.6*. It is constructed of steel plate in a box-type arrangement for rigidity. A shell-mounted seating is shown in *Figure 6.7*.

Sea tubes and inlet boxes

Most valves having a direct inlet or outlet to the sea are mounted on a sea tube which is fitted into the shell. A sea tube is a thick-walled steel tube with a flange on the inboard side which is machined flat to form a watertight joint with the valve. The tube is let into the lower side or bottom shell and fully welded inside and out (*Figure 6.8(a)*).

A number of sea tubes may be fitted into inlet boxes which are usually fitted in the forward corners of the engine room below the waterline. a box-like structure is fitted to the shell and opens to the sea through one or more holes with grids fitted. Several sea tubes can be let into this box, or valves can be mounted on to flanges welded directly to the inlet box (*Figure 6.8(b)*).

The sea tubes or inlet boxes also serve to strengthen the shell plating around the discontinuity resulting from the hole in the shell.

7

Outfit

Hatch covers

Hatch covers are used to make the cargo hatch watertight, to protect the cargo and to stiffen up the structure of the hatch opening. Two basic types are in general use—the wooden hatch cover fitted across hatch beams and the patent steel covers of various designs. The hatch covers fit on top of the hatch coamings, which have been described in Chapter 5. The weather deck coamings are at a height set by the load line rules (see Chapter 11). The tween deck coamings are set flush or almost flush with the deck to reduce interference with cargo stowage in this area.

Wooden hatch covers

A combination of transverse beams and longitudinal hatch boards make up the wooden hatch cover arrangement (*Figure 7.1*). I-section girders, the width of the hatch, are fitted at intervals along the length of the hatch and are known as hatchway beams, shifting beams or webs. The ends of the beams fit either into slots or carriers in the coaming side or lock into position on a trackway if they are of the sliding type. The beam ends are additionally stiffened by a doubling plate. The beams which take the ends of the hatchboards have a vertical flat fitted to hold the boards in place.

The hatchboards are fitted longitudinally over the hatch beams and are protected at their ends by a metal band. The boards are at least 60 mm thick, and more for a span greater than 1.5 m. The roller beam arrangement of hatchboards is the same, the roller beam simply speeding up the opening and closing of the hatch. At least two tarpaulins must be fitted over the hatchboards and suitably fastened down around the hatch coaming. Battens, cleats and wedges are used to 'dog' down the tarpaulins. Steel locking bars, or some other suitable additional locking device, are required to secure each of the hatch cover sections after battening down the tarpaulins.

Steel hatch covers

Patented steel hatch covers of a variety of designs are available from several manufacturers. Most designs employ a number of self-supporting steel covers

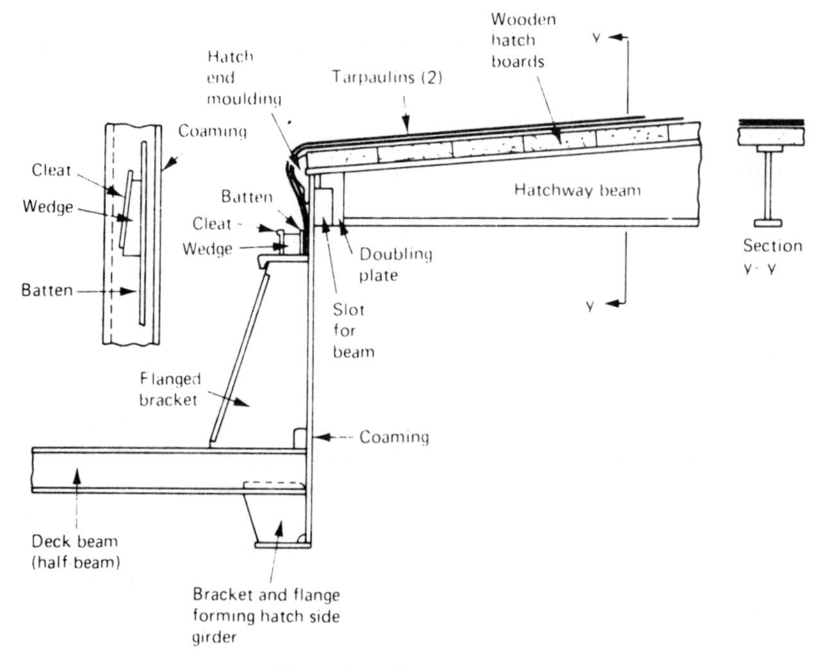

Figure 7.1 Wooden hatch cover

which completely enclose the hatch opening. Opening and closing arrangements utilise a 'single pull' via a winch wire or hydraulic or electric power. The covers run on wheels on a trackway along the hatch coaming top. The separate sections are either hinged together or joined by chains to one another. The covers finally stow at some point clear of the hatch opening.

A MacGregor steel hatch cover arrangement is shown in *Figure 7.2*. The hatch covers can be closed or opened by hydraulic power or a winch-operated single wire

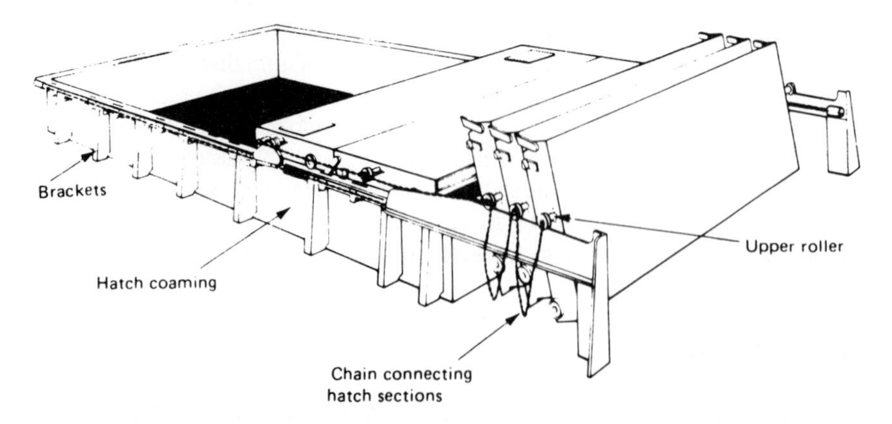

Figure 7.2 MacGregor steel hatch cover

pull. A trackway is formed for the hatch rollers by a platform top on the coaming. A vertical plate is positioned each side of the coaming at the stowing end of the hatch on the coaming trackway. The upper rollers on the hatch cover ride up on this plate and the cover then tips into the vertical position. The covers are thus compactly stowed clear of the hatch opening. The hatch covers run on eccentric rollers which act as wheels in the raised position and are clear of the coaming in the lowered position to enable the covers to be fastened down.

The covers are of fabricated steel plate with stiffeners or webs to strengthen the structure. The ends of the covers overlap in the closed position. Grooves fitted with compressible packing surround the outside edges of the covers. When the covers are fastened down by cleats on to a raised edge on the coaming, a watertight seal is formed and no tarpaulin is required. The athwartships joints between the covers have a similar sealing arrangement. The cleating arrangement shown in *Figure 7.2* is automatic. The cover wheels drop into slots in the coaming plate prior to cleating and are raised hydraulically after uncleating. Sliding bars are fitted along the side and end coamings under the top rail. Hooks are positioned at the cleating points and can pivot through a slot in the coaming rail. Double-acting hydraulic cylinders move the bars to raise or lower the hooks.

In the raised position the hooks engage cleat lugs which pull the hatch cover sections down on to the sealing strip. For transverse cleating a torsion bar arrangement is used. Lever arms on the end of the torsion bar are pushed up as the hatch closes and rotate the torsion bar. This presses cleating lugs on to pressure pads on the end of the adjacent hatch section. A peripheral cleat arrangement is shown in *Figure 7.3*.

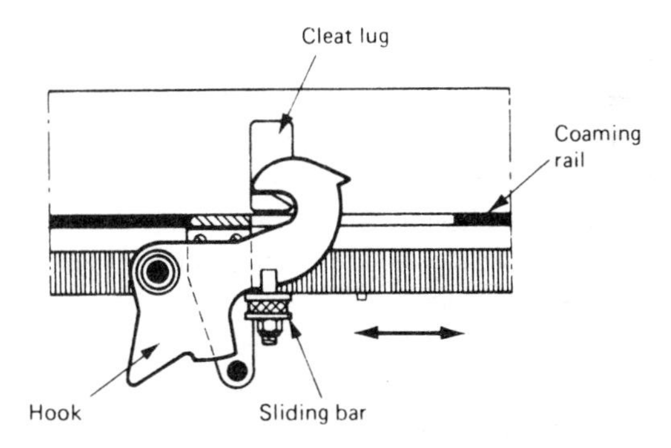

Figure 7.3 Automatic peripheral cleating

Minor hatch covers

A number of small access openings, tank entrances, etc., are fitted with minor hatch covers of steel construction.

A typical small hatch cover is shown in *Figure 7.4*. The coaming edge is forced into a rubber gasket by a number of fastening clips or 'dogs' around the cover, a watertight seal being thus formed. The handles are arranged for internal or external operation on accesses. A counterbalance weight is sometimes fitted to ease the opening of the cover.

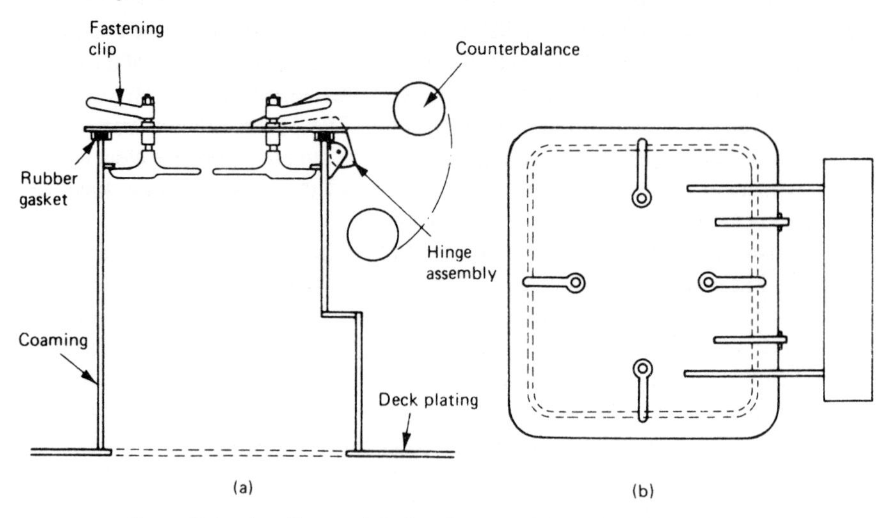

Figure 7.4 *Small watertight hatch cover: (a) section through hatch; (b) plan view of hatch cover*

Mooring equipment and arrangements

The winches and windlasses positioned on the forecastle and poop decks and sometimes the upper deck perform the mooring and warping duties required by the ship when arriving and departing its various ports of call. Various fittings are provided on the deck and around the deck edge to assist in the mooring operation and provide a clear run or lead for the mooring and warping wires. Examples of these fittings are bollards and the various types of fairlead which are found on board ship.

The windlass, as mentioned in Section D of Chapter 5, has warping ends which are used when mooring the ship. One or more warping winches are fitted on the poop deck aft for similar duties. Solid seatings, as mentioned in Chapter 6, transmit the loads to the deck and also stiffen the deck. Larger vessels have mooring winches fitted on the upper deck also. Bollards or mooring bitts are used to moor the ship once it is alongside and are welded or bolted to the deck or to a box-like structure which is welded to the deck, *Figure 7.5(a)*. Adequate structural support must always be provided in way of bollards and all mooring fittings, usually by additional stiffening to the deck beneath.

Fairleads are used to guide the hawsers or mooring wires to the bollards or mooring winches. Fairleads are attached to the deck, a raised seat or the deck and the bulwarks. Several different types are to be seen, such as the multi-angled fairlead, the pedestal fairlead, the roller fairlead and the panama fairlead. A multi-angled fairlead consists of two horizontal and two vertical rollers with the wire passing through the hole between the rollers, *Figure 7.5(b)*. A pedestal fairlead consists of a single horizontal or vertical roller mounted on a raised pedestal or seat, *Figure 7.5(c)*. A roller fairlead is one or more vertical rollers on a steel base which may fasten directly to the deck or to the deck and bulwarks, *Figure 7.5(d)*. The panama fairlead is an almost elliptical opening formed in a casting which is fitted into a suitably stiffened aperture in the bulwark, *Figure 7.5(e)*.

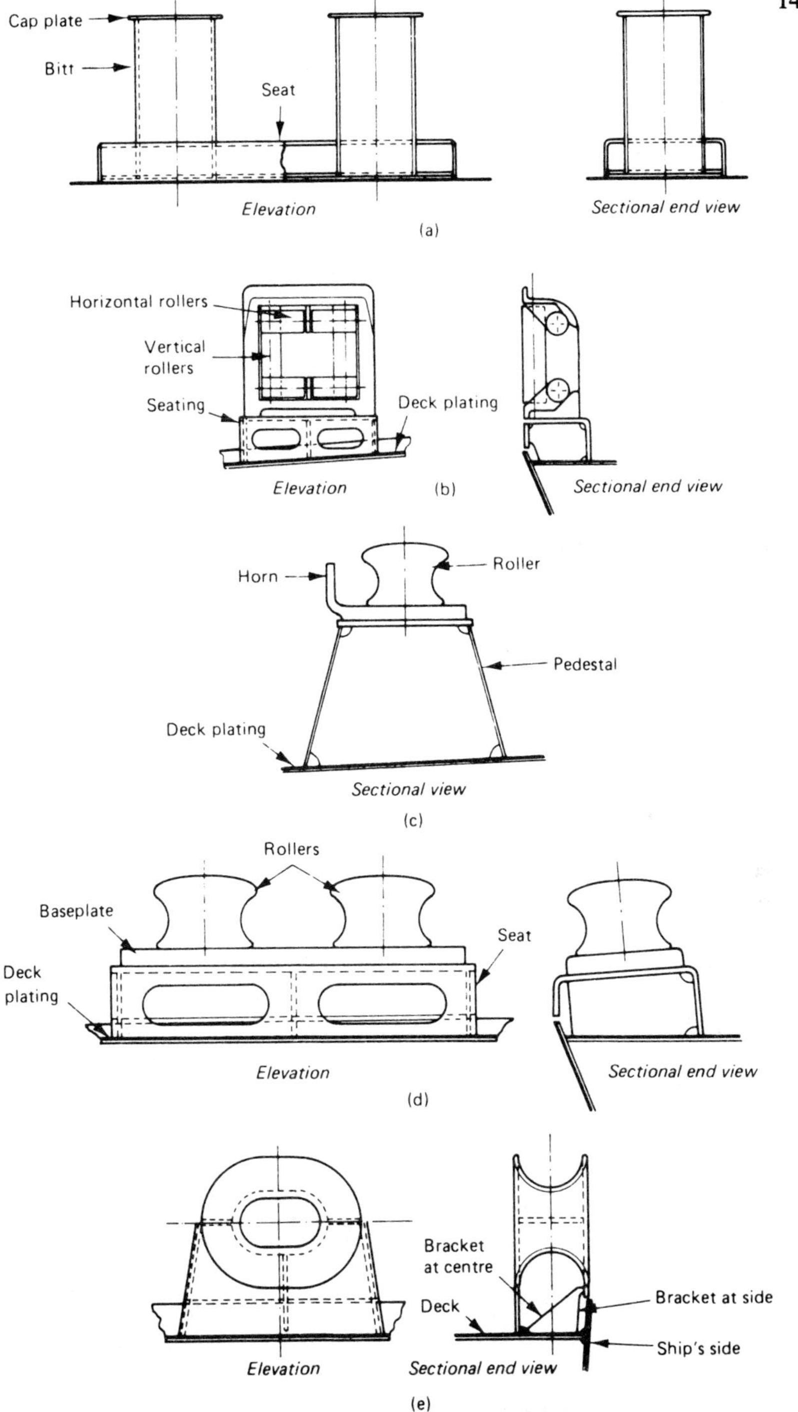

Figure 7.5 (a) Fabricated bollard; (b) multi-angle fairlead; (c) pedestal fairlead; (d) two-roller fairlead; (e) panama fairlead

The multi-angled fairlead is fitted at the deck edge and reduces the number of guide rollers or other fairleads required to give a clear lead of wire to the winch. The pedestal fairlead guides the wire across the deck to the winch clear of any obstructions. The roller fairlead is used at the deck edge to lead in the mooring and warping wires. A panama fairlead is fitted in the foremost position in the forecastle bulwark on the centreline of all ships which pass through the Panama Canal. Panama fairleads are also used in other positions around the deck edge as required.

For the various mooring and warping arrangements possible on a ship an 'arrangement of leads' drawing is provided. This shows the runs of the various wires

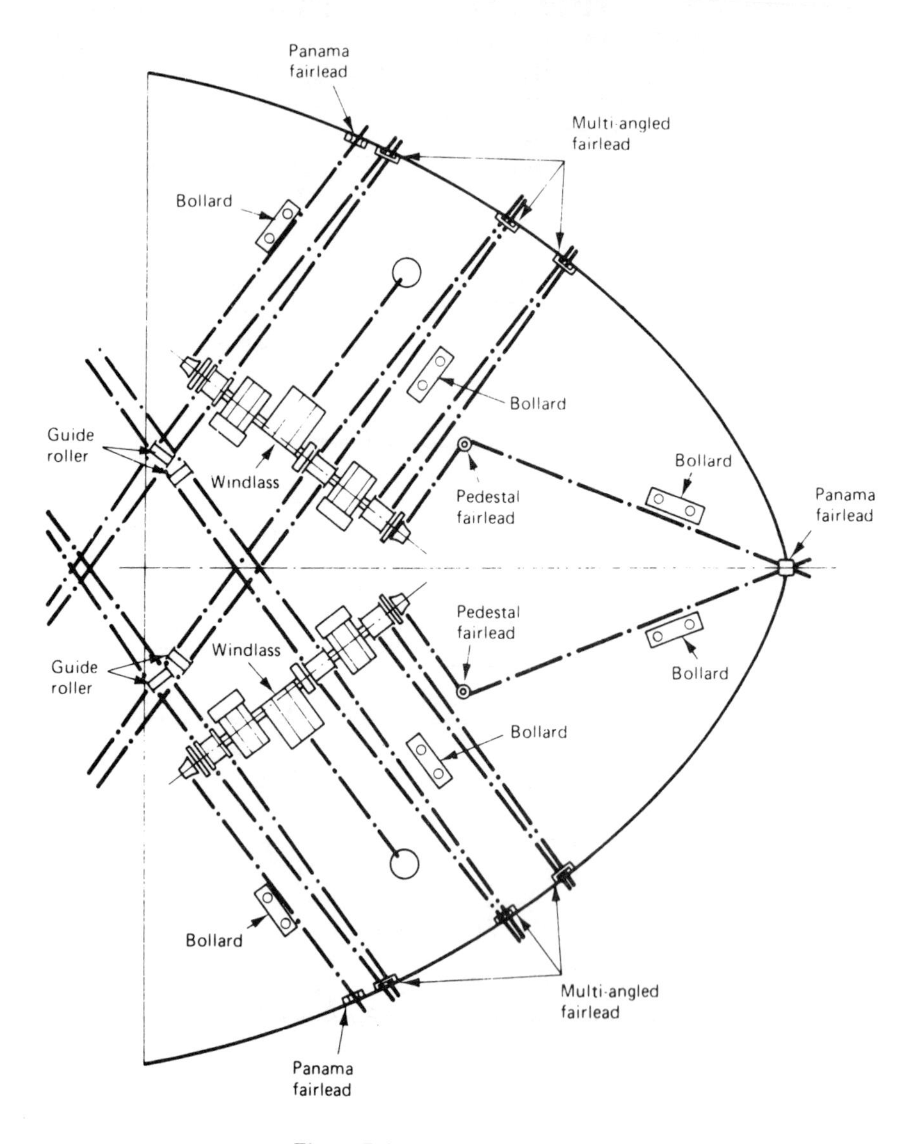

Figure 7.6 Arrangement of leads

through and over the various fairleads and winch warping drums on the decks of the ship. Such an arrangement for the fore end of a ship is shown in *Figure 7.6*.

Masts, derricks and deck cranes

Masts

The ship's mast acts as a lookout platform and a mounting point for navigation equipment such as lights, radar, aerials, etc. Access to the upper platform is by a ladder which, depending upon the mast size, may be fitted externally or internally.

A foremast, as fitted to an oil tanker, is shown in *Figure 7.7*. Construction is of light plate stiffened by internal webs. A D-type cross-section is often used for its streamlined, reduced-resistance form. The upper platform is additionally supported by brackets to the outer plating of the mast. The mast is fully welded to the

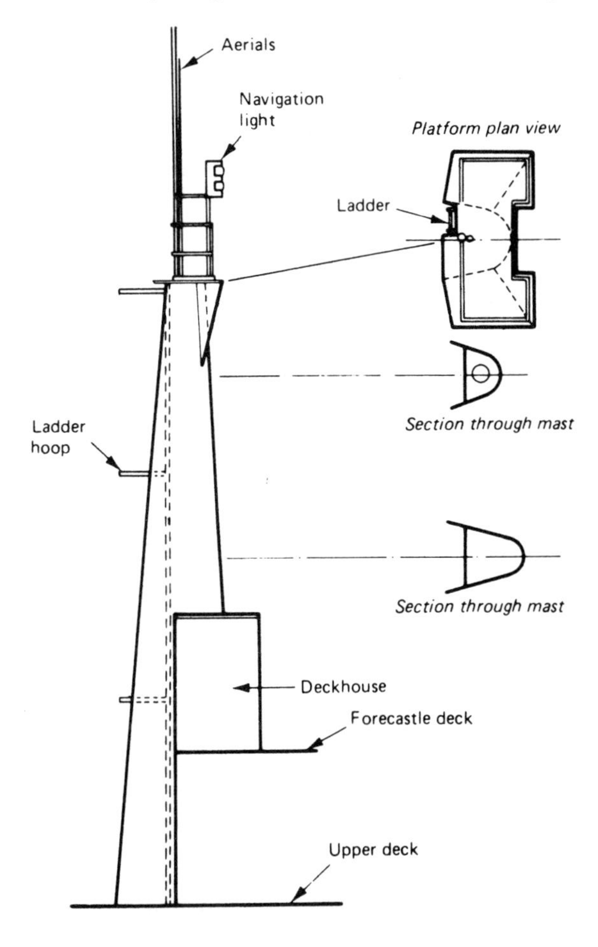

Figure 7.7 Oil tanker foremast

deckhouse on the forecastle deck and to the upper deck. A solid round bar is used to stiffen each of the free edges of plating and before erection the mast is coated internally with a bitumen solution.

Samson posts

Some masts on general cargo ships also double as support posts for the derricks used for cargo handling. Samson posts are also used more specifically for supporting derricks. Tied arrangements of samson posts, or bipod masts as they are sometimes called, are also used. The scantlings and construction of masts and posts used in cargo-handling work are given in the classification society rules and are dependent upon the safe working load (SWL) of the derrick boom. Most masts are self-supporting by virtue of their construction and attachment to the deck. Only special heavy-lift derricks require wire stays or preventers between the post top and the deck.

Samson post construction is of tubular steel section, stiffened internally by webs. Thicker plating or doubling plates are provided where attachments are made to the post. Derrick booms are of seamless tubing usually with a greater diameter at the middle region where the bending moments are greatest. The various goosenecks and end fittings are welded inserts in the tube ends.

The post attachment to the deck varies but must always provide adequate stiffening and support. Mast houses are fitted at the base of some masts or samson posts and may or may not assist in stiffening the structure. Some posts are let into the tween decks or are attached to the corners of superstructure to obtain support. The greater the derrick load the more stiffening is required, often by fitting additional webs below decks and heavier than usual bulkhead stiffeners and brackets below the mast or post.

Derrick rigs

The derricks used for cargo-handling work can be arranged or rigged in several different ways to provide for different manpower requirements, cargo-lifting capacities or lifting cycle times.

Union purchase

The union purchase rig is a much used arrangement for cargo loading and discharging. Two derricks are used, one arranged to plumb the hatch and the other to plumb the quay or over the ship's side. The falls or wires from both derricks are shackled to the same cargo hook. Thus, by using the two winch controllers separately and together the hook is raised or lowered over the hold, travels over the deck and can be raised and lowered over the ship's side.

This arrangement is safe as only the load moves, and it requires two reliable operators for the winches. It is, however, only suitable for light loads up to about 1.5 tonnes. A union purchase rig is shown in *Figure 7.8*.

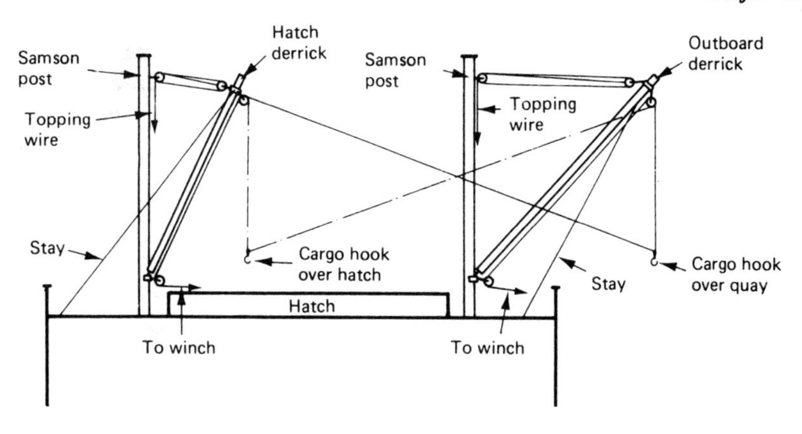

Figure 7.8 Union purchase rig

Swinging derrick

The fastest and most reliable method of cargo handling is achieved by the swinging derrick rig. A long derrick boom with a clear arc of swing is necessary for this arrangement. An adjustable span is usually arranged to facilitate the plumbing of the hatch and the quay over the ship's side. This is achieved by a topping wire and winch which is independent of the cargo winch. A swinging derrick rig is shown in *Figure 7.9*.

Heavy-lift derrick

For loads heavier than the safe working load of a single derrick, two derricks coupled together by a 'yo-yo' gear arrangement may be used, as shown in *Figure 7.10*. The

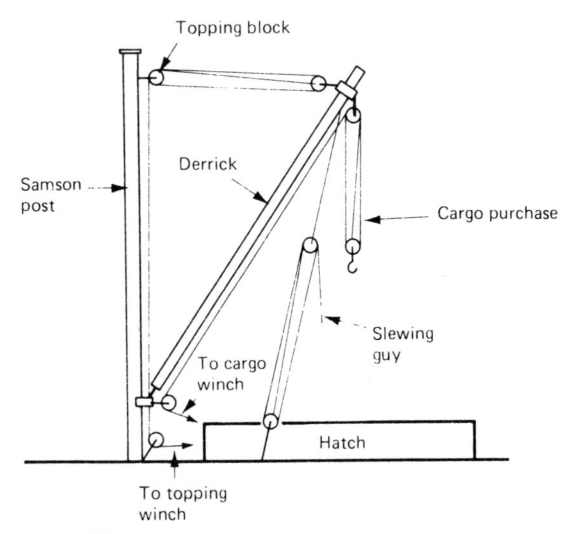

Figure 7.9 Swinging derrick rig

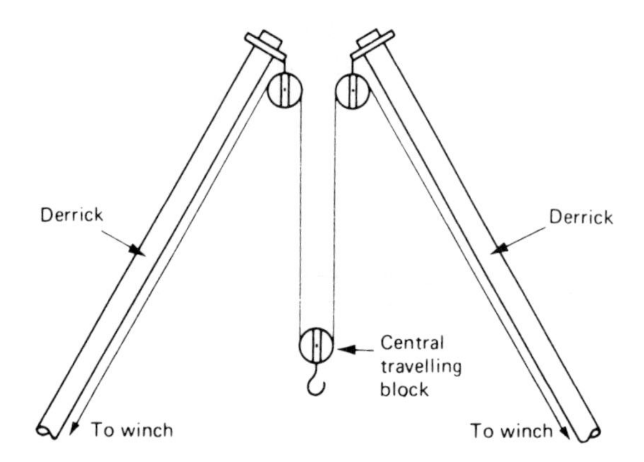

Figure 7.10 'Yo-yo' arrangement

derrick heads must be kept close together during operation and the central travelling block which equalises the load must have a safe working load greater than the cargo being lifted. A special heavy-lift derrick is fitted to many general cargo ships, with suitable rig and purchase gear for its designed safe working load.

Various patent heavy-lift derricks are available, one example being the Stülken derrick shown in *Figure 7.11*. The Stülken derrick has a safe working load up to 300 tonnes and is positioned between two outwardly raked tapering tubular columns. Several winches are provided for the various hoisting, slewing and topping duties. The controls are all arranged as levers in one console, which can be operated by one man. This heavy-lift derrick can be arranged to serve either of the hatches forward and aft of it. Smaller derricks are also rigged from the tubular columns for normal cargo work.

Deck cranes

Derricks have been replaced on many modern cargo ships by deck cranes mounted on platforms between the holds (*Figure 7.12*). The deck crane provides an immediately operational cargo-handling device with minimal rigging requirements and simple, straightforward one-man operation. The safe working load of the crane is determined by its cargo-handling duties, and designs are available from 3–5 tonnes and up to 10–15 tonnes as required. Double gearing is a feature of some of the larger cranes to enable speedier handling of lighter loads. Three basic types of cranes are available —general cargo cranes, grabbing cranes and twin-crane arrangements.

The general cargo crane is for use on cargo ships and bulk carriers. The grabbing crane is for use with a mechanically-operated grab when handling bulk materials. It requires a multiple-wire arrangement for the operation of the grab. Twin cranes utilise standard cranes which can be twinned or operated in unison to lift heavier loads such as containers, if required. A single operator is usual with this system, by utilising a master and slave control system in the two cranes. The use of a common revolving platform makes this arrangement possible.

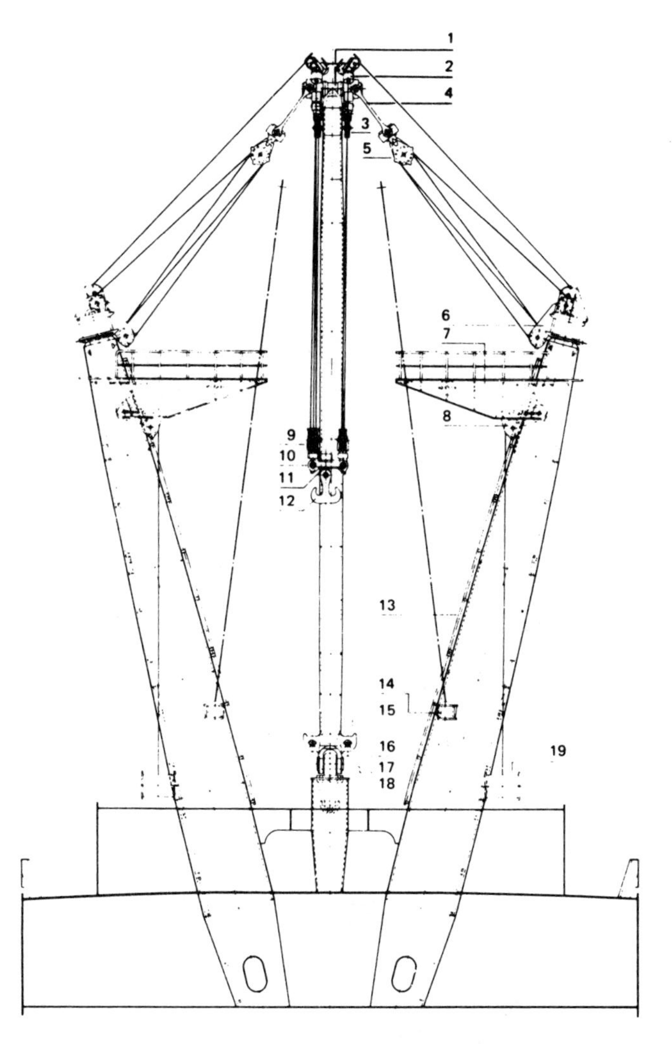

1 Derrick head fitting
2 Pendulum block fitting with guide rollers
3 Upper cargo blocks
4 Connecting flats
5 Lower span block
6 Span swivel
7 Cross tree
8 Inlet for the hauling part
9 Lower cargo blocks
10 Connecting traverse
11 Swivel eye for flemish hook
12 Flemish hook
13 Ladder
14 Gooseneck pin socket
15 Fastening device for lower cargo block
16 Heel fitting
17 Derrick pin
18 Gooseneck and gooseneck pin socket
19 Winches

Figure 7.11 Stülken heavy-lift derrick

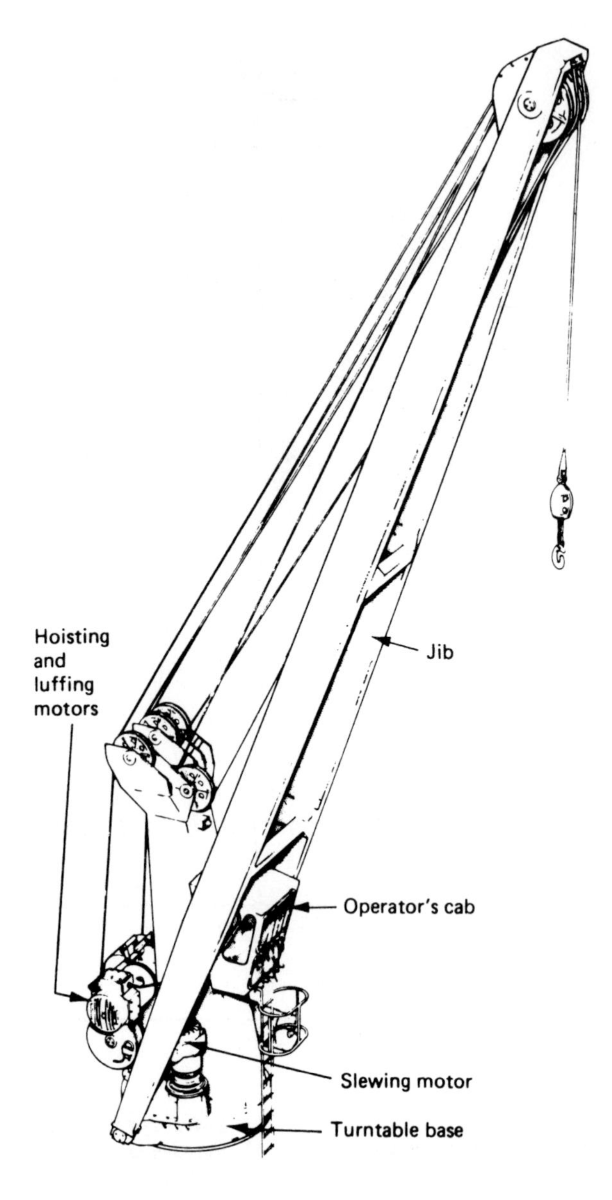

Figure 7.12 General cargo crane

Crane platform

The deck crane is located on a platform positioned some distance from the deck to provide the crane operator with a clear uninterrupted view of the hold and the quayside (*Figure 7.13*). The crane also revolves around this platform. The seat on which the crane rests is usually circular and of steel plate construction with closely spaced vertical ribs or brackets. This seat is usually welded to or is an integral part

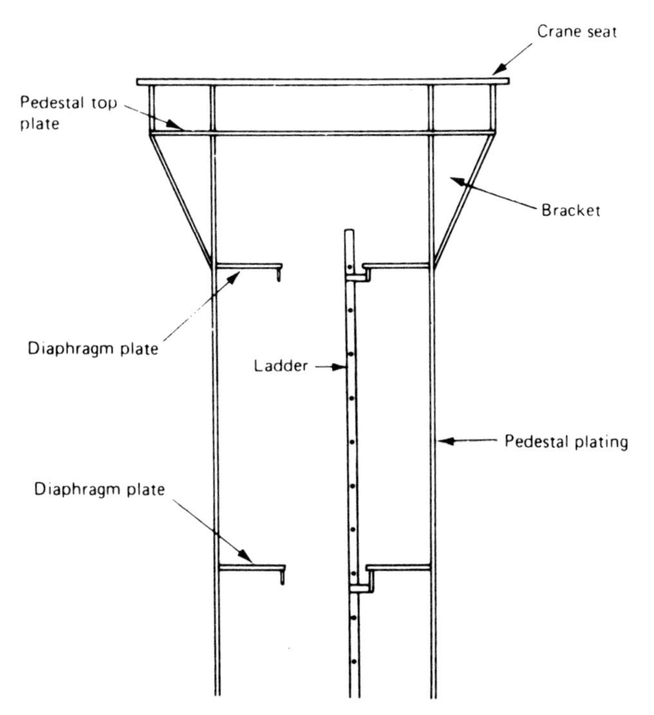

Figure 7.13 Crane pedestal and seat

of the raised post or platform which is welded to the deck of the ship. Adequate structural support and stiffening should be provided both around and under the seat.

Pumping and piping arrangements

Various piping and pumping systems are provided for the many services required on board ship. Some systems, such as bilge drainage and fire mains, are statutory requirements in the event of damage or fire on board ship. Each of the various systems will be examined in turn.

Bilge system

The bilge piping system of any ship must be designed and arranged such that any compartment can be discharged of water when the ship is on an even keel or listed no more than 5 degrees to either side. In the machinery space at least two suctions must be available, one on each side. One suction is connected to the bilge main and the other to an independent power-driven pump or ejector. An emergency bilge suction must also be provided and is usually connected to the largest capacity pump available. A diagrammatic arrangement of a bilge pumping system for a 26,000 deadweight tonnes bulk carrier is shown in *Figure 7.14*.

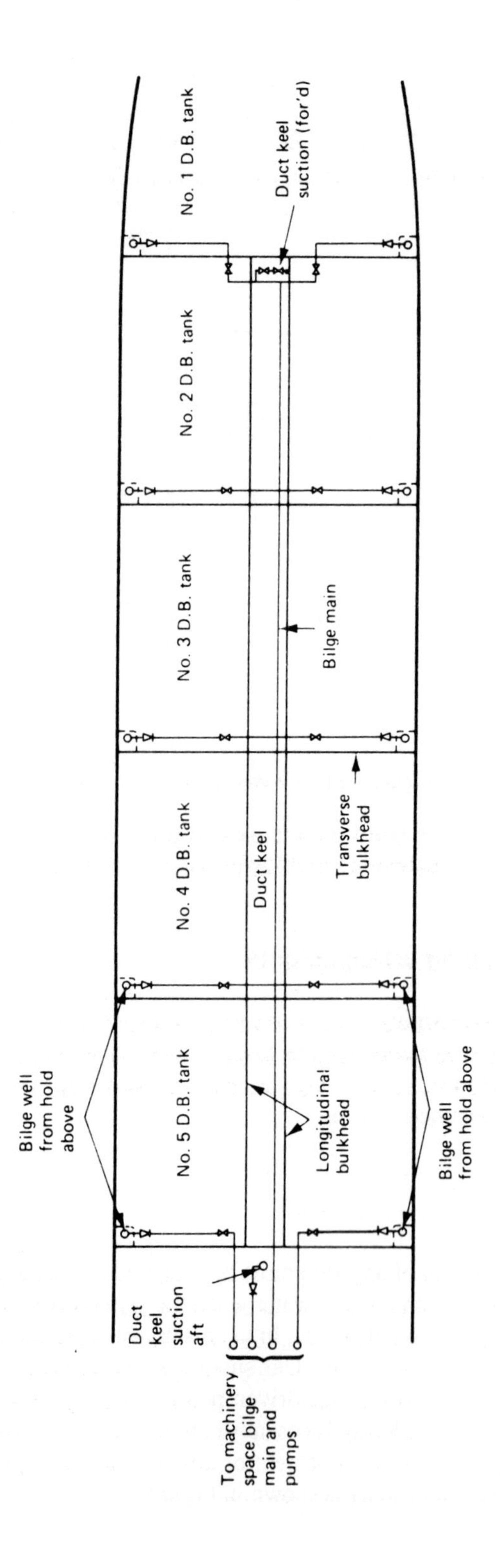

Figure 7.14 Cargo hold bilge system

Strum boxes are fitted on all but machinery and tunnel space suction pipes. Perforations of 10 mm maximum diameter are made in the plate to provide a suction area at least twice that of the suction pipe. In the machinery and tunnel space bilge lines, mud boxes are fitted. The mud box fits between lengths of piping and has a perforated centreplate. The use of strum and mud boxes prevents the entry of large objects to the pipeline and safeguards the internal parts of the pump (*Figure 7.15*).

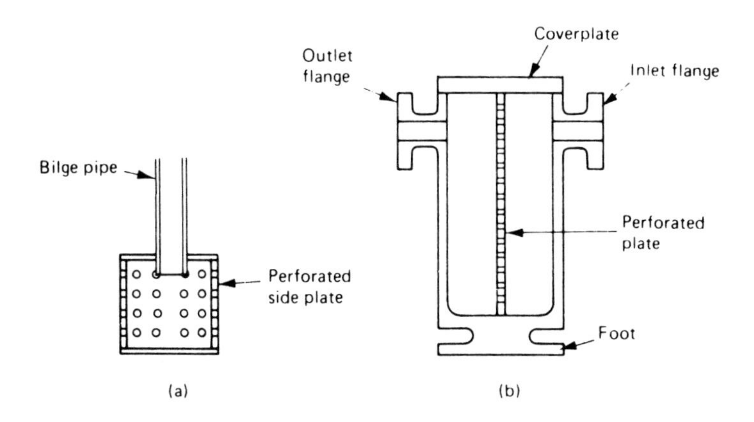

Figure 7.15 (a) Bilge strum box; (b) bilge mud box

Suction valves for the individual compartments must be of the screw-down non-return (SNDR) type to prevent reverse flow. All other valves must be of the non-return (NR) type. The port and starboard hold bilge valves are usually grouped in distribution chests at the forward end of the machinery space. Bilge piping is made up of the fore and aft mains and suction branches to the individual compartments. Piping is arranged, where possible, in pipe tunnels or duct keels to avoid penetrating watertight double-bottom tanks. Bilge pipes are independent of piping for any other duties such as ballast or fresh water. Passenger ship bilge mains must run at least 20% of the ship's beam inside of the side shell; in addition, any branches further outboard must have a non-return valve fitted.

Bilge pipe suction lines are sized according to an empirical formula. Minimum branch and main sizes are 50 mm and 65 mm, respectively, and the maximum size is 100 mm for both. Bilge piping may be constructed of cast iron, steel, copper or other suitable approved materials. It is usual to employ galvanised steel piping in bilge systems.

At least four independent power-driven pumps must be connected to the bilge main. Most ships employ two bilge pumps and have bilge main connections on the ballast and main circulating pumps. Where possible these pumps should be located in separate watertight compartments. One bilge system pump must be capable of operation under reasonable damage conditions. A submersible pump, remotely controlled, would provide this facility. Pumps fitted to the bilge system must be self-priming or connected to a priming system or device.

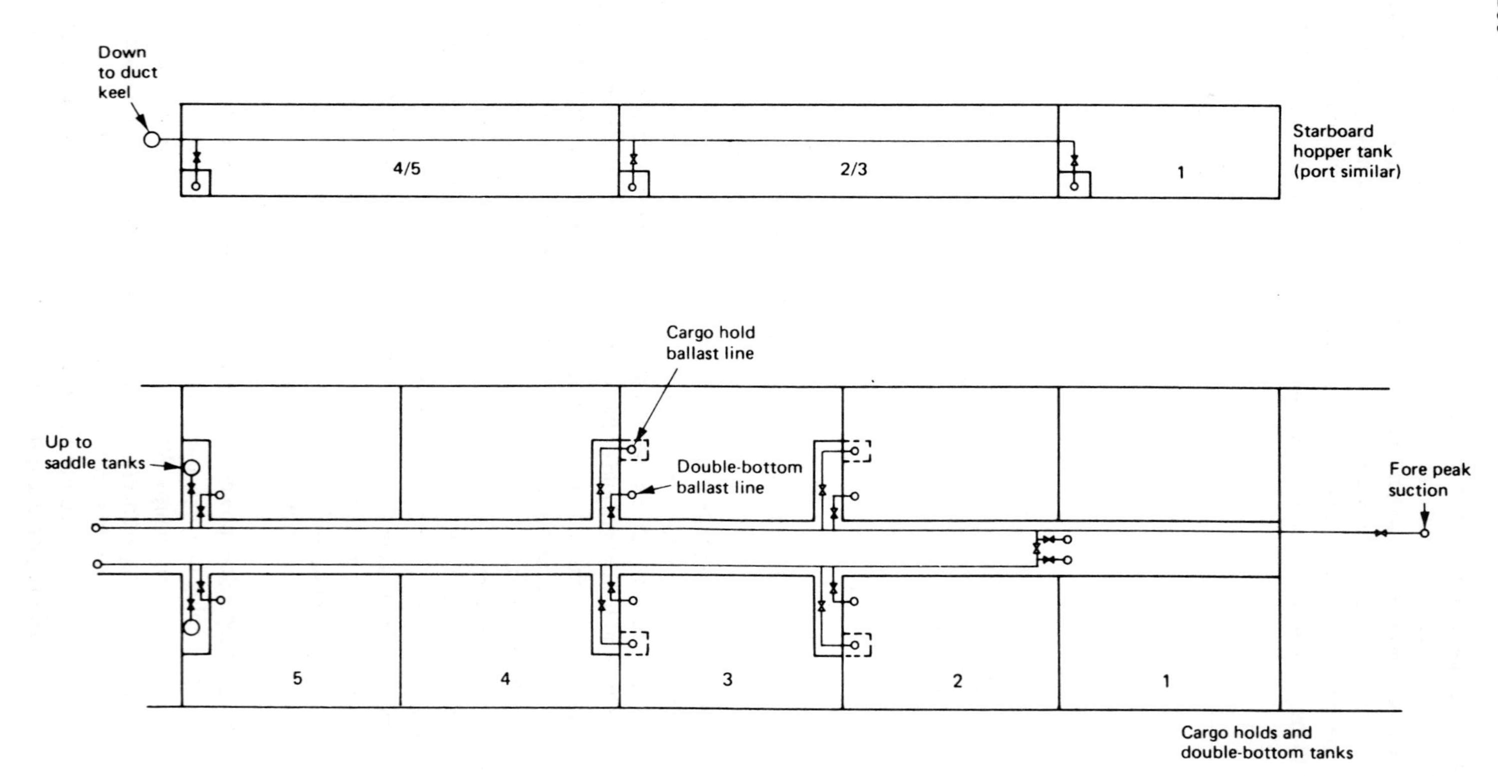

Figure 7.16 Ballast system for a bulk carrier

Ballast system

Requirements for the ballast system of a dry cargo ship are largely similar to those for the bilge system. There must be adequate protection provided against ballast water entering dry cargo or adjoining spaces. Connections between bilge and ballast lines must be by non-return valves. Locking valves or blanking arrangements must prevent accidental emptying of deep tanks or flooding. Where tanks are employed for oil fuel or ballast, effective isolating systems must be used.

A ballast pumping arrangement for a 26,000 deadweight tonnes bulk carrier is shown in *Figure 7.16*.

Fire main

All passenger ships of 4000 gross tons and above must have at least three power-driven fire pumps. All cargo ships in excess of 1000 gross tons must have at least two independently driven fire pumps. Where these two pumps are located in one area an emergency fire pump must be provided and located remote from the machinery space. The emergency fire pump must be independently driven by a compression ignition engine or other approved means. Water mains of sufficient diameter to provide an adequate water supply for the simultaneous operation of two fire hoses must be connected to the fire pumps. An isolating valve is fitted to the machinery space fire main to enable the emergency fire pump to supply the deck lines, if the machinery space main is broken or the pump is out of action.

A diagrammatic arrangement of a fire and washdeck system is shown in *Figure 7.17*. The system is designed to supply valves with hose connections on all the superstructure and upper decks. Relief valves are fitted at either end of the main to ensure that working pressure is not exceeded. The water may be supplied by the machinery space fire pump, the fire and tank-cleaning pump or the emergency fire pump located in the forecastle. Additional lines are led to the hawse pipe for anchor washing and the garbage tank for flushing.

The emergency fire pump in this arrangement is supplied by a booster pump fitted near the bottom of the ship. The booster pump is driven hydraulically from one end of the emergency fire pump, the other end having another sea water pump to further pressurise the water. A diesel engine drives the pumps fitted at either end.

General services

Many other pumping and piping services are fitted in ships for the various domestic, cargo and machinery requirements.

Scuppers

Direct drainage of the open decks above the freeboard deck is achieved by means of scuppers. A typical arrangement is shown in *Figure 7.18*. In enclosed spaces,

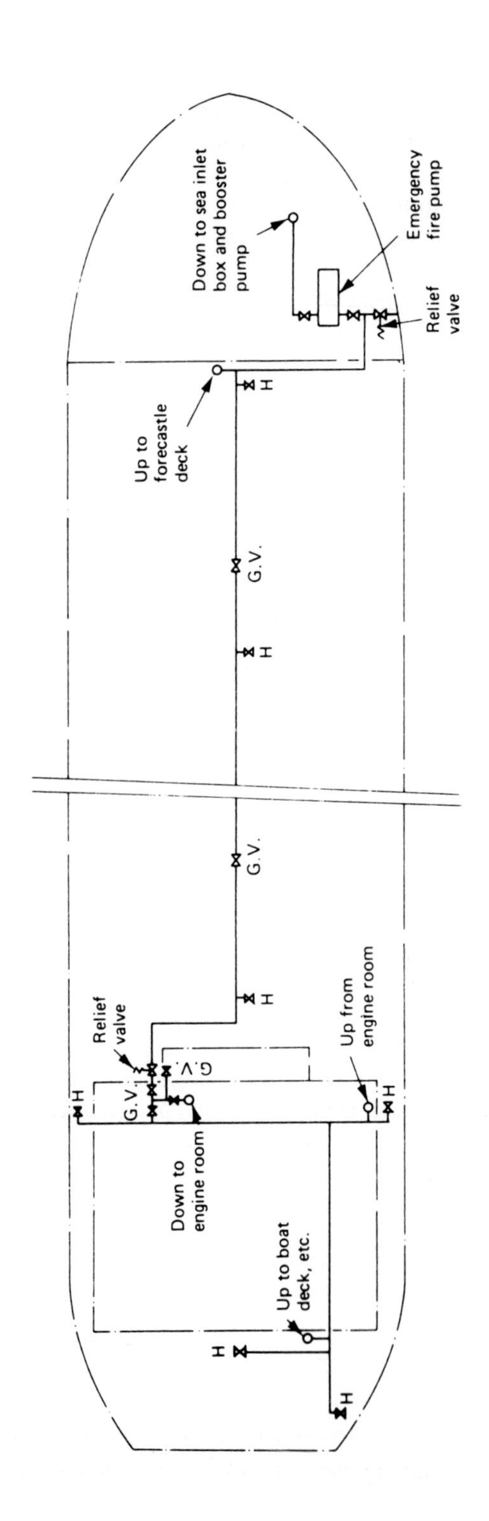

Figure 7.17 Fire and washdeck system (H, hydrant; GV, gate valve)

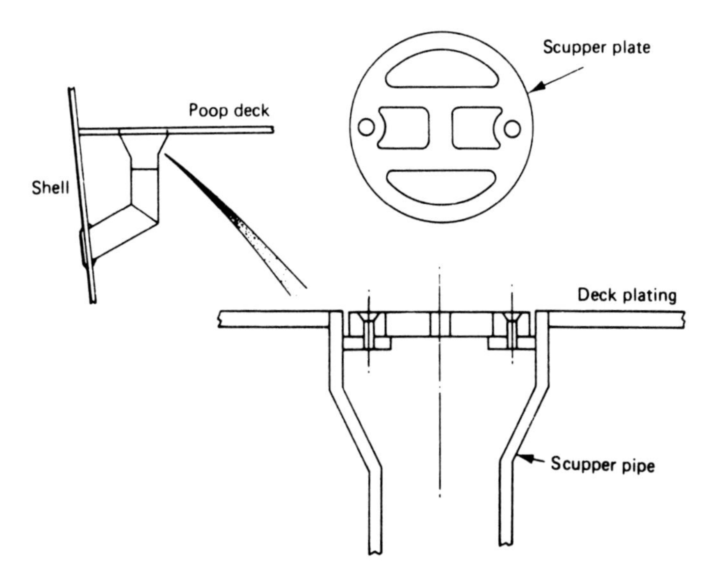

Figure 7.18 Deck scupper arrangement

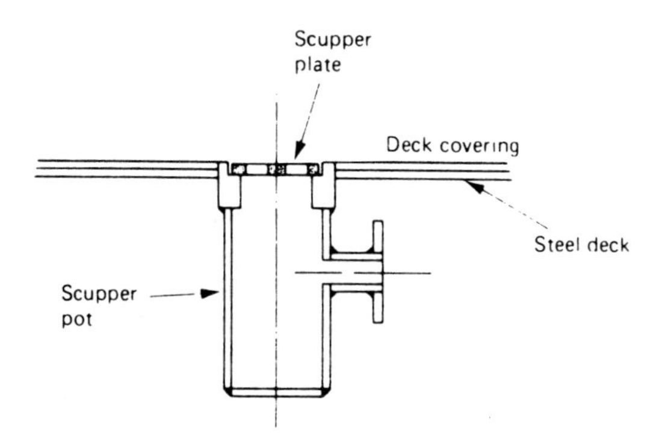

Figure 7.19 Accommodation scupper arrangement

such as bathrooms or galleys, the scuppers are led to the bilges. A scupper pot is fitted in a deck and acts as the collecting point for water. A pipe is connected to the underside to drain the water directly to the bilge (*Figure 7.19*).

Sounding pipes

Sounding pipes are fitted to all tanks to enable soundings to be taken and the depth of liquid present to be measured. Reference to the tank calibration tables will then permit the quantity of liquid present in the tank to be found.

Sounding pipes are made as straight as practicable and are led above the bulkhead deck, except for certain machinery space tanks (*Figure 7.20*). A minimum bore of

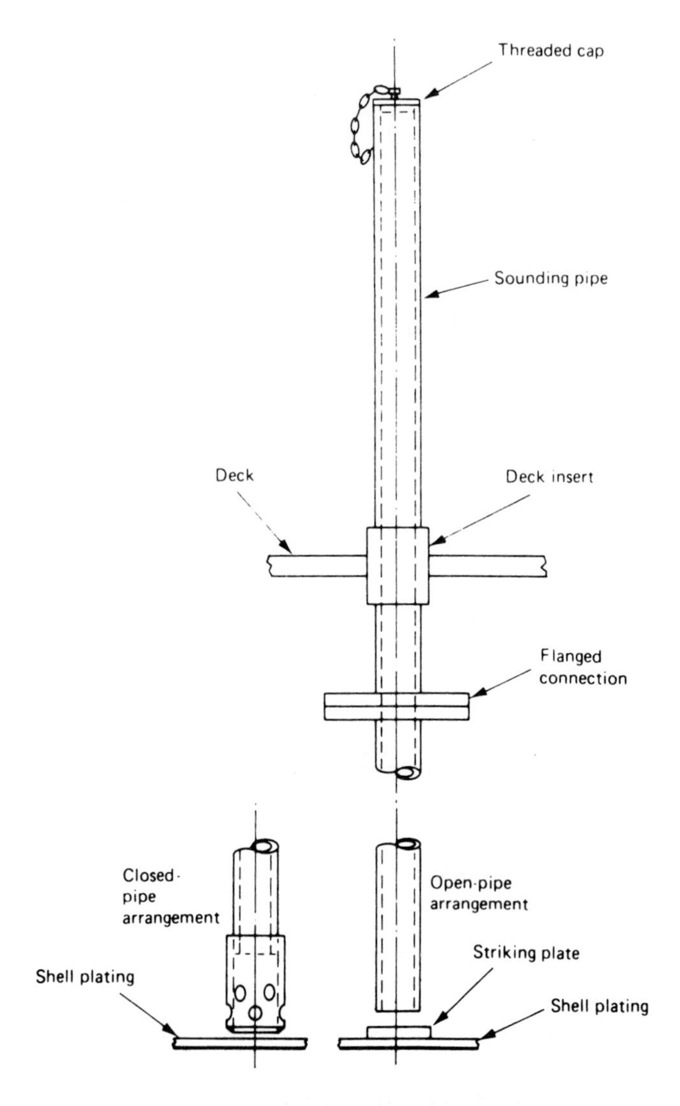

Figure 7.20 Sounding pipe arrangements

32 mm is required for sounding pipes. This may be greater where a refrigerated space is passed through to allow for icing up. Where the sounding pipe does not emerge above the bulkhead deck, some form of self-closing device should be fitted, e.g. a weighted cock. This would prevent flooding, in the event of an overflow, contamination due to the entry of other liquids or the escape of hazardous gases from the tank. A striking plate is fitted at the bottom of an open pipe where the sounding rod falls; alternatively, a closed pipe arrangement may be used (*Figure 7.20*). A number of patent sounding devices are available and may, with approval, be fitted instead of sounding pipes.

Cargo systems

Cargo pumps and piping systems are installed on tankers to discharge and load the liquid cargo. Separate ballast-pumping systems are also provided for ballast-only tanks which are filled during ballast voyages.

System choice and its flexibility depend upon the range of cargoes, the vessel's trading pattern and what the owner is prepared to pay for. The standard system employs several ring mains along the tank length with branches off to the individual tanks. Other systems are in use, for instance, employing large sluice valves to empty the tanks one to another. The pump suctions are then taken from the aftermost tank with the vessel trimmed by the stern.

An example of a ring system for a very large crude carrier is shown diagrammatically in *Figure 7.21*. Three mains are employed to serve the various tanks. This arrangement also enables different grades of oil to be carried in the tanks served by each main. Branches are led off into each of the centre and wing tanks and are fitted with isolating valves. Cross-connections are arranged between the mains, and direct-loading pipes from the deck manifolds join the mains. Two stripping mains are also fitted and led forward with branches off to the various tanks. The stripping lines are used to discharge the last few hundred tonnes of cargo which the main suctions cannot handle.

The main cargo pumps are steam-driven horizontal or vertical single-stage centrifugal pumps. For the system shown in *Figure 7.21* one pump is provided for each main. The driving motor or turbine is located in the machinery space and the drive passes through a gastight seal in the pumproom bulkhead.

The stripping mains are connected in the pumproom to two stripping pumps which are usually of the positive-displacement type.

Deck pipework

A particular feature of tankers is the large quantity of piping seen on deck. A typical arrangement is shown diagrammatically in *Figure 7.22*. The cargo pumps discharge into mains which pass up through the pumproom and along the upper deck to midships. The mains branch into crossovers to port and starboard and are fitted with Y-pieces at the manifolds which are grouped near to the ship's side.

Products tankers

More complex piping arrangements with independent lines are necessary on products tankers to avoid contamination between the different cargo 'parcels'. More than one pumproom may be fitted on such ships, or individual pumps in all tanks with no pumprooms. Arrangements for flushing lines using water or a portion of the cargo may increase the flexibility of a particular system.

Ballasting arrangements

Many tankers operate in the ballast condition on every other voyage. A sufficient

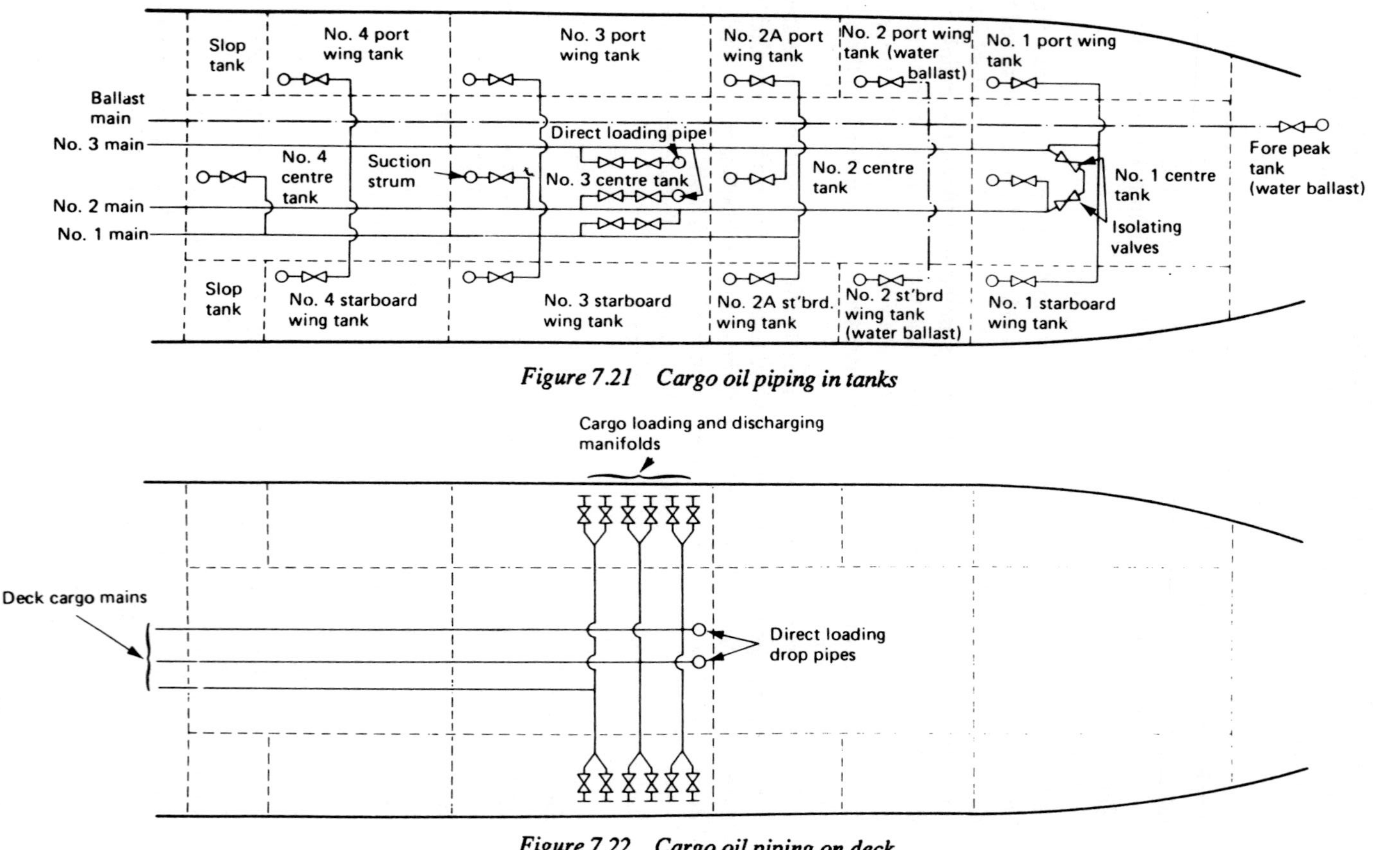

Figure 7.21 Cargo oil piping in tanks

Figure 7.22 Cargo oil piping on deck

quantity of ballast sea water must therefore be loaded on board to provide the ship with satisfactory seakeeping properties. Certain tanks are designated ballast only and are filled by the ballast pump and piping system.

Insulation

Thermal insulation

A ship's steel hull and structure will conduct heat very well. In way of heated tanks, refrigerated spaces and exposed accommodation spaces some form of insulation is necessary to reduce the heat flow to an acceptable level.

Various materials such as glass fibre, cork and some foam plastics are in use as insulation. Glass fibre matting or sheet is used in modern ships since it is easily fitted, is fire resistant, does not rot and does not support animal life. The amount of insulation fitted in a compartment is decided by the temperature which is to be maintained or accepted in the compartment (*Figure 7.23*).

Fastening is now largely by random pinning, using a stud gun to fix the pins to the steelwork. The pins penetrate the insulation, and caps fitted on the ends of the pins hold the insulation in place. Some slab insulation may be glued to the steelwork. Joins between sections of insulation are sealed, usually with an adhesive tape. In accommodation spaces, insulation will be behind decorative panels. In places where it is exposed to possible damage, a protective cladding or lining, such as galvanised mild steel sheeting, may be fitted. Insulation on tank-tops must likewise be protected from possible damage or be of a substantial nature in itself. Over oil tanks a space must be left to avoid possible contamination of the insulation. This space is not required when a bituminous covering is placed over the steel surface.

Plugs over manholes in cargo tanks and also hatch covers must be insulated to avoid any areas through which heat might be conducted. Special scupper arrangements are necessary to avoid heat transfer in refrigerated holds. This is achieved by a brine seal in an S-bend trap. The bilges may thus be pumped out but the sealing liquid, although diluted, will not be removed (*Figure 7.24*).

Acoustic insulation

Sound results from the movement of air particles and travels in the form of waves away from the source. There are many sources of sound on board ship, such as propulsion engines, auxiliary engines, large fans and ventilation plants. These would have a cumulative disturbing affect on personnel if allowed to continue unchecked.

Various countries now have either codes of practice for noise levels in ships, or regulations relating to noise levels in ship spaces. Maximum noise levels are given for particular spaces using a weighted sound pressure level or db(A) value. Most ships at sea, however, would not meet these criteria. New ship designs will require consideration of noise levels in the very early stages if an acceptable noise environment is to be obtained.

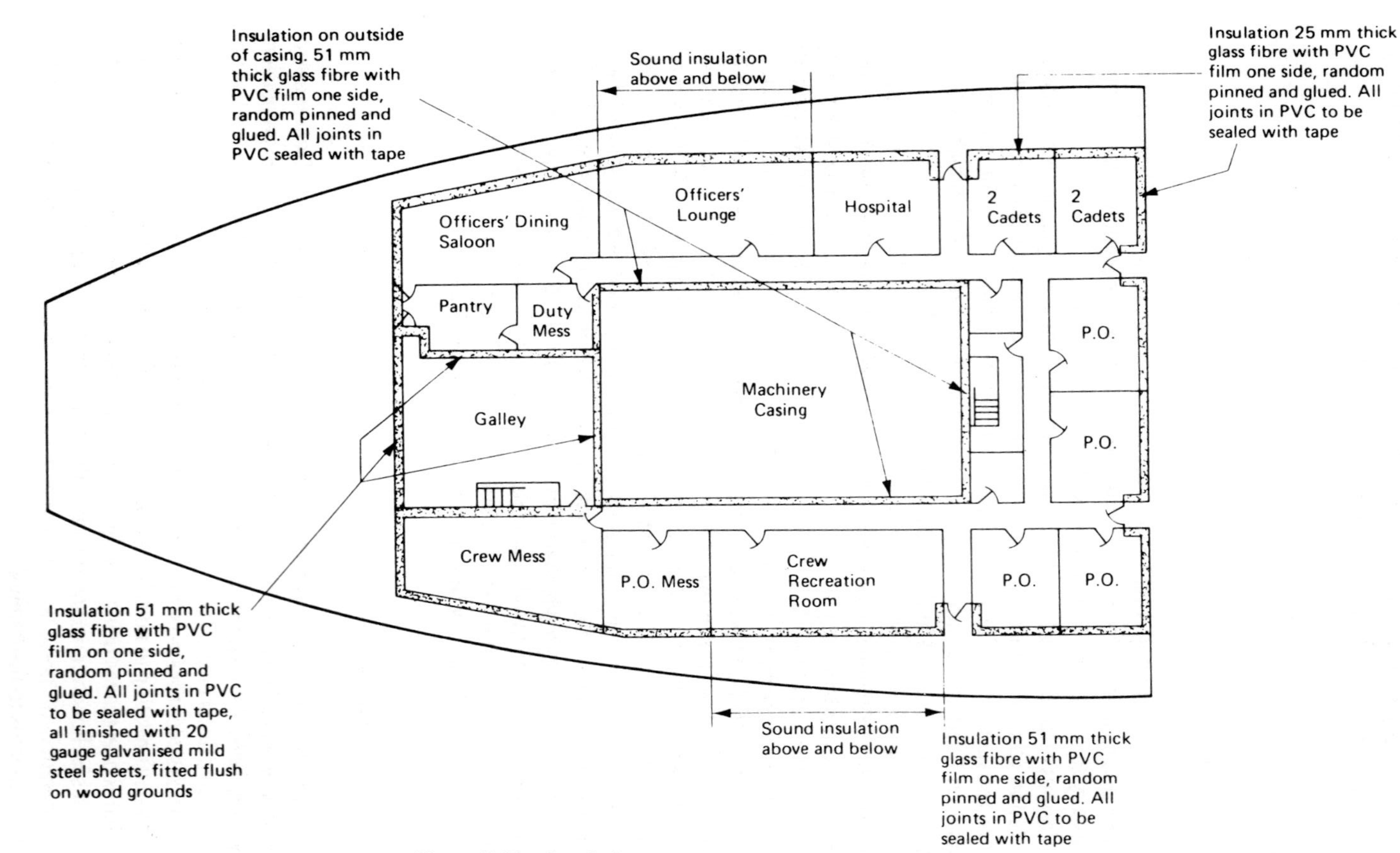

Figure 7.23 Insulation arrangements in accommodation spaces

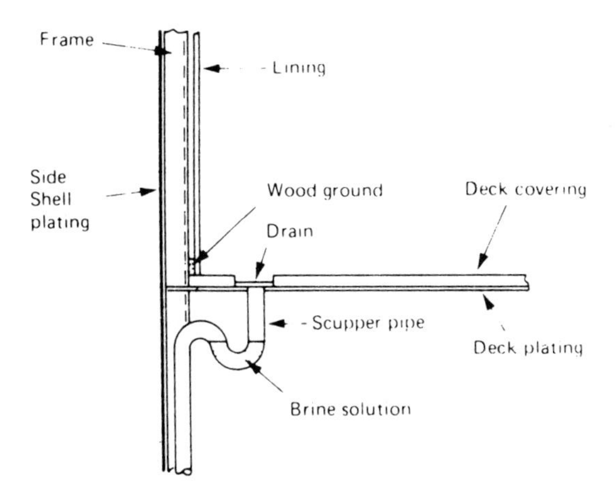

Figure 7.24 Refrigerated hold scupper trap

Two approaches are made to the solution of the problem. First, rooms and areas which are occupied for any length of time are fitted out in such a manner as to be as sound absorbing as possible. The second method is to isolate or silence the sound from occupied spaces.

Increasing the sound-absorption capacity of a room is achieved by using a variety of sound absorbers. These include membrane absorbers such as thin panels, resonant absorbers such as perforated ceiling boards and porous connections in ducting, flexible mountings on machinery, and sound insulating the surroundings of a noisy space. Air-conditioning plant noise can be eliminated by the use of duct and baffle silencers and sound attenuating supply and exhaust fittings. *Figures 7.25(a)* and *7.25(b)* illustrate the problems to be found in a ship's accommodation and the various solutions that can be adopted.

Watertight doors

Watertight bulkheads are, of course, specifically designed and constructed to ensure their watertightness. Where openings are necessary in these bulkheads special watertight doors must be fitted. On cargo ships with a shaft tunnel, the tunnel entrance will have a watertight door fitted. On passenger ships, with their large areas of accommodation and access requirements, a greater number of watertight doors will be fitted.

Where openings are cut into bulkheads they must be reinforced to maintain the strength of the bulkhead. This is particularly so in the lower regions of watertight bulkheads, where the greatest loading occurs. Where stiffeners are cut or increased in spacing in way of a watertight door, adequate reinforcing is required. The watertight door has a heavy framework which further stiffens the bulkhead in way of the opening. The size of the opening is kept as small as possible.

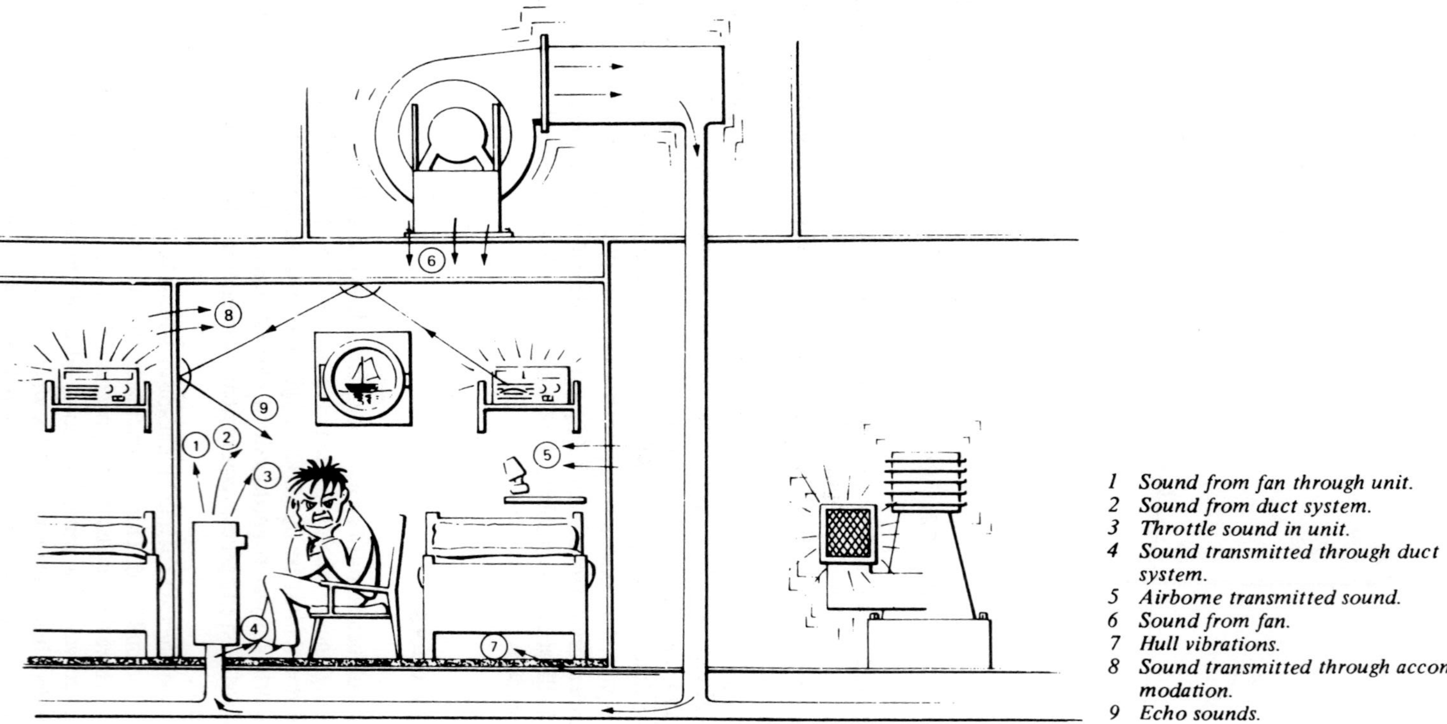

1 *Sound from fan through unit.*
2 *Sound from duct system.*
3 *Throttle sound in unit.*
4 *Sound transmitted through duct system.*
5 *Airborne transmitted sound.*
6 *Sound from fan.*
7 *Hull vibrations.*
8 *Sound transmitted through accommodation.*
9 *Echo sounds.*

Figure 7.25(a) **Sound insulation—accommodation with bad sound comfort**

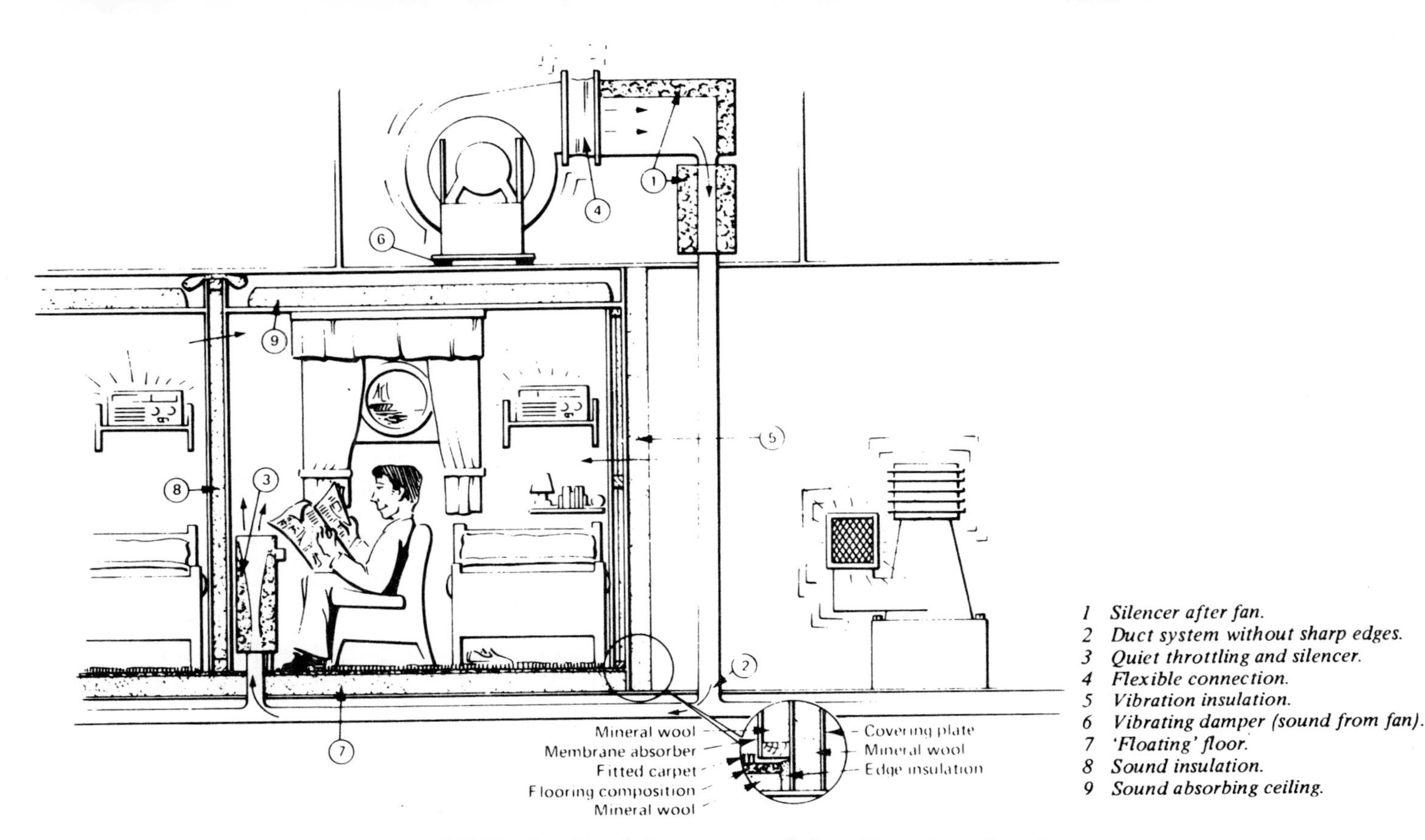

1 *Silencer after fan.*
2 *Duct system without sharp edges.*
3 *Quiet throttling and silencer.*
4 *Flexible connection.*
5 *Vibration insulation.*
6 *Vibrating damper (sound from fan).*
7 *'Floating' floor.*
8 *Sound insulation.*
9 *Sound absorbing ceiling.*

Figure 7.25(b) Sound insulation—accommodation with good sound comfort

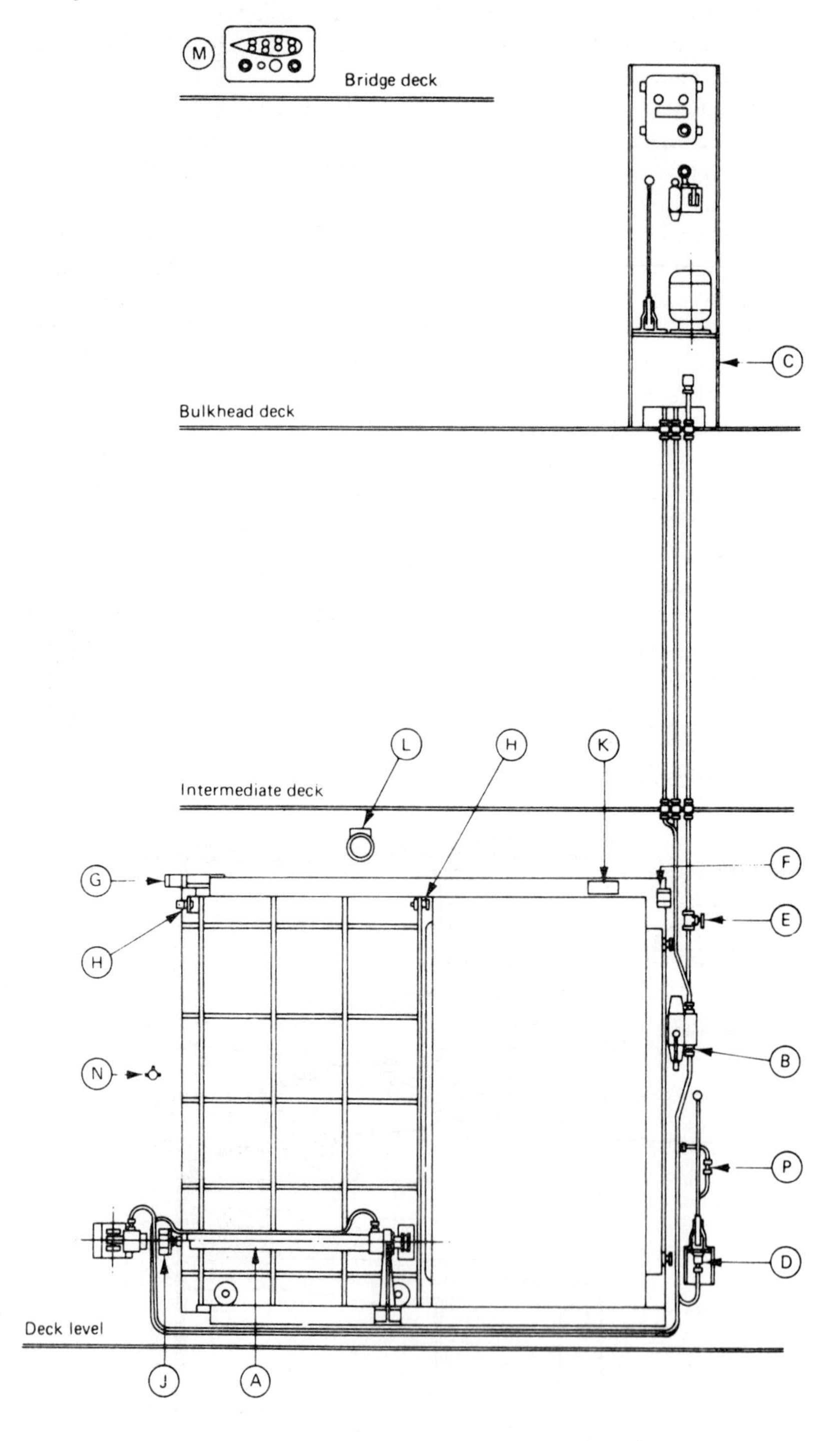

Figure 7.26 Horizontal sliding watertight door

All doors fitted below the waterline are of the sliding type, either horizontal or vertical in operation. It is usual to use horizontal sliding doors, except where space limitations require the vertical type.

The sliding door must be able to close against a list of 15 degrees to port or starboard. It must be operable from the vicinity of the door, and from a point above the bulkhead deck. The remote operating point must have an indicator showing the door position.

A horizontal sliding watertight door of Stone Manganese Marine Ltd manufacture is shown in *Figure 7.26*. A stout door frame is fitted directly into the bulkhead and provides the trackway along which the door slides. The door is moved by a hydraulic cylinder which may be power operated or hand pumped. A special solenoid spool valve which may be remotely or manually operated provides the basis of the control system. Bridge operation, local manual over-ride operation and local emergency control of the door are possible. Operating the hand pump together with manual movement of the solenoid valve provides local or remote emergency operation. Powered operation is possible from the bridge or by manual movement of the solenoid valves at either the local or remote pumping stations.

Bridge operation is only usual on passenger ships where there may be a large number of watertight doors.

Watertight doors are pressure tested under a head of water corresponding to their bulkhead position in the event of the ship flooding. This usually takes place at the manufacturers' works.

Above the waterline, in certain approved positions, hinged watertight doors are permitted. These will be similar in construction to the weathertight doors described in Section F of Chapter 5.

Stabilisers

The motions of a ship in a seaway can result in various undesirable effects, examples of which are cargo damage and human discomfort. Only the rolling of a ship can be effectively reduced by stabilisation. Two basically different stabilising systems are used on ships—the fin and the tank. Both systems attempt to reduce rolling by producing an opposite force to that attempting to roll the ship.

A Door-operating cylinder
B Door-control valve, solenoid/manual operated
C Power unit comprising:
Pump and motor unit
Motor starter
Door control valve (manual)
Relief valve and pressure gauge
Red and green light indication
Hand pump (emergency remote)
Supply tank
Level gauge (dipstick)
Oil filter and strainer
D Hand pump
E Stop valve (servicing)
F Combined alarm closing limit and indicator light switch
G Opening limit switch
H Switch strikers
J Door stop sited behind door cylinder 'A'
K Warning plate
L Alarm
M Bridge controller/indicator
N Key-operated isolating switch (1 each side of the bulkhead)
P Non-return valve

Fin stabiliser

One or more pairs of fins are fitted on a ship, one on each side (see *Figure 7.27*). The size or area of the fins is governed by ship factors such as breadth, draught, displacement, and so on, but is very small compared with the size of the ship. The fins may be retractable, i.e. pivoting or sliding within the ships form, or fixed. They act to apply a righting moment to the ship as it is inclined by a wave or force on one side. The angle of tilt of the fin and the resulting moment on the ship is determined by a sensing control system. The forward speed of the ship enables the fins to generate the thrust which results in the righting moment.

The operating system can be compared to that of the steering gear, in that a signal from the control unit causes a movement of the fin which, when it reaches the desired value, is brought to rest. The fin movement takes place as a result of a hydraulic power unit incorporating a type of variable displacement pump.

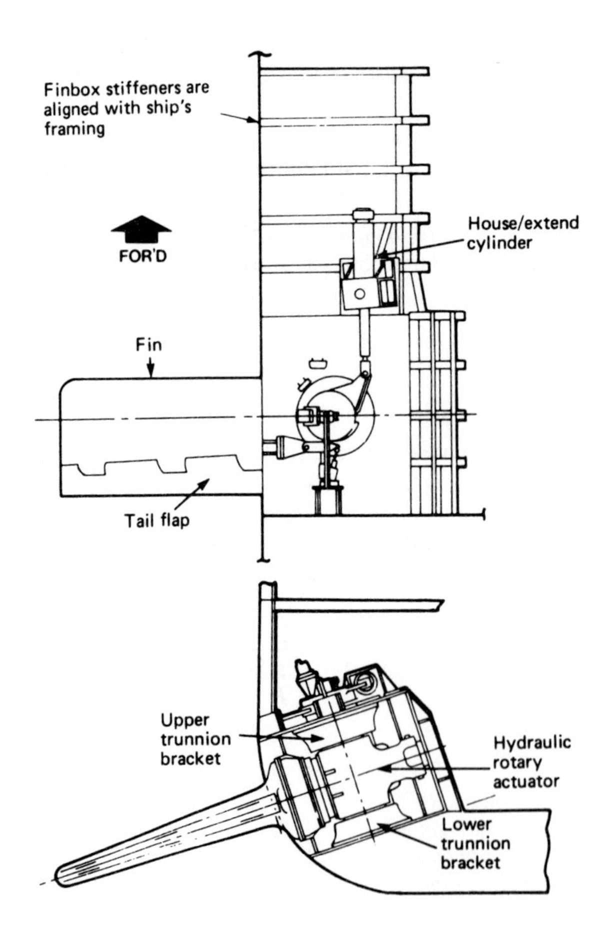

Figure 7.27 Fin stabiliser

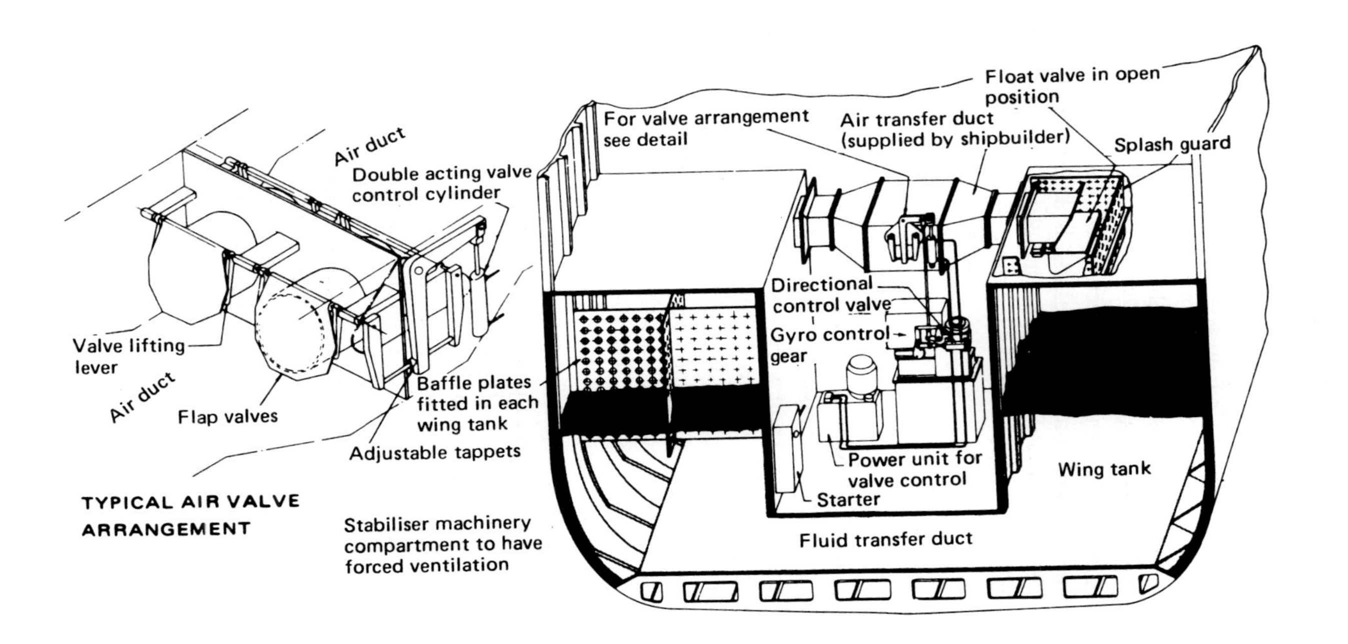

Figure 7.28 Air controlled tank stabiliser

The effectiveness of the fins as stabilisers depends upon their speed of movement, which must be rapid from one extreme point to the other. The fins are rectangular in shape and streamlined in section. The use of a moveable flap or a fixed and movable portion is to provide a greater restoring moment to the ship for a slightly more complicated mechanism.

The control system is based upon an acceleration sensor. This unit provides a signal which after electronic integration provides a measurement of roll velocity and angle. These various parameters are all used to bring about a suitable fin movement which will oppose the roll.

Fin stabilisers provide accurate and effective roll stabilisation in return for a complex installation which, in merchant vessels, is usually limited to passenger ships. It is to be noted that at low ship speeds the stabilising power falls off, and when stationary no stabilisation is possible.

Tank stabiliser

A tank stabiliser provides a righting or anti-rolling force as a result of the delayed flow of fluid in a suitably positioned transverse tank. The system operation is independent of ship speed and will work when the ship is at rest.

Consider a mass of water in an athwartships tank. As the ship rolls the water will be moved, but a moment or two after the ship rolls. Thus, when the ship is finishing its roll and about to return, the still moving water will oppose the return roll. The water mass thus acts against the roll at each ship movement. This athwartships tank is sometimes referred to as 'flume'. The system is considered passive, since the water flow is activated by gravity.

A wing tank system arranged for controlled passive operation is shown in *Figure 7.28*. The greater height of tank at the sides permits a larger water build-up and thus a greater moment to resist the roll. The rising fluid level must not however fill the wing tank. The air duct between the two wing tanks contains valves which are operated by a roll sensing device. The differential air pressure between tanks is regulated to allow the fluid flow to be controlled and 'phased' for maximum roll stabilisation.

A tank system must be specifically designed for a particular ship by using data from model tests. The water level in the system is critical and must be adjusted according to the ship's loaded condition. Also there is a free surface effect resulting from the moving water which effectively reduces the stability of the ship. The tank system does however stabilise at zero speed and is a much less complex installation than a fin stabiliser.

8

Oil Tankers, Bulk Carriers and Container Ships

Oil tankers, because of their sheer size and numbers at sea, are worthy of special consideration. These vessels require special forms of construction and outfitting because of the liquid nature of their cargo. Container ships are likewise increasing in size and numbers at sea. Large hatch openings and the need for structural rigidity create special constructional aspects for these vessels. The bulk carrier, in its many forms, is increasing in its unit size and numbers such that it too is worthy of individual attention.

Oil tankers

Longitudinal and transverse bulkheads divide the cargo-carrying section of the vessel into a number of tanks. In addition to separating different types of oil, the individual tanks reduce the effects of the liquid's free surface on the stability of the ship. Since oil contracts and expands with changes of temperature, tanks are rarely completely full and movement of the liquid takes place. The bulkheads, decks, etc., must therefore be oiltight even when stressed or loaded by the movement of the oil in addition to the normal static loads. Longitudinal stresses are considerable in tankers and great strength is therefore required to resist bending and stiffen the hull structure.

Fire and explosion are an ever-present hazard on tankers and special systems of ventilation are necessary. Void spaces or cofferdams are also fitted in places to separate the cargo tank section from other parts of the ship, such as pumprooms and fore peak tanks. Cargo-handling equipment is provided in the form of pumps located in a pumproom, usually positioned between the machinery space and the cargo tanks. More than one pumproom may be fitted depending upon the cargo carried or the piping arrangements. Suction pipelines run through the cargo tanks, and discharge lines leave the pumproom and travel along the deck to the crossover lines and manifolds situated at midships.

Two main types of oil tanker are to be found at sea today. The very large crude carrier (VLCC) and the products carrier. The main difference is in size and the products carrier has a larger number of tanks with a more complex piping system. This enables the carriage of many different cargo 'parcels' on any one voyage. The various aspects of tanker construction will now be examined.

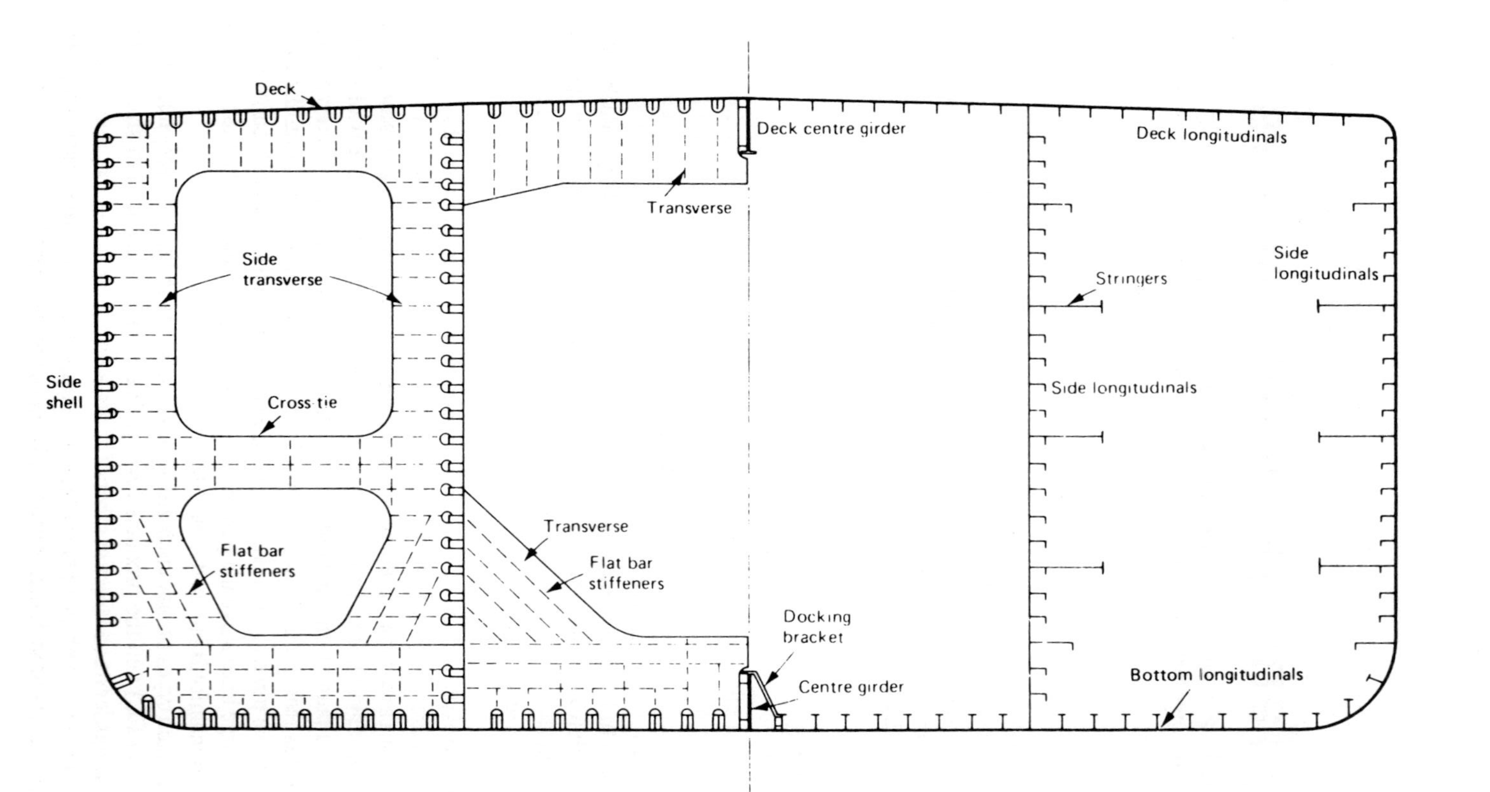

Figure 8.1 Oil tanker—midship section (longitudinal framing)

Framing

All tankers are constructed using either the longitudinal or the combined type of framing system. Ships greater than 198 m in length must be framed longitudinally. A fully longitudinal system of construction will have longitudinal stiffeners along the ship's sides throughout the tank length. These longitudinals are usually offset bulb plates of increasing dimensions towards the bottom shell of the ship. Built-up stiffeners, consisting of webs with symmetrical flat plate flanges, have also been used. Side transverses are fitted in line with the bottom transverses to support the longitudinals against compressive loadings (*Figures 8.1* and *8.2*). The combined framing system uses side frames with intermediate deep transverse webs. A number

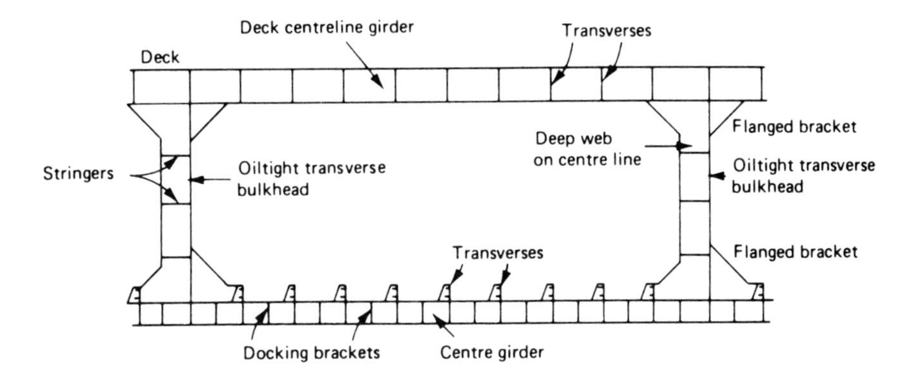

Figure 8.2 Elevation at centreline of tank (longitudinal framing)

of longitudinal stringers are fitted, depending on the depth of the tank. Brackets and knees are used to tie the side frames to the underside of the deck, the bottom plating and the stringers (*Figures 8.3* and *8.4*).

Bottom structure

The bottom structure is longitudinally framed over the cargo tank length. Bulb plates and built-up T-sections are usually employed. The bottom transverses provide support and are spaced at intervals of around 3.8 m on smaller ships and up to 5 m on longer vessels. The longitudinals are continuous and pass through notches cut in the transverses (*Figure 8.5*). Flat bar make-up plates are fitted to the transverses where the longitudinals pass through. At watertight bulkheads a fully welded collar is fitted (*Figure 8.6*). The longitudinals are also bracketed to the transverses. The transverses are usually a plate web with a heavier flat bar flange. Horizontal stiffeners are fitted where a considerable transverse depth is employed (*Figure 8.1*).

A centre girder is fitted, except where there is a centreline bulkhead. Various arrangements of continuous or intercostal longitudinal side girders are also sometimes fitted. The arrangements used will determine the scantlings of the members

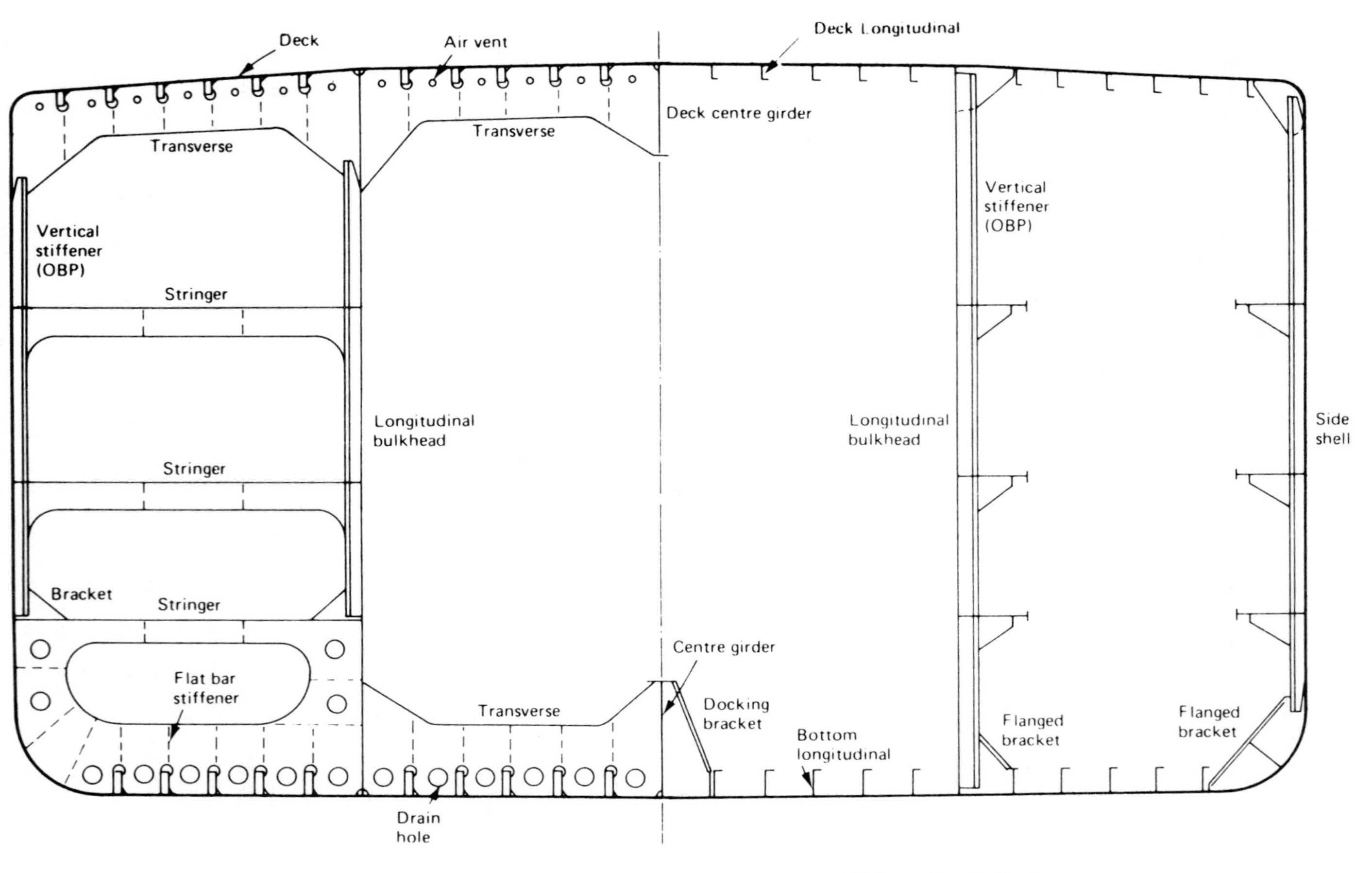

Figure 8.3 Oil tanker midship section (combined framing): OBP = offset bulb plate

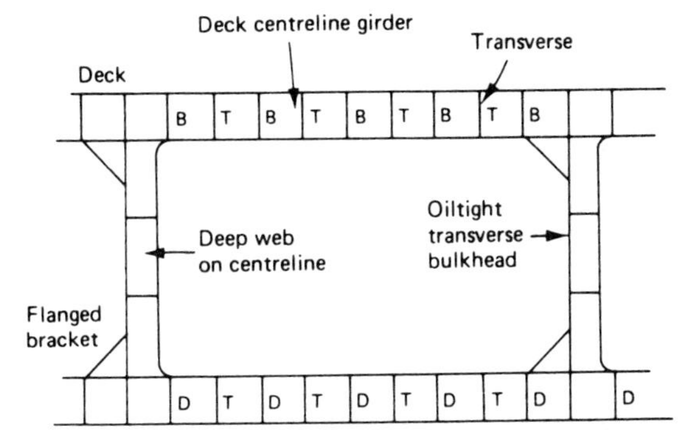

Figure 8.4 Elevation at centreline of tank (combined framing) (T, transverse; D, docking bracket; B, bracket)

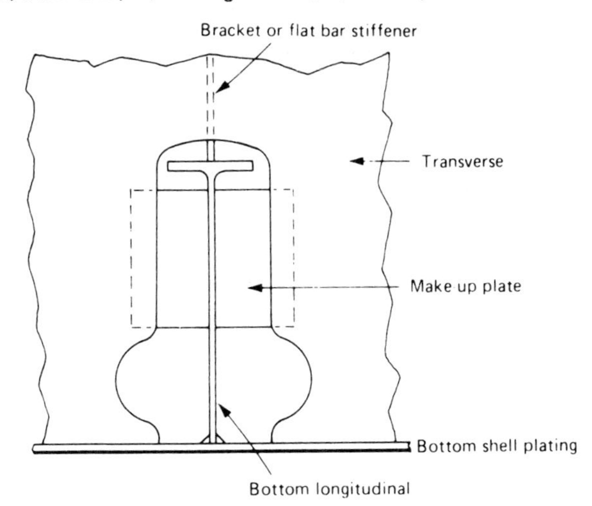

Figure 8.5 Notch arrangement

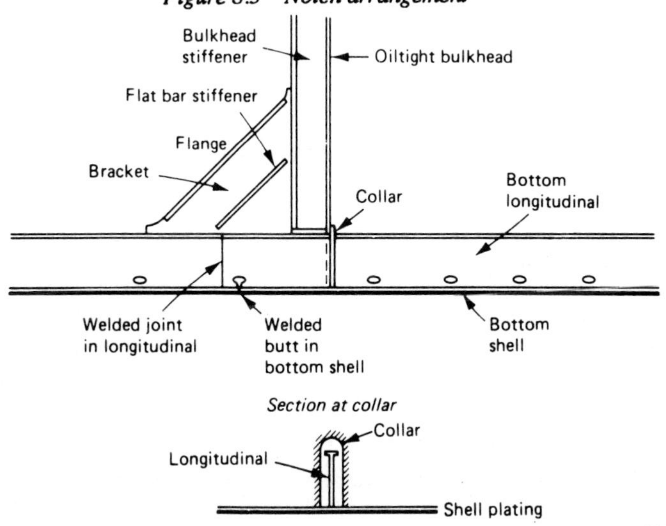

Figure 8.6 Continuous longitudinal arrangement through a watertight bulkhead

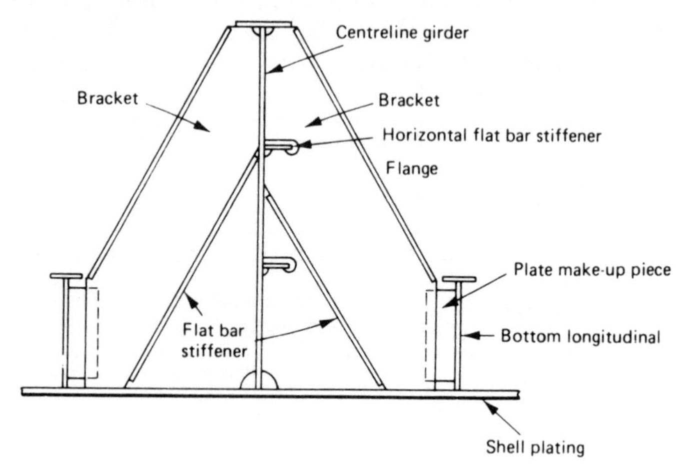

Figure 8.7 Docking bracket

employed in the construction. The centreline girder is stiffened and supported by vertical docking brackets fitted between each transverse (*Figure 8.7*).

A heavier plate flange is fitted at the upper edge of the centreline girder. Additional stiffening of the centreline girder is provided either by horizontal or vertical flat bars.

Underdeck structure

This is largely the same as that for the bottom structure, with transverses fitted in line with those below. A continuous centreline girder and perhaps intercostal or continuous side girders are fitted beneath the deck.

Bulkheads

Three types of bulkhead are to be found on tankers—longitudinal, transverse and wash.

Longitudinal bulkheads

Flat stiffened or corrugated oiltight bulkheads may be employed. The stiffening is largely the same as that of the side shell, i.e. horizontal stiffeners along the bulkhead where longitudinal shell stiffening is used. Brackets fasten the stiffeners to the transverse bulkheads at the ends. Where side transverses are fitted to the shell, correspondingly positioned vertical webs are fitted at the bulkhead. Horizontal stringers at the ship's side are matched by horizontal stringers on the bulkheads. A continuous ring-type structure of considerable strength is thus built up within the tank space.

This ring-type structure is further braced by the use of beams known as cross-ties fitted between the transverses or side stringers and the longitudinal bulkheads.

Where corrugated bulkheads are employed the corrugations must run horizontally. Vertical webs are fitted at every bottom transverse, in order to support the bulkhead.

Transverse bulkheads

Transverse bulkheads are similar in construction to longitudinal bulkheads and may be flat with stiffeners or corrugated. Vertical webs must be fitted to transverse bulkheads in line with the centre girder and may be fitted in line with side girders. Corrugated bulkheads may have vertical or horizontal corrugations with stiffening webs fitted at right-angles to the corrugations. Longitudinal stiffeners are arranged continuously through transverse bulkheads and are attached by brackets.

Transverse bulkheads must not be spaced greater than one-fifth of the ship's length apart. Where the tank length is greater than one-tenth of the ship's length, or 15 m, a perforated or wash bulkhead must be fitted.

Wash bulkheads

A wash bulkhead is similar in construction to a transverse bulkhead but is not oiltight. Large holes or perforations exist in the plating. These holes, while allowing the oil to move through, restrict the speed and force of its movement and provide additional transverse strength to the ship.

Double-hull and mid-deck tankers

MARPOL 73/78 details various construction requirements with regard to oil tankers. These are outlined in Chapter 11. New tankers will now have to have double bottoms and wing tanks extending the full depth of the ship's side. Mid-height deck tankers with double sided hulls or any other method of design and construction may also be accepted, provided they offer the same level of protection against pollution in the event of collision or stranding.

The US Oil Pollution Act of 1990 stipulated that any tanker ordered after 30 June 1990 or delivered after 1 January 1994 should be fitted with a double hull if it is to enter US waters. Various designs and methods of construction to meet these requirements are currently being proposed by shipbuilders throughout the world and a number of these are outlined.

A cross section of a double-hull VLCC design is given in *Figure 8.8*. Wing and centre cargo tanks are provided within the double-hull. The double bottom and side tanks are three metres deep, which is greater than the two metre minimum. This is to permit better access and venting of these enclosed spaces. Various locations of the stiffening structure are also being proposed. While enclosing the structure within the double hull will improve cargo handling and tank cleaning, there may be problems in relation to ship construction, corrosion protection and cleaning of these

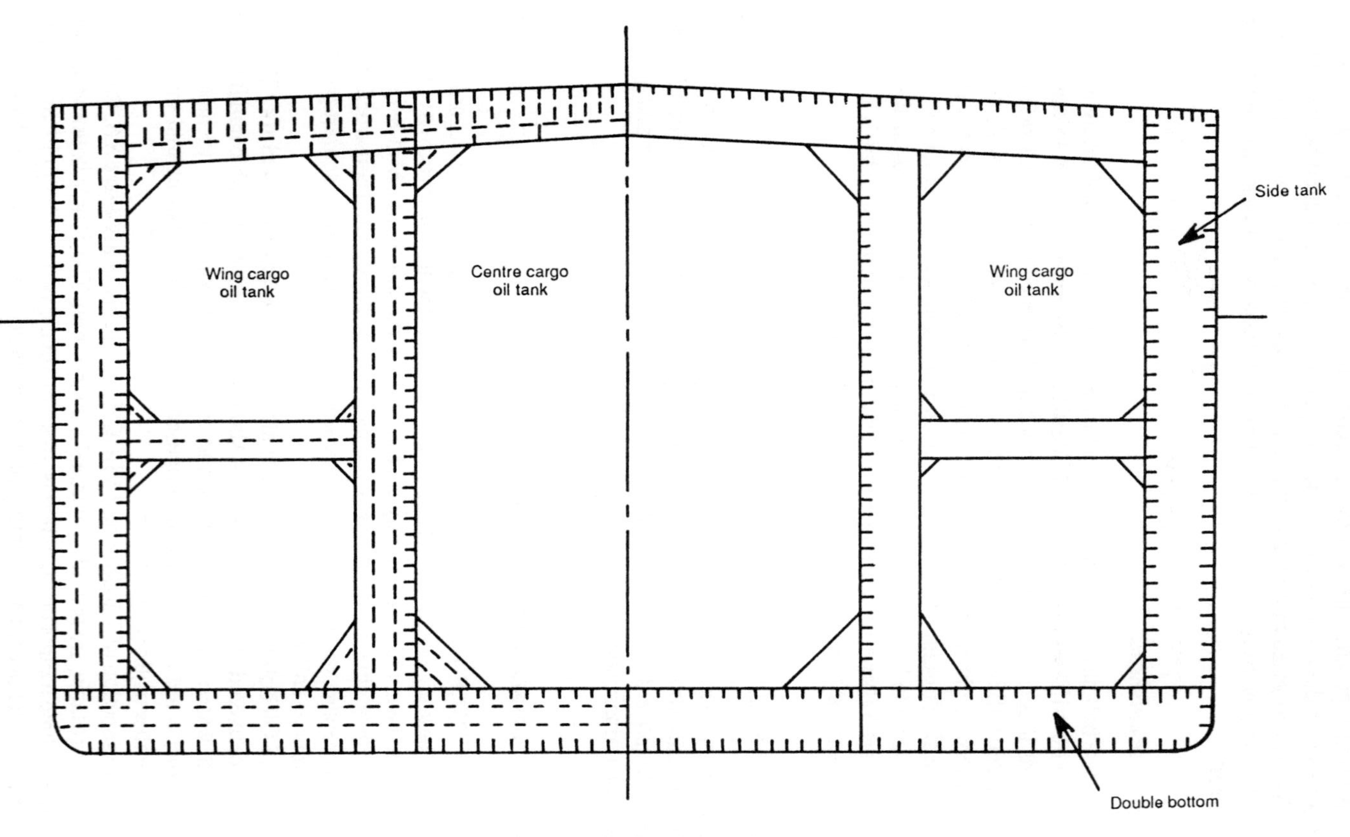

Figure 8.8 Double-hull tanker

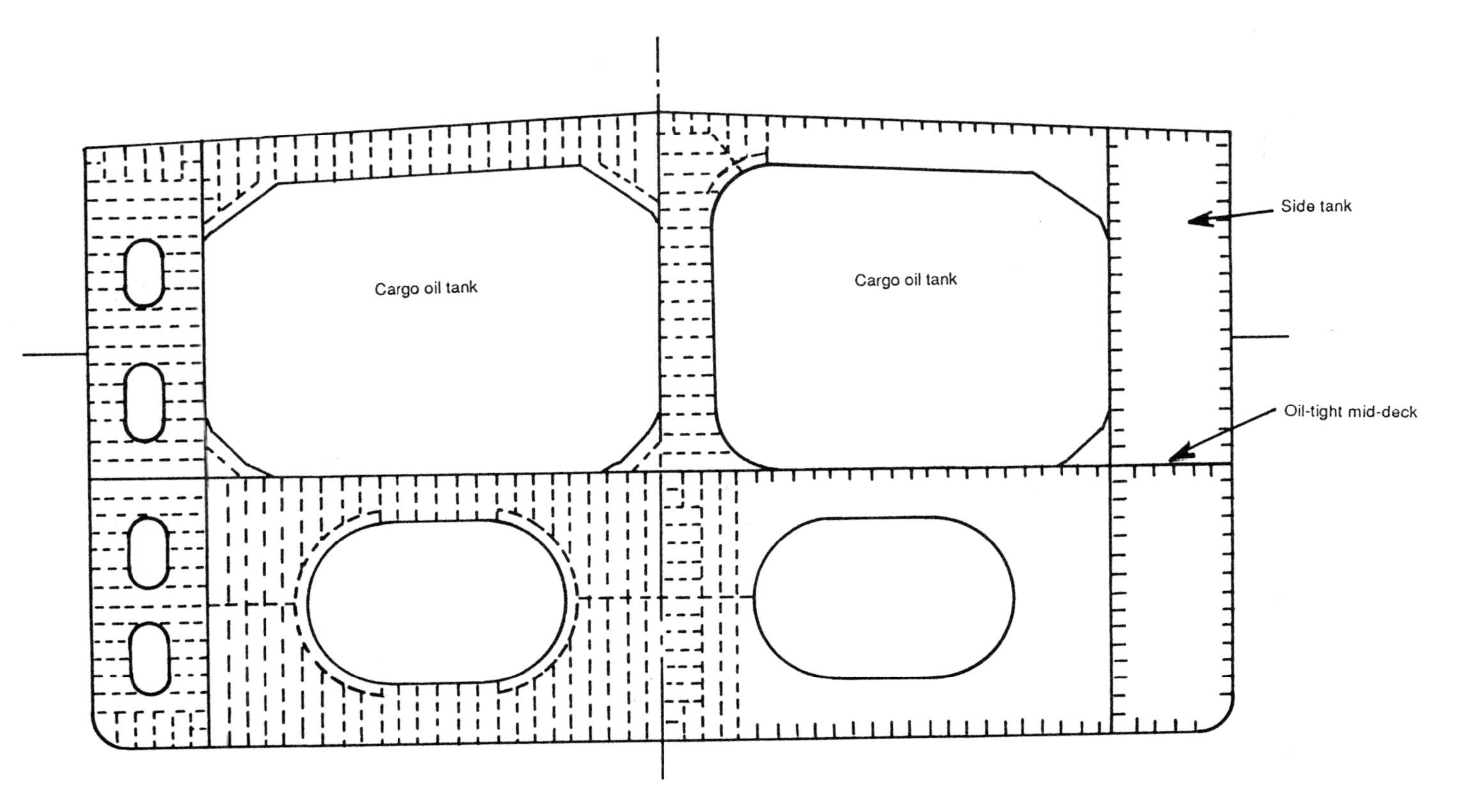

Figure 8.9 Mid-deck tanker

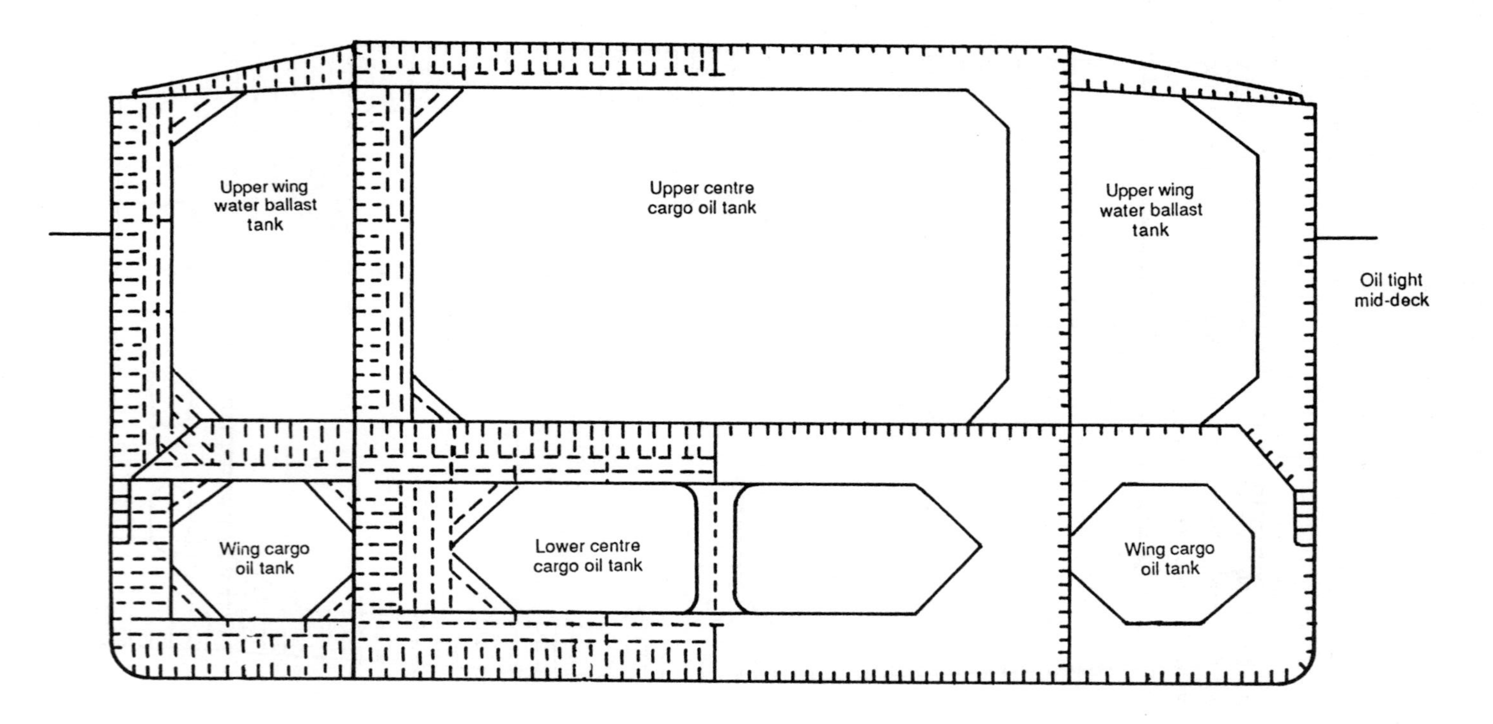

Figure 8.10 'Coulombi Egg' mid-deck tanker

water ballast tanks. The general stiffening of the bulkheads and the structure will be as outlined for single hull tankers.

The use of a mid-deck, rather than a double-hull, is claimed to reduce oil spills in the event of high energy groundings, when compared with a double hull design. IMO has accepted the mid-deck arrangement and a cross-section of one such design is given in *Figure 8.9*. The concept is based upon the cargo oil pressure in the lower tank being less then the external sea water pressure. If the bottom shell were penetrated, little or no oil would flow out. The side tanks are typically more than five metres wide, thus giving extra collision protection.

The position of the full-width mid-deck oiltight bulkhead must be carefully determined and is normally below the minimum draught level to ensure an oil pressure which is less than the external sea water pressure. The cargo lines, cargo vent and inert gas lines, access trunks and fixed tank cleaning machines would be positioned in the lower tank. Access trunks would be led to each lower tank forward and aft and could be used for various fittings and services, thus keeping the upper tank clear.

A consortium of European shipyards are developing the E3 tanker, so called because it is intended to be European, Economic and Environmentally friendly. Three prototype designs are being considered. Perhaps the simplest is a double-hull vessel with cargo tanks divided into pairs by a centreline bulkhead. The cargo tanks are the maximum MARPOL size and the double bottom is three metres deep. The side ballast tanks are four metres wide. The more conventional second design uses two longitudinal bulkheads to give centre and wing cargo oil tanks. The wing tanks are to the maximum MARPOL size. The third prototype is a novel design with a six metre deep double bottom which can be loaded with cargo. A pair of cargo tanks are above and the side tanks are increased to six metres wide. This, then, is a variant of the mid-deck design.

Numerous variants are being proposed by shipowners and naval architects around the world. One further patented design will be mentioned, which is the 'Coulombi Egg' mid-deck tanker (*Figure 8.10*). Cargo oil is carried in the upper and lower centre tanks and the lower wing tanks. Only upper wing tanks are used for water ballast. The cargo in the lower wing tanks is considered to be protectively located and a hydrodynamic automatic cargo transfer system is provided which works on the same principle as the mid-deck grounding protection provided by hydrostatic forces. A reception tank is provided to receive oil which is forced out of a holed cargo tank. Furthermore, the construction and stiffening arrangements for the structure are considered to be much simpler than other proposed double-hull or mid-deck designs.

The designs which are ultimately adopted will take into consideration building costs, steel weight, corrosion protection, tank cleaning and maintenance considerations, in addition to the regulatory requirements of IMO as outlined in the MARPOL 73/78 Convention.

Framing at ends

Beyond the cargo tank length the vessel may be transversely or of combined framing construction and must have certain additional strengthening fitted. A deep tank or tanks is often fitted forward of the cargo tank space. Where transverse framing is employed, solid floors are fitted at every frame space. Intercostal side girders of depth equal to the floors are also fitted in line with every other bottom shell longitudinal in the deep tank space. The deep tank is fitted with web frames not more than five frame spaces apart. A centreline bulkhead must also be fitted, unless the main longitudinal bulkheads extend through the deep tank. With longitudinal framing, transverses are fitted in the deep tank not more than 3 m apart. Intercostal side girders are also fitted either side of the centreline. On larger vessels the cargo tank structure may extend into the deep tank itself. Panting and pounding arrangements are also necessary and will be similar to those described in Chapter 5.

All modern tankers now have the machinery space and accommodation located aft. Web frames are fitted not more than five frame spaces apart in the machinery space, with fixed or portable beams across the casing opening. Transverse framing of the bottom is usual in the machinery space and construction is similar to that mentioned in Chapter 5. Transverse or longitudinal framing of the sides and deck may be used from the machinery space to the after end of the ship. Deck longitudinals must extend into the machinery space a distance equivalent to one-third of the ship's breadth. Panting arrangements are also fitted in the after peak, as described in Chapter 5.

Superstructures

These are of much the same construction as described in Chapter 5. The load line rules require protective housings around openings in the freeboard and other decks and a forecastle extending 7% of the ship's length from forward. Because of a tanker's high bending stresses extra care must be taken with discontinuities at the superstructure ends.

General

Cofferdams are fitted between oil tanks and other compartments and must be at least 760 mm wide. Pumprooms or water ballast tanks may, subject to certain conditions, be accepted instead of cofferdams. Special arrangements are necessary in tankers because of the reduced freeboard to clear the decks of water. Open rails are fitted for at least half the length of the weather deck. Solid bulwarks are usually fitted only at the forecastle and around the superstructure.

Hatches

Access to the cargo tank spaces is by oiltight hatches. Circular or oval shapes are usually employed with coamings at least 225 mm high. Steel covers with suitable oiltight fastening arrangements are usual, (*Figures 8.11(a)* and *8.11(b)*). Patented covers of other approved materials are also available. Other tanks and cofferdam spaces may have similar hatches or manholes for access (*Figure 8.12*).

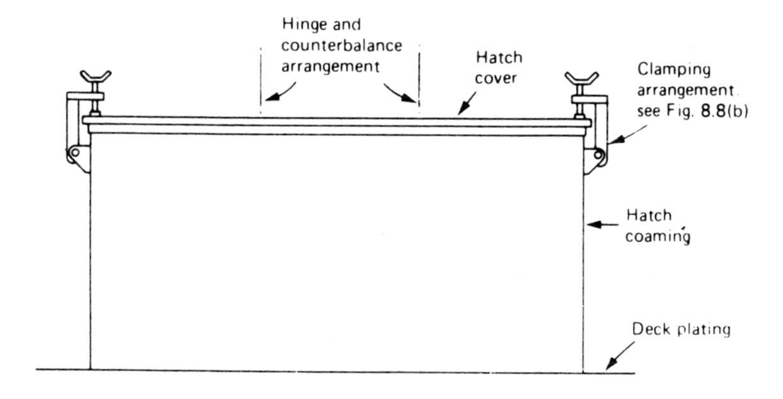

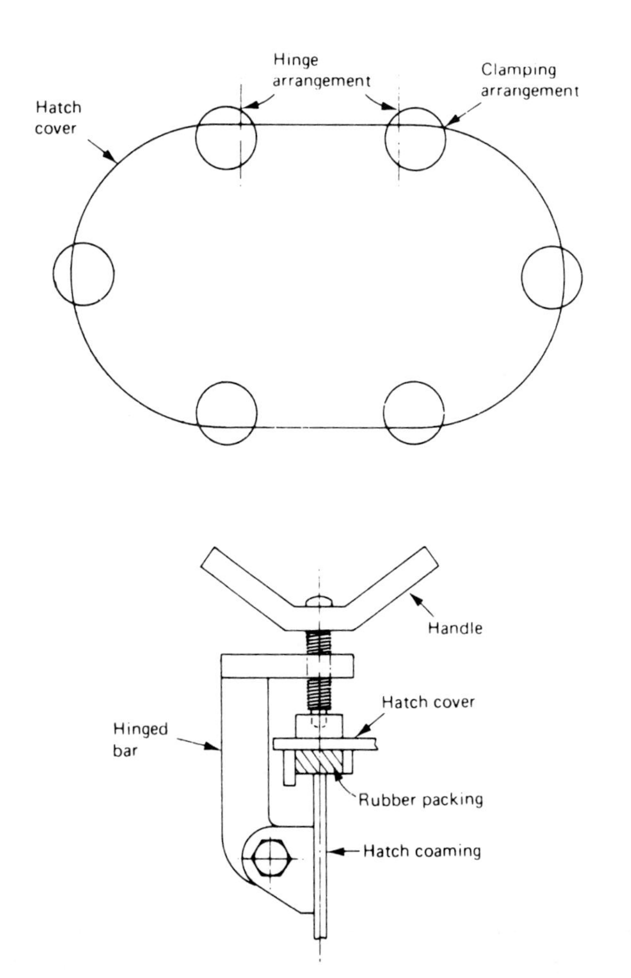

Figure 8.11 (a) Cargo tank hatch; (b) detail of hatch clamping arrangement

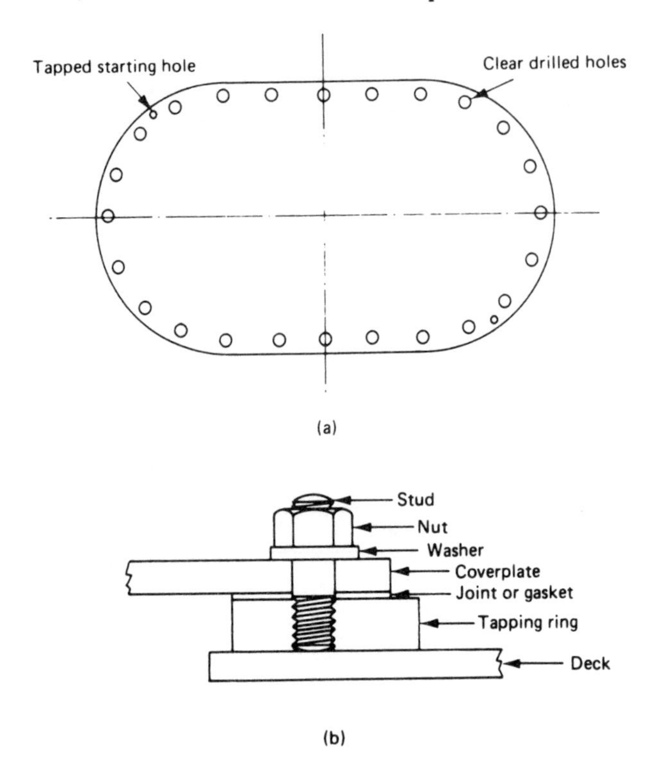

Figure 8.12 Manhole cover: (a) plate; (b) detail of securing arrangement

Ventilation

Ventilation arrangements are fully described in Chapter 10.

Inert gas plants

Inert gas plants are being fitted to an ever-increasing number of tankers to improve their operational safety. The plant provides an inert gas blanket over the surface of the cargo to stop the build-up of flammable vapours which might lead to explosions.

A typical system is shown in *Figure 8.13*. The plant uses exhaust gas which is drawn from the boiler flue uptakes, where available, or from a separate combustion chamber. The gas enters a scrubbing tower via a water seal which is circulated by sea water. The gas is cooled, solids and unwanted gases are scrubbed out and it then passes through a demister which removes water vapour. The inert gas which contains less than 5% oxygen is then pumped into the cargo tanks, using fan units to drive the gas along the supply main. A deck-mounted water seal is fitted in the main to prevent the back-flow of flammable gases from the cargo tanks.

During unloading the inert gas provides a positive pressure on the cargo surface which assists discharging in addition to ensuring a safe operation. Inert gas is fed

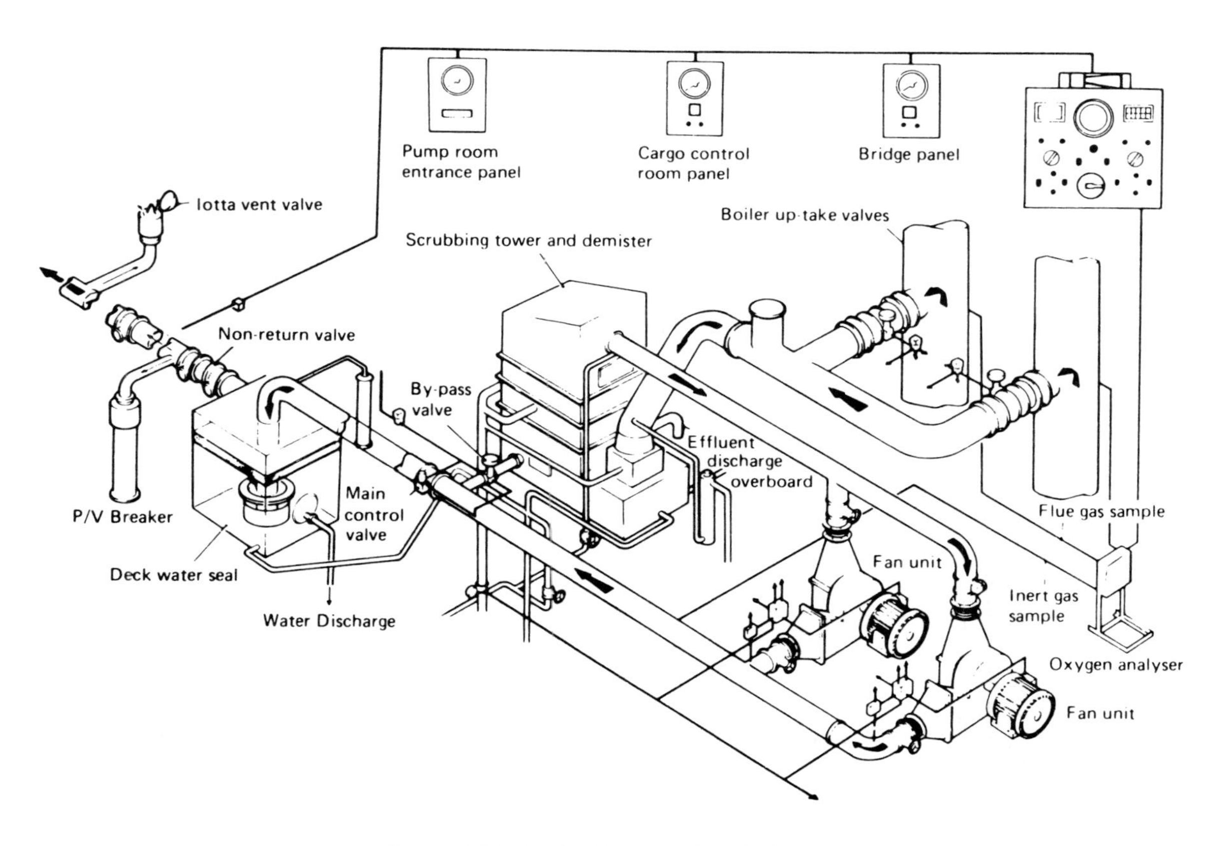

Figure 8.13 Typical inert gas installation

into tanks prior to loading and when full the fans are stopped. During loading the high velocity venting valves are opened to vent the inert gas to atmosphere. When loading is complete the valves are closed and inert gas is supplied to produce a slight pressure in the tanks. During loaded passage the inert gas pressure is monitored and maintained.

Other outfit items

Special circular openings with removable gastight covers are provided for tank-cleaning operations. A number of fixed or portable tank-cleaning machines are lowered into the cargo space through these openings (see *Figure 8.14*). Hot or cold

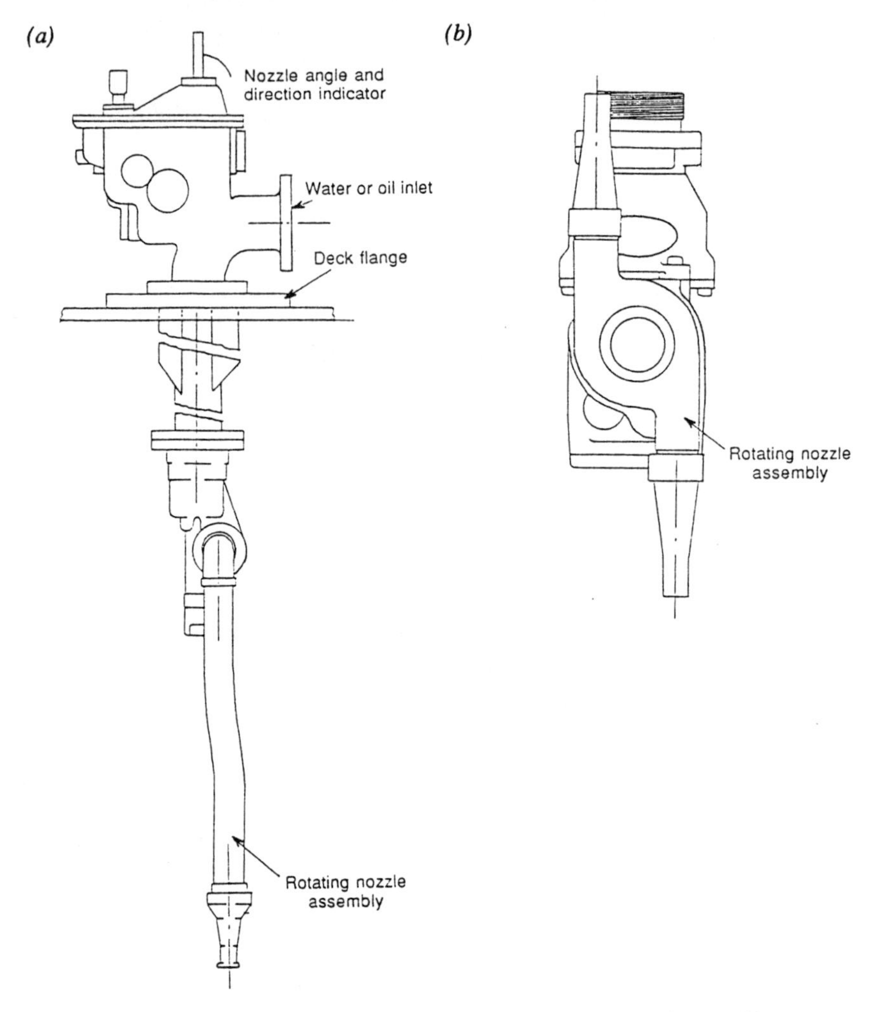

Figure 8.14 Tank cleaning machines: (a) fixed tank washing machine; (b) portable tank washing machine

water is then sprayed around the tank in order to clean oil from all the surfaces. Many tankers now use crude oil washing where crude oil (cargo) is sprayed around the tank by tank cleaning machines.

Tank sounding gauges, which give local and, often, remote readouts of liquid depths, are fitted to each cargo tank usually on to a 'pot' or cylindrical seat.

Heating coils are fitted in many tankers to improve the discharging of the oil. Steam is passed through coils fitted on the tank bottom to heat the cargo prior to discharge. Gases will be released during heating and the venting system must therefore be open.

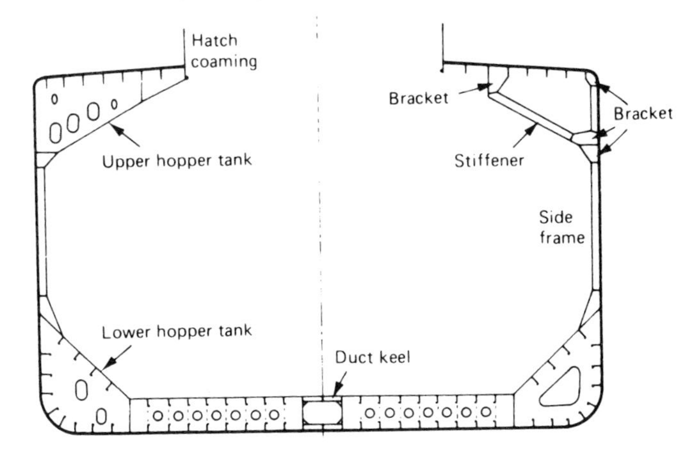

Figure 8.15 Bulk carrier transverse section

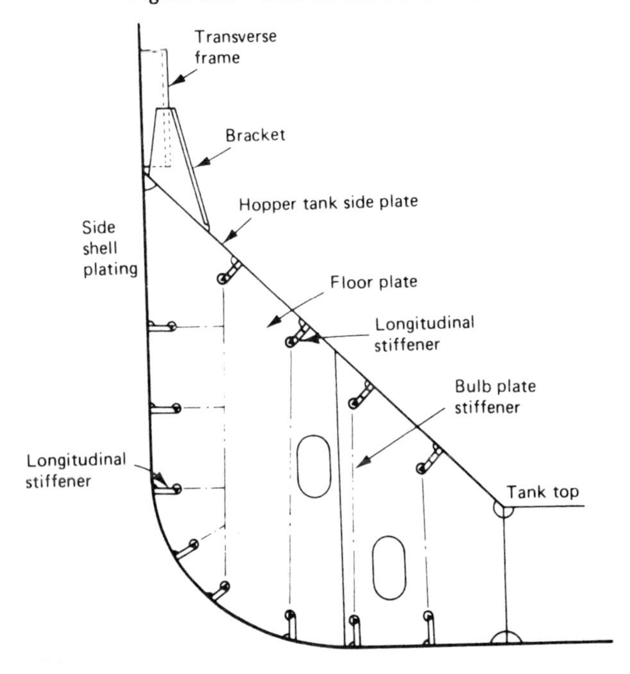

Figure 8.16 Solid floor arrangement in a lower hopper tank

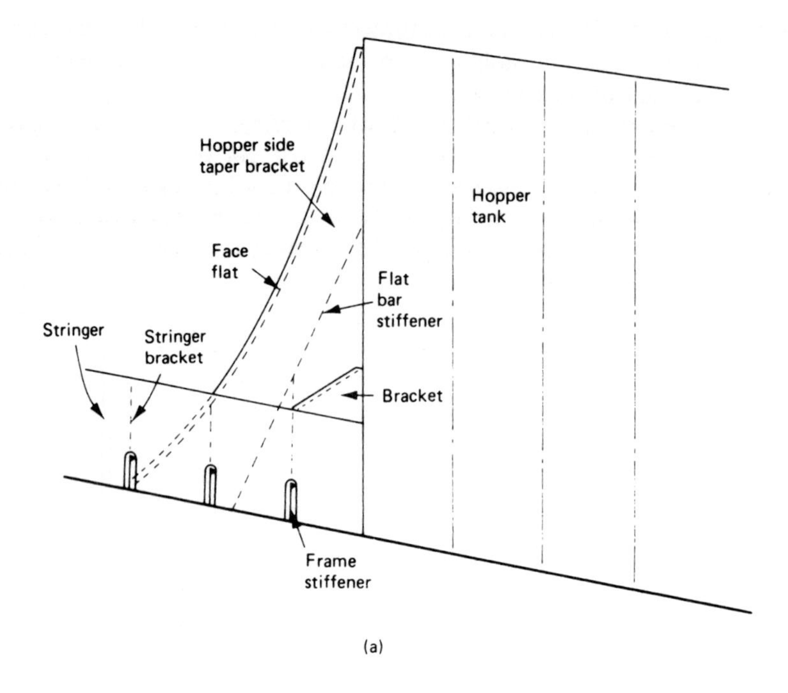

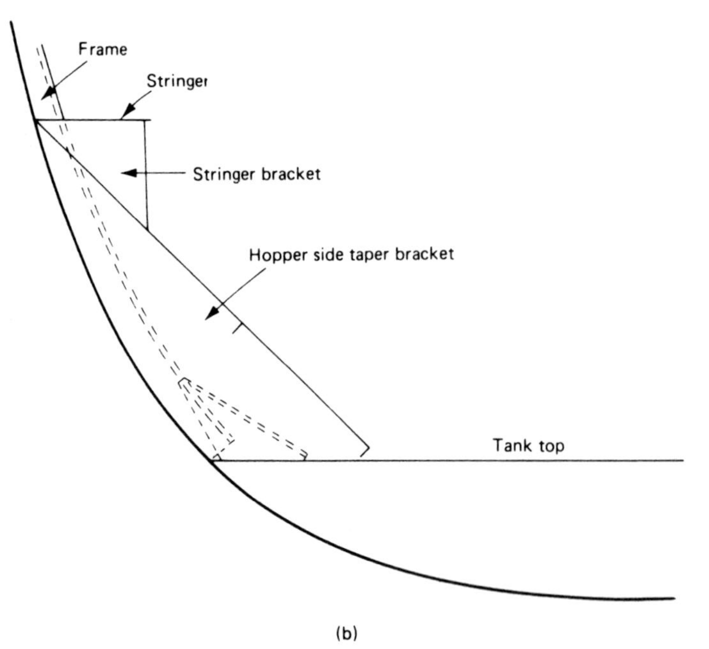

Figure 8.17 Tapering off of hopper tank at after end: (a) plan view on hopper tank end; (b) section on hopper tank end

Bulk carriers

The bulk carriage of single-commodity cargoes has been a continually advancing trend with the development of specialist types of ship to suit. The desire for flexibility of operation has also led to various designs to enable different bulk cargoes to be carried on different voyages. Such vessels have become known as combination bulk carriers; oil/bulk/ore (OBO) and oil/ore (OO) are examples.

Some particular aspects of bulk carrier construction will now be examined in detail. A transverse section through a general-purpose bulk carrier is shown in *Figure 8.15*. The cargo hold is seen to be shaped by the upper hopper or saddle tanks, the lower hopper tanks and the double bottom. A composite framing system is used in common with most bulk carriers. Transverse framing is employed in the machinery space, the side shell in way of the cargo tanks, the saddle tanks or upper hopper tanks, the main deck inside of the line of hatches, the forecastle deck and the fore and aft peak tanks. Longitudinal framing is employed at the bottom shell, the tank top and the upper deck outside of the line of hatches.

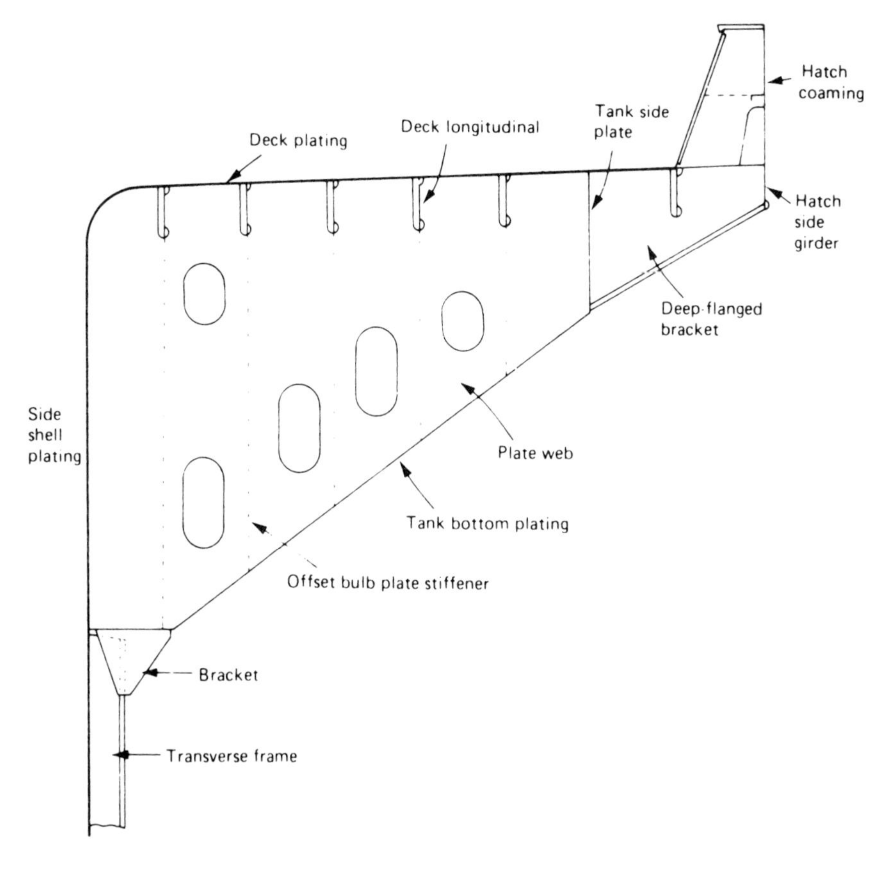

Figure 8.18 Section through upper hopper tank

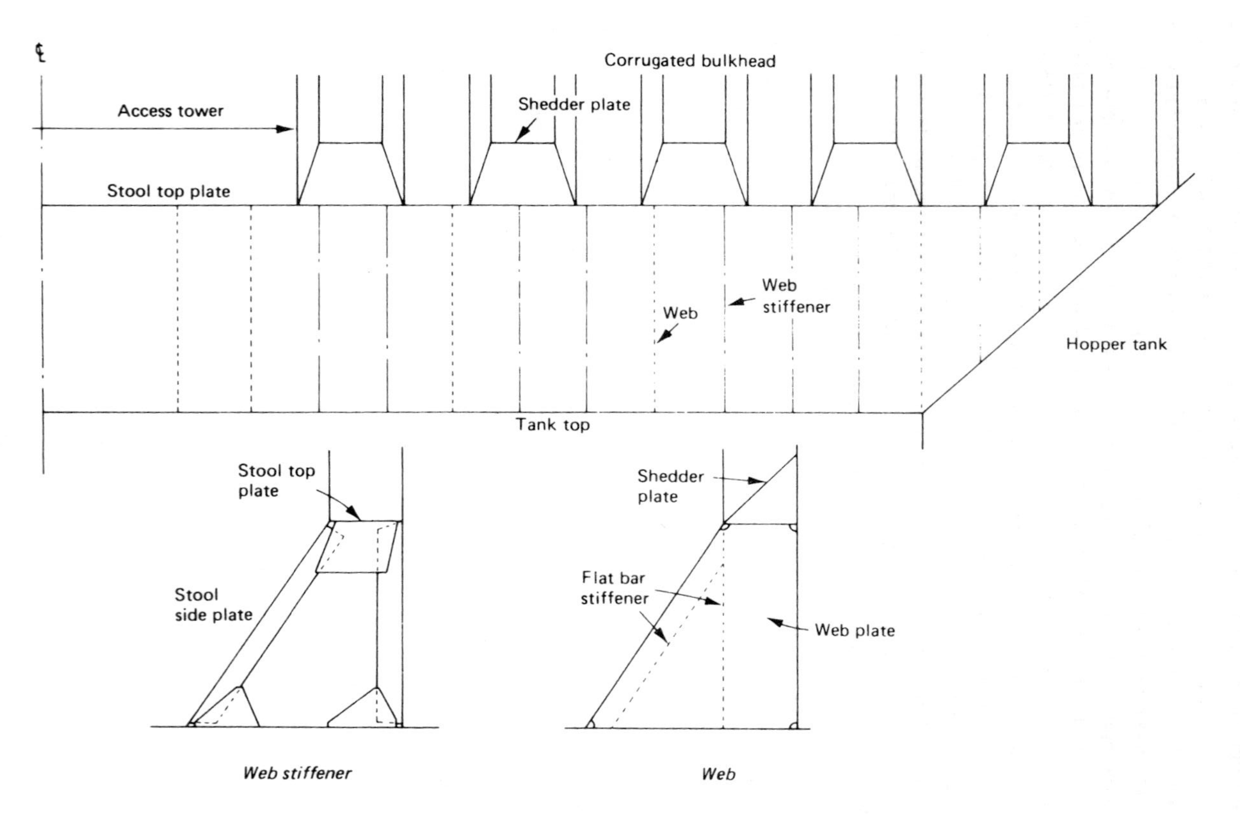

Figure 8.19 Stool arrangement below corrugated bulkhead

A section through a typical floor in a lower hopper is shown in *Figure 8.16*. The longitudinal framing structure can be clearly seen. Above the hopper tank can be seen the transversely framed hold with the bracket connecting the frame to the hopper tank. At the ends of the hopper tank region a considerable change in section occurs. The construction used to reduce the effect of this discontinuity is shown in *Figure 8.17*. A large tapered bracket is used which is connected to the surrounding transversely framed structure as shown.

A section through an upper hopper tank or saddle tank is shown in *Figure 8.18*. The longitudinal framing under the deck can be seen as well as the bracket connecting the upper edge of the transverse frame to the tank. The side shell portion of the tank is transversely framed by offset bulb plates with plate webs, as shown in *Figure 8.18*, fitted at every fourth frame. A deep-flanged bracket joins the inner tank side to the hatch side girder.

Details of a bulkhead stool are shown in *Figure 8.19*. With a corrugated transverse bulkhead as shown, the stool arrangement is used to shape the forward and after lower regions or the cargo hold. This flush tapering shape permits easy discharge of bulk cargoes and simplifies cargo hold cleaning. Shedder plates are fitted inside the troughs of the corrugated bulkhead for the same reason.

Container ships

The cargo holds of a container ship create large open spaces which are uninterrupted by any structure or framing. The rigidity of the structure must be provided by the bulkheads and transverse webs in-between the cargo holds. The regular box shape of the container results in any curved region of the ship being unsuitable for the stowage of containers. The ship structure outboard of the cargo hold is, therefore, used for water ballast tanks or access passages, in addition to providing longitudinal strength for the structure. The loss of cubic capacity in the regular shaped holds is, to a large extent, offset by the stacking of containers on the hatch covers and the deck. Suitable lashing arrangements are then necessary for the various tiers of containers. Pure container ships do not carry cranes but rely on the shoreside gantry cranes at container berths to discharge containers. Hatch covers may be of the hydraulically hinged type, although pontoon-type covers which are lifted on and off by the container terminal gantry cranes are sometimes used.

Framing

Container ships are longitudinally framed throughout all the continuous structural material. This consists of the wing tanks on either side of the cargo holds and the double bottom. A deep girder is fitted at the upper deck level and runs continuously through the cargo holds. Smaller box girders are located below the upper deck at the level of every second container.

To strengthen this open-box type structure, deep transverse webs are fitted at the ends of each of the cargo holds and the upper deck above the bulkheads, see

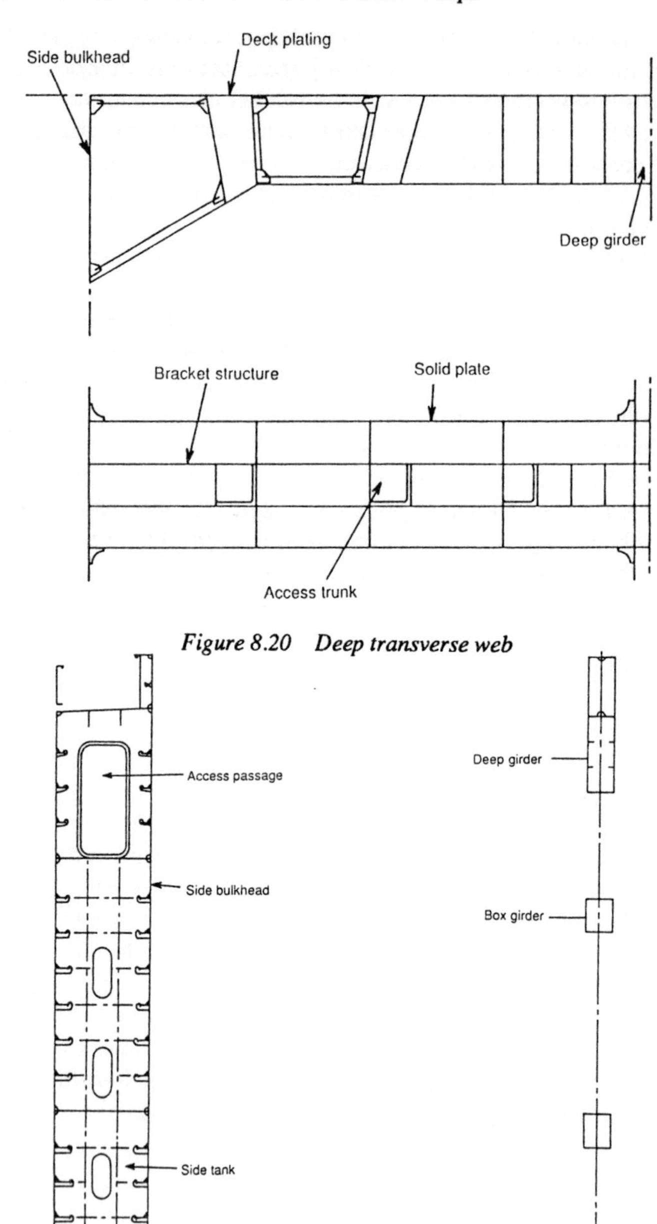

Figure 8.20 Deep transverse web

Figure 8.21 Cross-section through a hold

Figure 8.20. This rigid box structure will resist torsion and racking stresses acting on the ship and extends over four frames. The webs are of solid plate construction at each end with bracket structures in-between.

The fore and after ends of the ship are transversely framed with appropriate strengthening for panting and pounding.

Bottom structure

A double bottom exists along the full length of the ship and is longitudinally framed. Plate floors are fitted every fourth frame in the cargo hold and at every frame in the machinery space. In the pounding region forward, solid floors exist initially at alternate frames and then at every frame. The tank top plating is increased in thickness in the cargo hold and is suitably strengthened for the carriage of either 40 foot or 20 foot containers to the required height.

In the arrangement shown in *Figure 8.21*, an extra longitudinal stiffener is located on either side of the vertical keel plate for support during docking. Pipe tunnels are located port and starboard in the double bottom with access via watertight doors from the machinery space. The sides of the pipe tunnels are formed from watertight side girders. Intercostal side girders are fitted beneath the side bulkheads and outboard of the pipe tunnels.

Side bulkheads

Side bulkheads are used to create a box-like structure along the shell. The side tanks formed are used for the carriage of water ballast with the upper spaces port and starboard used as an access passage and a cable tunnel respectively. These side bulkheads are transversely stiffened with web frames in line with the plate floors. Continuous horizontal stiffeners are fitted to the side shell and the bulkheads and increase in scantlings as they progress to the bottom shell.

Bulkheads

Watertight bulkheads are fitted at the hold boundaries. They are vertically stiffened across their width and have deep horizontal stringers, (see *Figure 8.22*). The stringers also serve as inspection and access galleries and are two frames deep. Two additional deep webs are fitted on either side of the centreline. All stringers and webs are fitted with facing plates. The transverse deep girder is fitted between the upper deck and the top of the bulkhead.

Container guides and fittings

The cargo holds are fitted with vertical cell guides at the corner points of all containers. Angle bars of about 15 × 150 × 12 mm are used. These are supported at

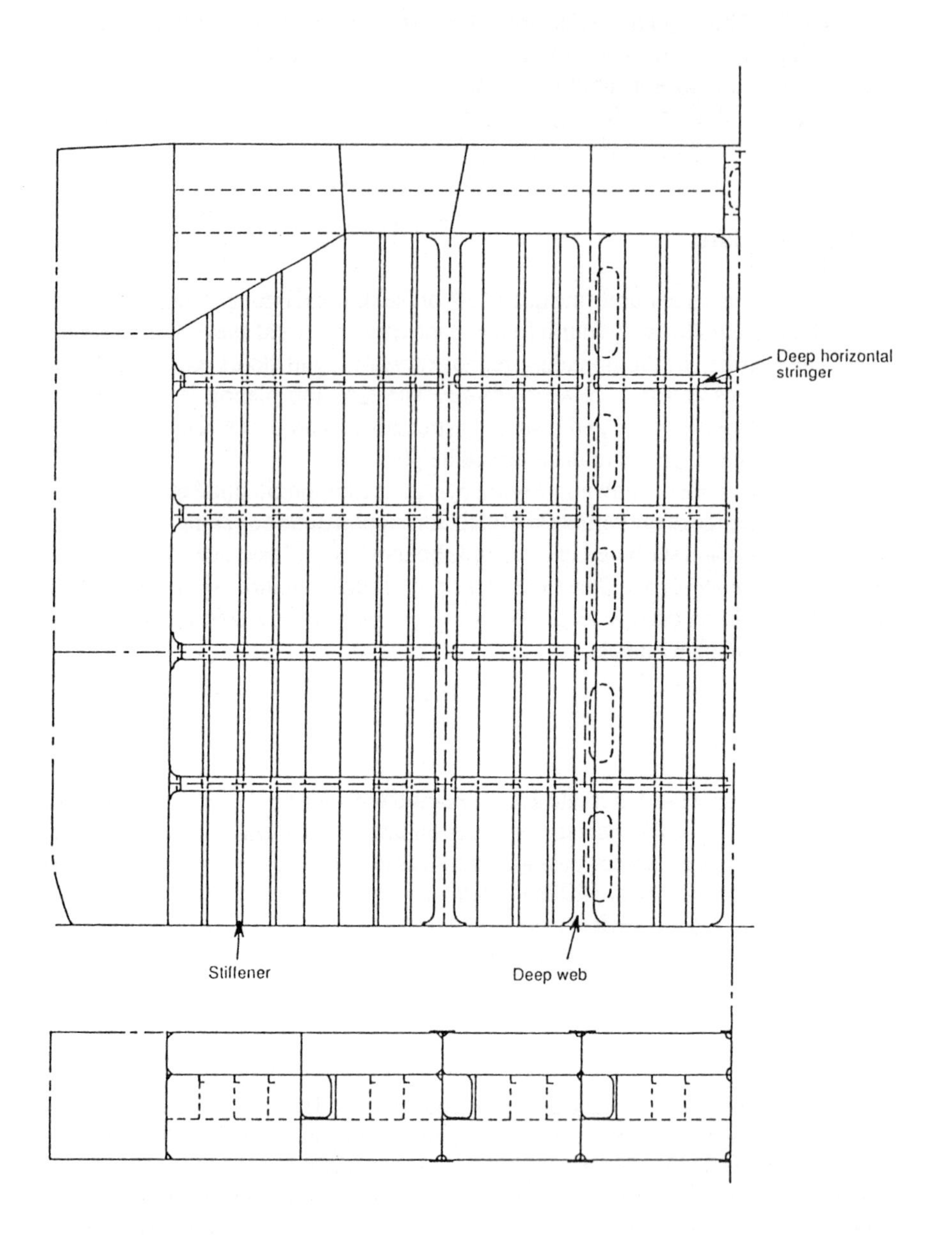

Figure 8.22 Watertight bulkhead

intervals by brackets welded to cross ties of channel bar section. The lower end of the guide is welded to a stool about 50 mm thick which is in turn welded to the tank top. The tops of the guides have entry arrangements which may be fixed or movable and serve to assist in aligning the container both fore and aft and athwartships. The guide system may be for 40 foot or 20 foot containers depending upon the owner's

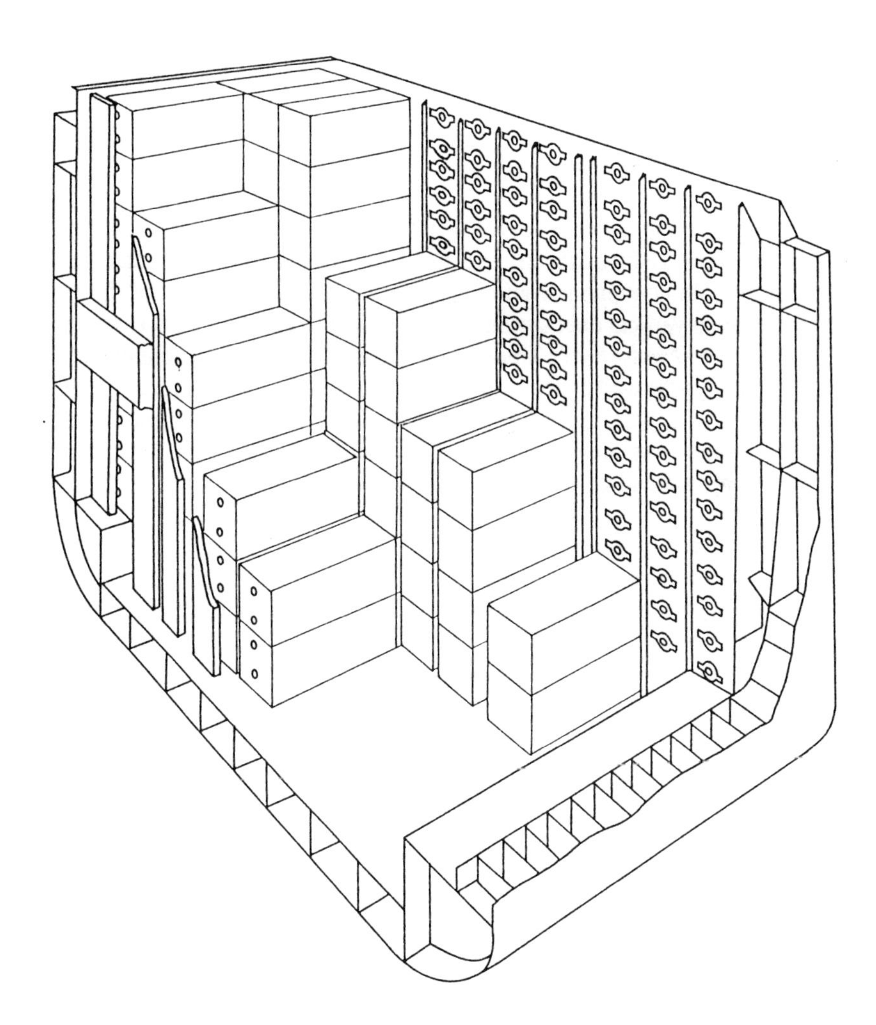

Figure 8.23 Vertical duct arrangement for refrigerated containers

requirements. Where guides are provided for 40 foot containers, temporary intermediate guides may be available for use with 20 foot containers.

Cell guides must be robustly constructed since they are designed to resist container loading and unloading loads, prevent container movement and to transmit any dynamic loading into the main hull structure.

Where containers are carried on deck the hatch covers must have provision for suitable locking fittings to secure the corners of the containers. Where containers overhang the hatch coamings they must be adequately supported at their corners by stanchions of suitable height and provided with locking arrangements. Where containers are stacked, the tiers must be connected by locking devices at adjacent corners and bridging pieces across the tops.

Lashing arrangements may also be required depending upon the loading calculations or particular company practice. The cell guide structure and all container securing devices will be subject to classification society rules and regular surveys.

Refrigerated containers

Vessels designed specifically for refrigerated container carrying may have built-in ducting systems. These can be in two forms; a horizontal finger duct system in which are fed up to 48 containers from one cooler situated in the wings of the ship or, alternatively, a vertical duct system in which each stack of containers has its own duct and cooler (*Figure 8.23*). This type of system is employed for containers having two port holes in the wall opposite the loading doors. Air is delivered into the bottom opening and, after passing through a plenum, rises through a floor grating over the cargo and returns via another section of the plenum to the top port. The connection between the duct and container is made by couplings which are pneumatically controlled.

Where only a small number of refrigerated containers are carried they will probably have refrigeration units integrally fitted which are operated by electricity. These containers are usually stowed on deck as air cooling of the refrigeration plant is required.

9

Liquefied Gas Carriers and Chemical Tankers

The bulk transport of liquefied gases requires the use of specialised vessels. Natural gas and petroleum gas each require different transport arrangements and hence the vessel types are particular to their cargo. Chemical tankers, on the other hand, may carry dangerous chemicals or liquids such as wine or vegetable oils. Special constructional arrangements are therefore necessary for this versatile type of bulk carrier.

Liquefied gas carriers

The past 25 years have seen the emergence of the bulk transport of natural gases both for use as fuel and as a refrigerant. Specialist ships are now used to carry the various types of gas in a variety of tank systems, combined with arrangements for pressurising or refrigerating the gas.

Natural gas is found and released as a result of oil-drilling operations. It is a mixture of such gases as methane, ethane, propane, butane and pentane. The heavier gases, propane and butane, are separated by liquefaction and are termed 'petroleum gases'. The properties and therefore the behaviour of these two basic groups vary considerably, thus requiring different means of containment and storage during transportation.

Natural gas is, by proportion, 75–95% methane and has a boiling point of –162°C at atmospheric pressure. Methane has a critical temperature of –82°C. The critical temperature is the temperature above which it cannot be liquefied by the application of pressure. A pressure of 47 bar is necessary to liquefy methane at –82°C. Thus, natural gas cannot be liquefied by pressure at normal temperatures. Liquid natural gas tankers are therefore designed to carry the gas in its liquid form at atmospheric pressure and a low service temperature in the region of –164°C. The problems encountered, therefore, deal with protecting the steel structure from the low temperatures, reducing the loss of gas and avoiding the leakage of gas into the occupied regions of the ship.

Petroleum gas consists of propane, propylene and butane or mixtures of these gases, all of which have critical temperatures above normal ambient temperatures. Thus they can be transported either as a liquid at low temperature and pressure or at normal temperature and under pressure. The design problems for this type of ship are similarly protecting the steel hull where low temperatures are employed, reducing gas loss and avoiding gas leakage, with the added consideration of pressurising the tanks.

Liquefied natural gas tankers

The tank types of LNG carriers are self-supporting and either prismatic, cylindrical or spherical in shape or a membrane construction which is supported by insulation. Materials used include aluminium, 90% nickel steel or membranes composed of stainless steel or nickel iron.

Tank designs are split into three categories, namely self-supporting or free standing, membrane and semi-membrane. The self-supporting tank is strong enough by virtue of its construction to accept any loads imposed by the cargo it carries. A membrane tank requires the insulation between the tank and the hull to be load bearing, such an arrangement being termed an integrated tank design. Single or double metallic membranes can be used, with insulation separating the two membrane skins. The semi-membrane or semi-integrated design is similar to the membrane, except that the tank has no support at its corners.

A double-hull type of construction is used with each of the above designs, the space between being used for water ballast. The basic configurations are shown in *Figure 9.1*.

Comparison of tank types

Membrane and prismatic tanks use the underdeck cubic capacity most effectively. Cylindrical and spherical tanks involve constructional problems by penetrating the upper deck but provide greater safety in the event of collision or grounding. Membrane tanks are cheaper to build but the insulation, which must be load bearing, is more expensive. The insulation of spherical tanks need not be load bearing since it is only a partial secondary barrier, if needed at all in this respect. The hull and machinery costs are about equal for each type. All the different types are in service, with the firmly established designs being prismatic, spherical and membrane types.

Boil-off

Liquefied natural gas is continually boiling in tanks when transported by sea. There is therefore a need to release this gas to avoid a pressure build-up in the tank. It may be vented directly to atmosphere or burnt in boilers or in specially adapted dual fuel engines. Burning the boil-off gas in a flare mounted on a boom remote from the ship is another possible solution. Re-liquefaction is not economical because of the large power and huge cost of the machinery necessary.

Liquefied petroleum gas tankers

Three basic types of liquefied petroleum gas tankers are currently used—the fully

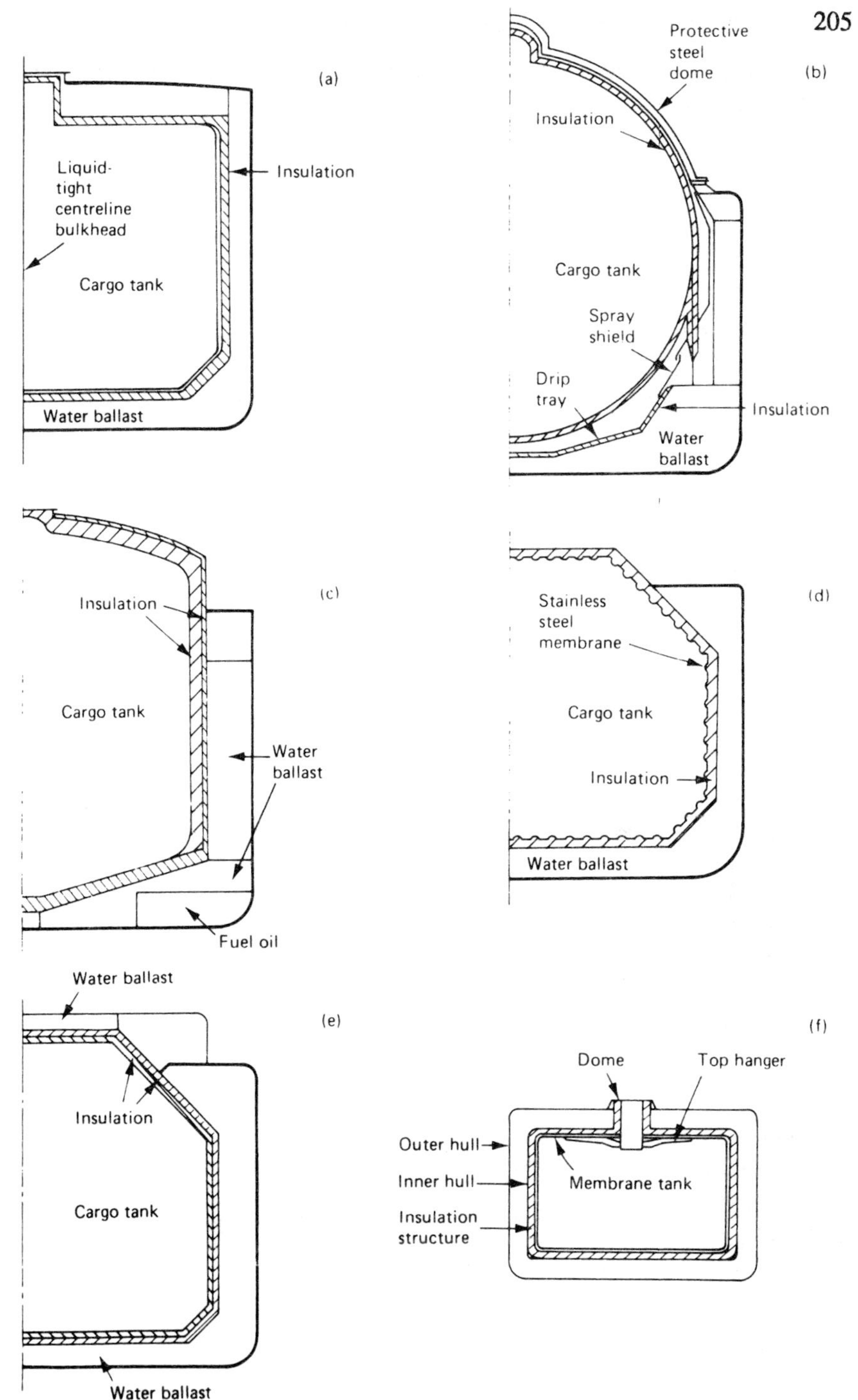

Figure 9.1 Tank arrangements for liquefied natural gas: (a) prismatic tank; (b) spherical tanks; (c) cylindrical tank; (d) membrane tank; (e) double-membrane tank; (f) semi-membrane tank

pressurised tank, the semi-pressurised partially refrigerated tank, and the fully refrigerated atmospheric pressure tank.

The fully pressurised tank operates at about 17.5–18.0 bar and requires heavy, expensive tanks of carbon steel which are usually cylindrical in shape. This high pressure is equivalent to the vapour pressure of the cargo at the highest possible ambient temperature, usually taken as 45°C. The tank domes penetrate the upper deck and have fitted all the necessary connections for loading, discharging, sampling, etc.

Semi-pressurised tanks operate at about 8 bar and a temperature of about –7°C must be maintained in the tanks. Insulation is therefore required around the tank and, since some cargo will boil off, a re-liquefaction plant is needed. Horizontal cylindrical tank configurations are again used. Low temperature steels for temperatures down to around –45°C must be used for the tanks.

Fully refrigerated atmospheric pressure tank systems have service temperatures about –50°C and maximum working pressures of 0.28 bar. The tanks are insulated, self-supporting and prismatic in shape. The tank material must be ductile at low temperatures and is usually a fine-grain heat-treated steel such as Arctic D or a low alloy nickel steel. A secondary barrier capable of retaining the cargo in the event of main tank fracture is required by classification society rules. Three tank types are used with fully refrigerated LPG ships:

(1) A central trunk runs along the top for the length of the cargo tank. Wing ballast tanks are fitted, their inner surface acting as the secondary barrier (*Figure 9.2*).
(2) A large dome is situated aft at the top of the tank and wing ballast tanks are fitted (*Figure 9.3*). The inner surface of the wing tanks acts as the secondary barrier.
(3) A large dome is situated aft at the top of the tank but no wing ballast tanks are fitted (*Figure 9.4*). Hopper tanks are used for ballast when necessary. The hull itself acts as the secondary barrier and must be of low temperature carbon steel in way of the cargo tanks.

Comparison of tank types

The reduction in weight of tank material in a semi-pressurised tank design is offset by the need for refrigerating plant and insulation around the tank. The use of low pressure tanks does, however, permit better utilisation of the underdeck cubic capacity of the vessel. The fully pressurised tank has no need of insulation nor a secondary barrier.

Construction aspects of LNG and LPG carriers

The various regulatory bodies have rules for the construction and classification of ships carrying liquid gases in bulk. These rules follow closely the IMO code for this type of vessel.

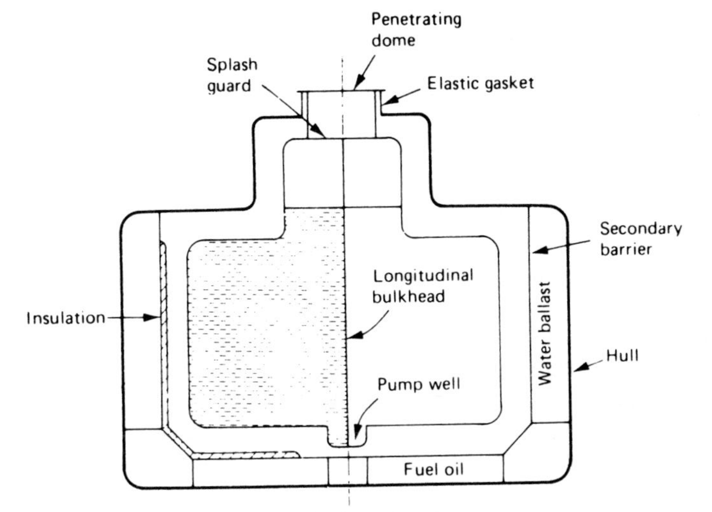

Figure 9.2 Cylindrical trunk tank arrangement

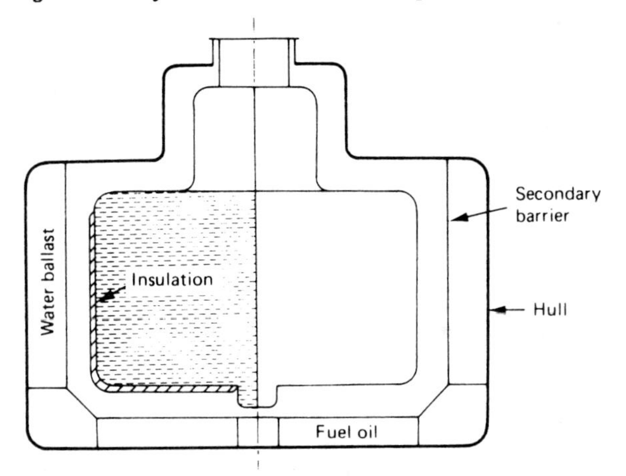

Figure 9.3 Aft dome tank arrangement

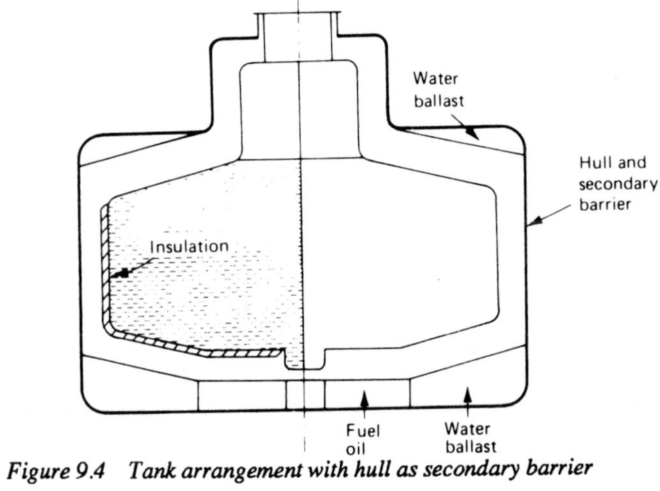

Figure 9.4 Tank arrangement with hull as secondary barrier

A complete or partial secondary barrier is required in all but pressure vessels operating at ambient temperatures down to –10°C. This secondary barrier is a liquid-resisting outer skin which will temporarily contain any leakage of the liquid cargo from the primary barrier or tank. The secondary barrier should also prevent the structure temperature from dropping and should not fail under the same circumstances as the primary barrier.

Bulkheads or cofferdam arrangements are necessary between cargo tanks, depending upon the temperature of the cargo carried.

Cargo-pumping pipework systems must have no interconnection with other systems. Where a cargo tank has no secondary barrier a suitable drainage system must be provided which does not enter the machinery space. Where secondary barriers are used drainage must be provided to deal with any leakage, again from outside the machinery space.

Special ship survival arrangements are required which limit the width of tanks in relation to the ship's breadth. Double-bottom tank heights are also stipulated.

Arrangements of tank design or internal bulkheads where possible must be used to restrict cargo movement and the subsequent dynamic loading of structure. Membrane tanks, for instance, cannot have internal bulkheads and are tapered off in section towards the top.

Materials of construction and those used in piping systems are dealt with in considerable detail in the rules.

Chemical tankers

The hazardous nature of many, but not all, of the cargoes carried in chemical tankers has resulted in various rules and regulations relating to tanker construction in order to safeguard both the ships and the environment.

The International Maritime Organisation (IMO) has produced a 'Code for the Construction and Equipment of Ships carrying Dangerous Chemicals in Bulk'. This code provides a basis for all such vessel designs and an IMO Certificate of Fitness must be obtained from the flag state administration to indicate compliance. Also, Annex II of the Marpol 73/78 Convention and Protocol is now in force and applies to hazardous liquid substances carried in chemical tankers.

IMO ship types

The IMO Code sets out three ship types—I, II and III, which correspond to different classes of hazardous chemicals and the suitable location of the vessel's tanks. The length *L* and breadth *B* are defined in the International Convention on Load Lines 1966 and the configurations are given in *Figure 9.5*. Damage considerations following collision, stranding and minor ship side damage and also survival assumptions were the criteria considered in producing the tank configurations. Ship type I is designed to provide maximum preventive measures with respect to the escape of it's cargo under the assumed conditions. Ship type II requires significant preventive

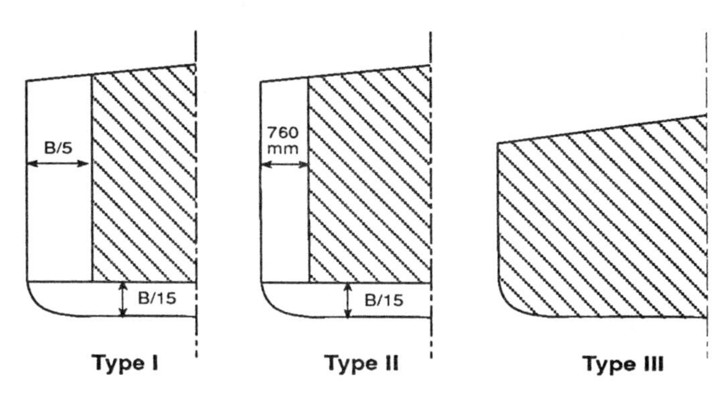

Figure 9.5 Chemical tankers IMO ship types

measures. Ship type III is for products of a sufficient hazard to require a moderate degree of containment.

Ship structure

The number of tanks, their volume and layout, will further be determined by the required frame spacing in the cargo space. The tanks must be designed to withstand the dynamic forces within partially filled tanks and also the high specific gravity of some cargoes.

The bottom structure may be either single or double bottom throughout or a double bottom beneath the centre tanks and a single bottom beneath the wing tanks. The choice will be influenced by the fact that IMO types I and II must have a double bottom and double bottom ballast tank capacity is needed for trimming and heeling.

Bulkheads may be either horizontally or vertically corrugated or plane with stiffeners on the outside of the tank to facilitate tank cleaning. Sandwich or double skin bulkheads have also been used to provide easily cleaned tank surfaces in both wing and centre tanks.

The hull structure may be single or double skin. IMO Type II cargoes require a double hull and cargoes requiring heating or cooling can benefit from the insulating effect of a double skin.

Deck structure can be conventional with stiffeners in the tank space or may use a double skin or cofferdam in order to provide plane surfaces within the tanks. Single decks with stiffeners outside the tank space have been used.

Cargo handling

The large numbers of tanks and the need to avoid contamination between different chemicals usually results in the use of deepwell pumps in each tank. The pump may also be used as the filling line for the tank.

Tank ventilation may use open or closed vent piping depending upon the type of cargo. The height of the main vent may be as low as 4 metres for less toxic and as high as B/3 for highly toxic cargoes. Pressure/vacuum valves are used to guard against overpressure in the tanks.

Heating coils may be provided in some or all of the tanks. Steam, heating oil or warm water can be used as the heating medium. Tank cleaning systems are also required and must include a slop tank system to comply with Marpol 73/78.

Tank coatings

Protection of the structural components is important and various types of coating are used in the cargo tanks. Tanks may be constructed of mild steel, clad steel or stainless steel. The choice of paint or other coating will depend upon the various cargoes to be carried and compatibility is essential. The main types of coatings used are epoxy, phenolics, zinc silicate and polyurethane. Rubber coatings are used in tanks carrying liquids such as hydrochloric acid.

10

Ventilation

An ocean-going ship is required to operate in a variety of very different climates. Air temperatures may range from –15°C to 50°C and sea water temperatures from 0°C to 38°C. The moisture content of the air will vary considerably and solar radiation may affect one or more of the ship's exposed surfaces. All the various forms of good and bad weather will also be experienced. The air from the air-conditioning and ventilation plants is therefore required to provide an acceptable climate for the crew to live and work in, sufficient air for machinery use and to maintain temperature and humidity at acceptable levels to the cargo. All this must be achieved regardless of the conditions prevailing external to the ship. The design of suitable systems will therefore require information about the ship's trade routes, types of cargo and machinery installation.

Accommodation

Most ship's air-conditioning systems employ centrally situated units. These units are self-contained and supply the cabins and spaces within a particular area via trunking. The control possible in individual cabins or spaces depends upon the nature and complexity of the central unit. Three basic systems are in use—the single duct, the twin duct and the twin duct with reheat. In each case the central unit will supply warm or cool air, or clean, humidify or dehumidify the air supplied to the cabins.

The single duct system

In the single duct system the central unit mixes outside air with some returned or recycled air. This air is then filtered, heated and perhaps humidified or cooled. This conditioned air is then distributed along a single duct to the individual supply units in the different spaces. The amount of supply air can be controlled within the particular cabin or space. *Figure 10.1* shows the arrangement of the single duct system.

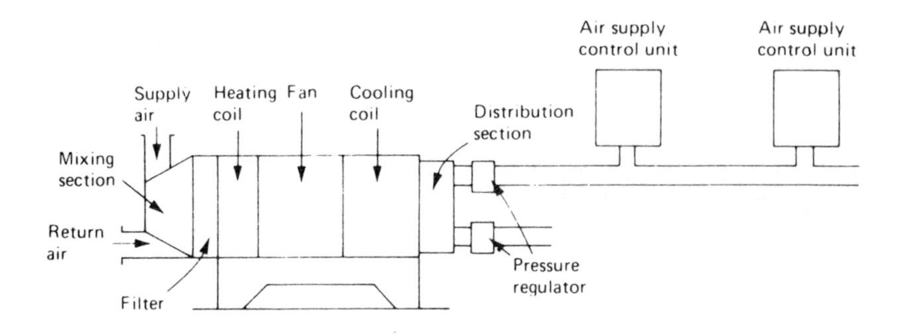

Figure 10.1 The single duct system

The twin duct system

Again, outside and returned air are mixed in the central units then filtered, preheated and perhaps humidified. Some of the air leaves the unit before it reaches the cooler, to be reheated; the amount is increased as the outside temperature falls. The remainder of the air passes over the cooling coil. The two air supplies at different conditions are passed through separate ducts to controlled mixing units in the individual spaces. The air temperature and condition can then be selected for the particular space. *Figure 10.2* shows the arrangement of the twin duct system.

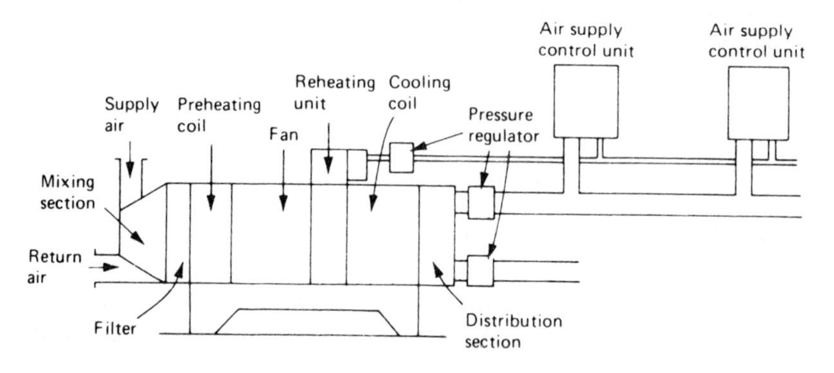

Figure 10.2 The twin duct system

The single duct with reheat system

The central unit mixes outside and return air, filters, preheats and humidifies or cools the air to the lowest required temperature of any part of the system. The air then passes along one duct to individual units in the spaces. Within these units is a controlled heater over which the air passes. Heating may be achieved by circulating hot water or an electric heater. The air supply and its temperature may therefore be regulated. *Figure 10.3* shows the arrangement of the single duct with reheat system.

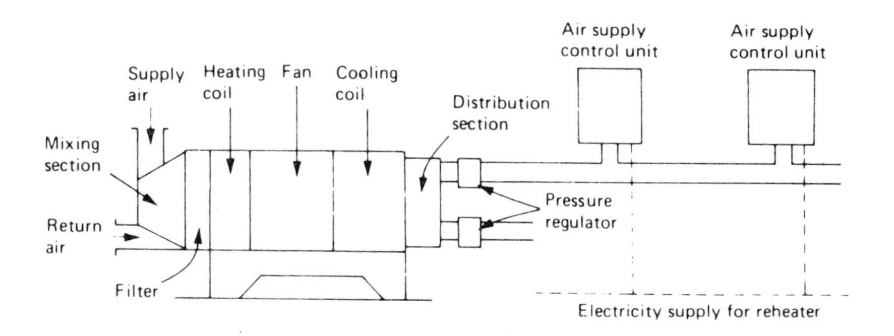

Figure 10.3 The single duct with reheat system

Cargo spaces

The primary function of ships is to transport goods from place to place. The cargo must be delivered in good condition and, in addition to careful loading and discharge, the storage and ventilation must be suitable and satisfactory. Inadequate, poor quality air supplied can seriously damage most cargoes. Fairly simple systems of cargo ventilation and attendant procedures can prevent such damage. Different cargoes react to the climate on board in as complex a manner as the human body, with often irreparable damage as the result.

Certain general cargoes, some fruit and vegetable cargoes and hygroscopic (water-absorbing or emitting) cargoes are carried in non-insulated holds. As a result they are exposed to all climatic changes which may cause condensation on the hull or cargo. Ventilation of the holds in which they are carried is therefore necessary. Refrigerated and frozen cargoes are carried in insulated holds but because of the living, gas-producing nature of the cargo they also require ventilation.

Ventilation of non-insulated cargo holds

The purpose of ventilation in non-insulated holds is to remove surplus heat and humidity, to prevent the condensing of moisture on cargo or hull and to remove gases produced in the ripening process of some fruit and vegetable cargoes. Natural and mechanical ventilation systems are used for this purpose.

Natural ventilation is accomplished by inlet and outlet pipes and trunking to each cargo space. These inlets and outlets consist of cowls or ventilators of various designs. Air is forced in by the action of the wind or drawn in as a result of an ejector type of exhaust drawing air out which is then replaced. Where the force of the wind is utilised the cowls must be manually positioned, and are large cumbersome fittings which must be well stayed to the deck. *Figure 10.4* shows a natural ventilation arrangement for a tween deck or workshop. Most modern ships utilise mechanical ventilation for reliability, improved performance and the reduced size of cowls necessary.

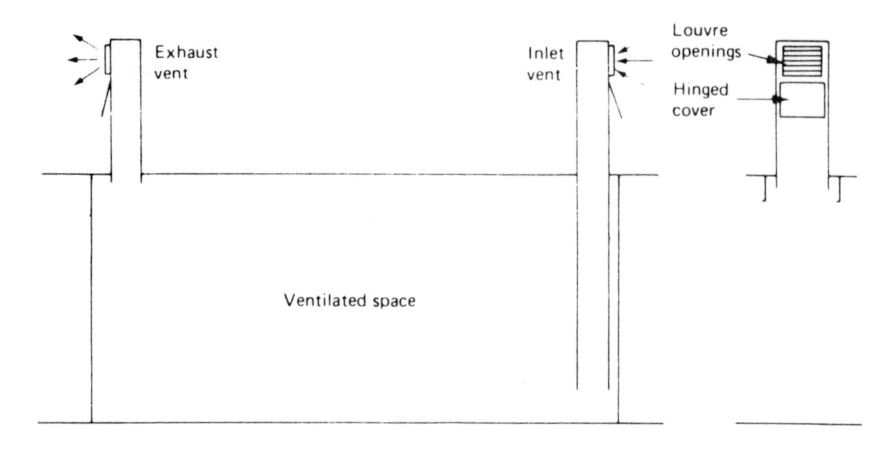

Figure 10.4 Natural ventilation of tween-deck space or workshop

Mechanical ventilation operates in two distinct systems—the open and the closed.

The open system uses axial flow fans fitting in the inlet and exhaust trunks. The trunks may have separate cowls or be incorporated into samson posts or masts. The air is supplied along trunking and ducts to the bottom of the hold.

The air is drawn from the top of the hold just below the decks. The exhaust fans can be reversed if condensation is likely near the deckheads, for example with a low

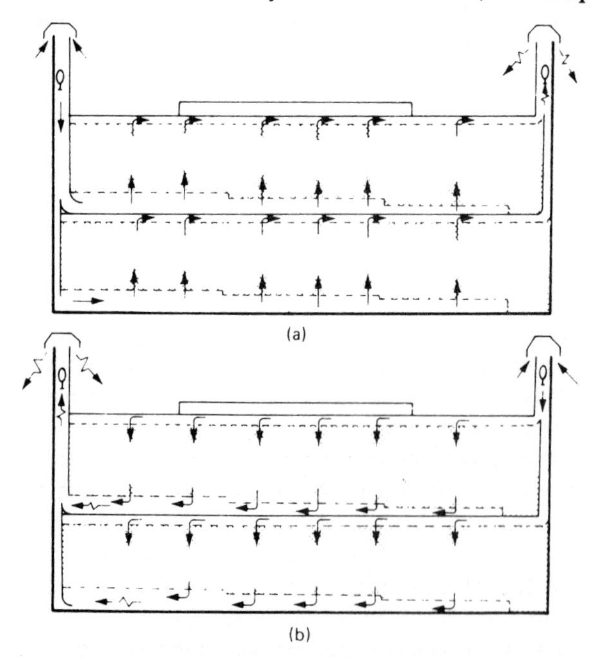

Figure 10.5 Open ventilation system: (a) normal circulation; (b) reversed circulation—to prevent underdeck circulation at low outside temperature

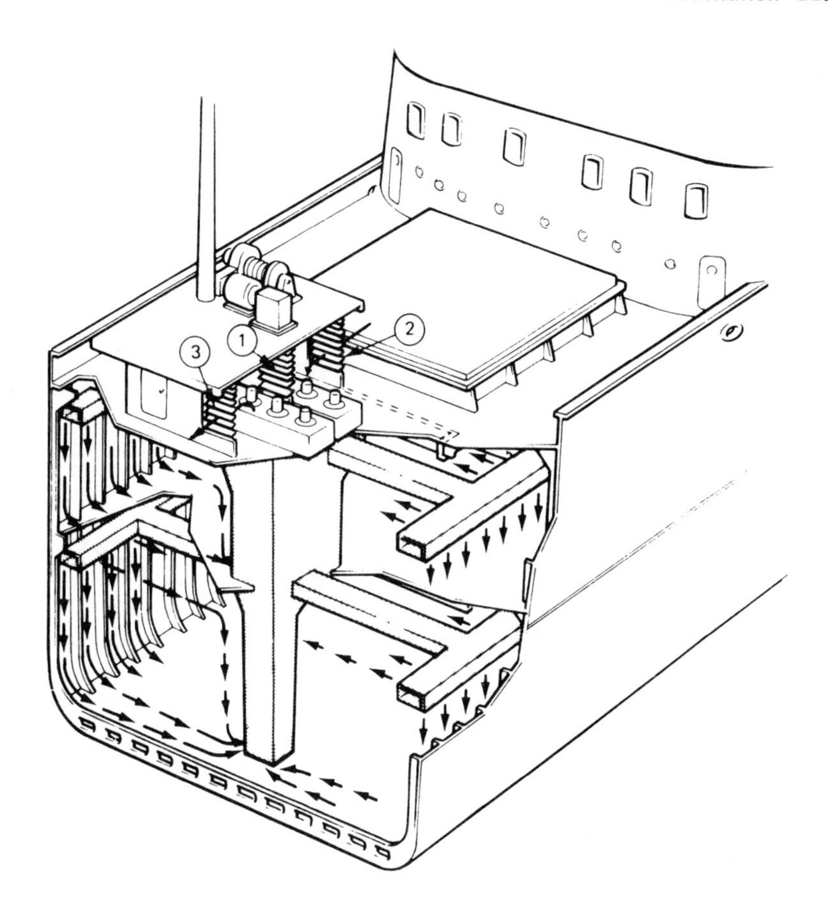

Figure 10.6 Closed ventilation system (1, recirculating damper; 2, inlet air damper; 3, exhaust air damper)

outside air temperature. *Figure 10.5* shows the arrangement of the open mechanical ventilation system.

The closed system recirculates air and a controlled amount of fresh air can be admitted. The ventilating air is distributed around the hold and cargo, forming an insulating wall or curtain between the two. Exhaust air is drawn from the bottom of the hold. This system affords every possible mode of control and is widely used in somewhat varied forms. *Figure 10.6* shows the closed ventilation system.

Ventilation of refrigerated cargo holds

Refrigerated cargo holds require a carefully controlled air-replacing system for each individual space. Cooled air is supplied to the refrigerated hold where it gains heat from ripening cargoes and entrains the gases produced. This air is then exhausted and a careful balance must be maintained between inlet and exhaust gas quantities, regardless of the outside climatic conditions.

One system achieves this by drawing outside air down to a bank of cooler tubes via a central unit. The dehumidified air then passes into the cargo holds. The exhaust gases are drawn from the hold through ducts back to the central unit and then returned to the outside atmosphere. The linking of inlet and outlet valves ensures a constant air supply at all times to the hold. *Figure 10.7* shows the arrangement of such a system.

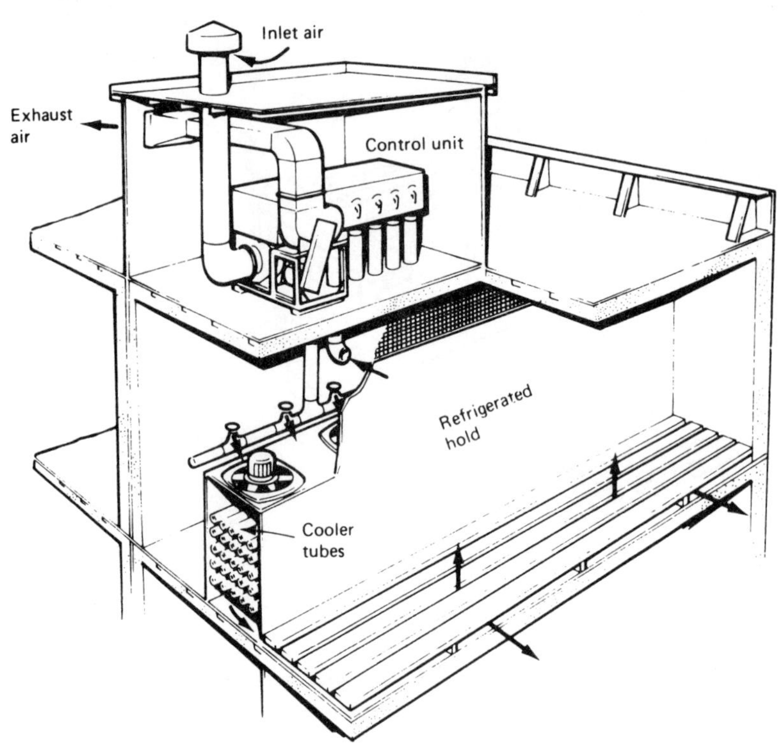

Figure 10.7 Balanced air renewal system for refrigerated cargo spaces

Particular types of ship have their associated cargo ventilation problems, e.g. 'roll-on, roll-off' ships, and the vehicle exhaust fumes during loading and discharging. Bulk carriers usually only require natural ventilation. The particular problems for each ship type must be considered early on at the design stage to ensure a suitable system is provided.

Machinery spaces

The machinery space requires an air supply for the operation of boilers, combustion engines, compressors, etc., and to maintain a satisfactory climate for the operating staff to work in.

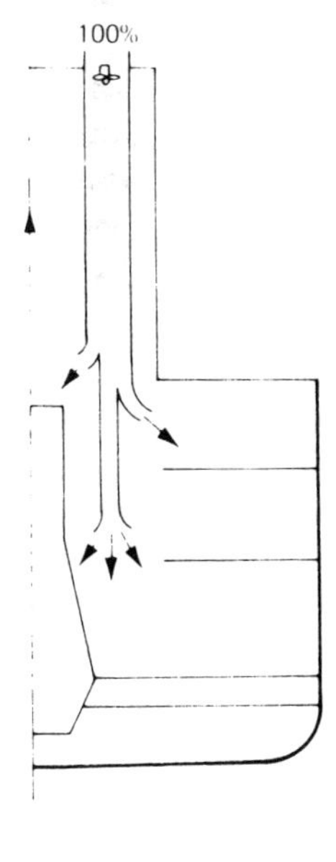

Figure 10.8 (left) *Machinery space ventilation using medium pressure axial flow fan*

Figure 10.9 (bottom left) *Machinery space ventilation using low pressure axial flow fan and high pressure centrifugal fan*

Figure 10.10 (bottom right) *Machinery space ventilation using medium pressure axial flow fans and a through trunking system*

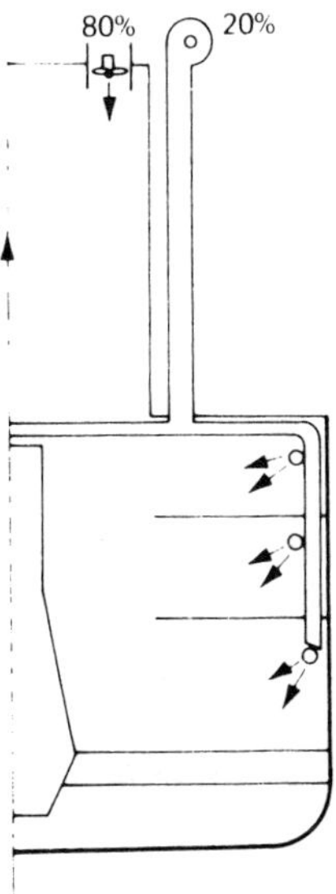

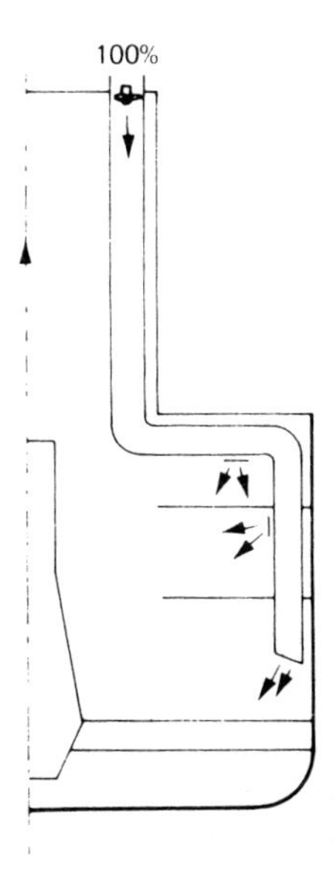

Certain machinery consumes or requires air for its operation and sufficient air at as low a temperature as practically possible should be provided. Underpressure occurring in the machinery space will affect the efficiency and performance of internal combustion engines. Overpressure may lead to leakage of hot air into the accommodation. Ventilation is also necessary to remove the heat generated within the machinery space and thus provide a reasonable climate for staff to work in. This very difficult task is achieved by the provision of ducted supplies of filtered but uncooled air to as many regions as possible. Particular areas such as workshops and control rooms, being small, may be air conditioned and more readily provided with an acceptable working climate.

Various systems of air supply to the machinery spaces and casing are in use and are shown in *Figures 10.8—10.10.*

Figure 10.8 utilises a medium pressure axial flow fan supplying air down a trunking, which is proportionally released at the various platform levels and exhausts through the top of the casing. *Figure 10.9* uses a low pressure axial flow fan to supply air into the casing area. Also, a high pressure centrifugal fan provides air through ducts to outlets at the various platforms. *Figure 10.10* uses medium pressure axial flow fans to provide a through trunking system to the various outlets at the various platforms. This method has proved to be the best. A diagrammatic arrangement of medium pressure axial flow fans and trunking in a machinery space is shown in *Figure 10.11*.

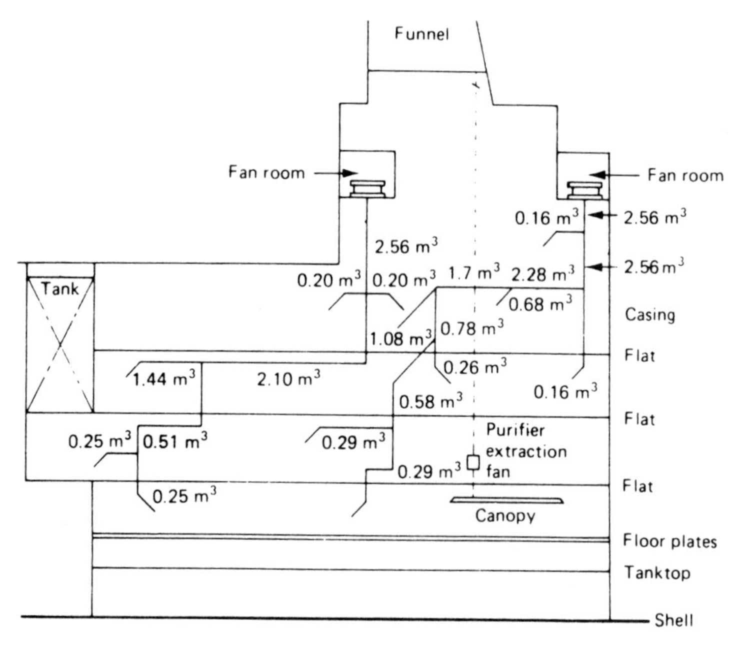

Figure 10.11 Machinery space ventilation—diagrammatic arrangement

Control rooms

The provision of control rooms in most modern machinery spaces ensures close careful control of the climate in such spaces, often with the provision of air conditioning in addition to ventilation. This climate control provides the personnel with a comfortable working area isolated from the main machinery space. Also, delicate equipment in need of careful climatic control is able to receive it. The satisfactory operation and continuous performance of modern control equipment requires a carefully controlled environment which, by using a control room, can be achieved.

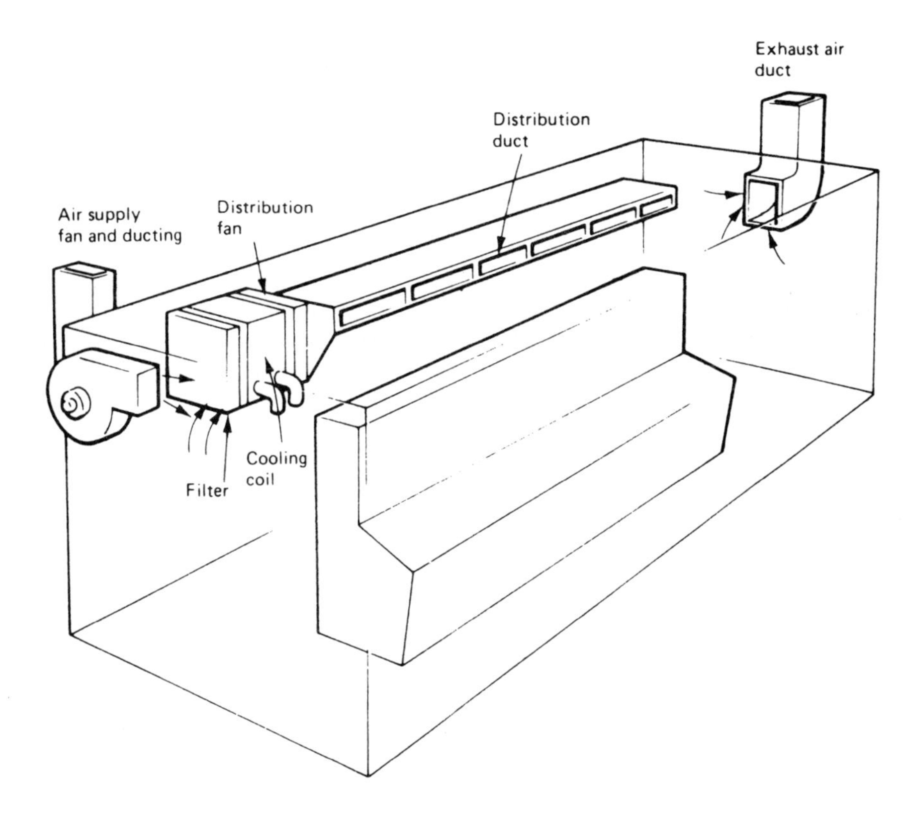

Figure 10.12 Control room ventilation

A separate ducted supply is led into the control room and, usually, through a filtering air-conditioning plant or unit which is set to function automatically with controls located in the control room. A matched exhaust will remove stale warm air from the control room. *Figure 10.12* shows such an arrangement.

Pumprooms

Tanker pumprooms require ventilation to carry away poisonous cargo fumes resulting from leaking glands or pipe joints. The working climate in this space well below deck level must also be comfortable for any personnel present. Mechanical exhausting of air is achieved by the use of axial flow fans and trunking. The trunking draws from the pumproom floor and emergency intakes at a height of 2.15 m from the working platform. These emergency intakes must be fitted with dampers which can be opened or closed from the weather deck or the working platform. The fan motors are located in the machinery space and drive the fans through gastight seals in the bulkhead. Supply is through cowls or louvres at the top of the pumproom. An arrangement is shown in *Figure 10.13*.

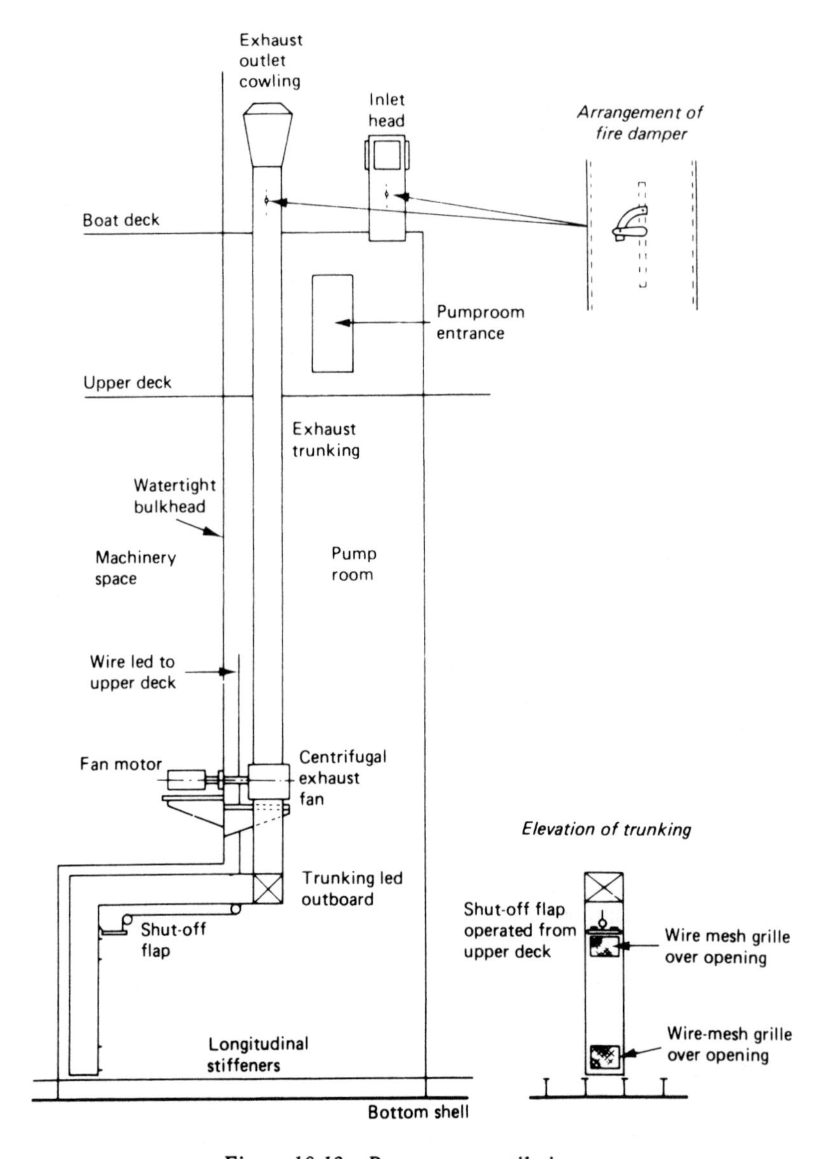

Figure 10.13 Pumproom ventilation

Double-bottom tanks

Ventilation of double-bottom tanks is provided by means of an air pipe situated remote from the filling pipe and usually at the highest point in the tank to avoid unventilated pockets. The air pipe, is led up to the weather deck to a gooseneck or patent type of head. Air pipes from fuel tanks are positioned in low risk areas and have flame screen gauzes fitted (*Figure 10.14*).

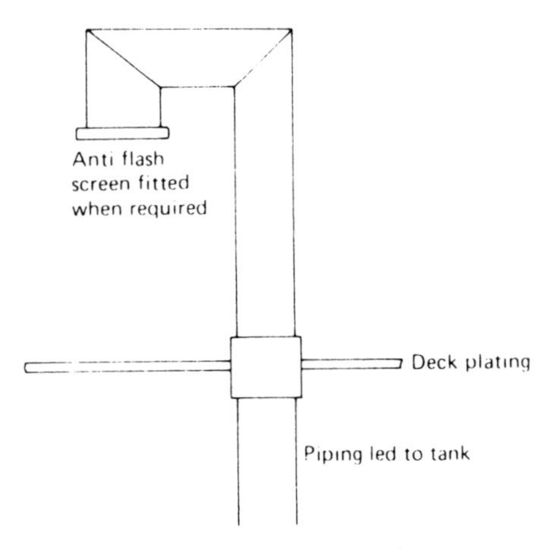

Figure 10.14 Air pipe head

Cargo tanks

Ventilation of cargo tanks avoids overpressure or partial pressure conditions which could occur during loading and unloading of cargo. Temperature fluctuations during a voyage could have a similar effect. Vapour pipelines from the cargo hatch are led to pressure/vacuum relief valves which are usually mounted on a standpipe some distance above the deck. Individual vent lines are fitted for each tank on large

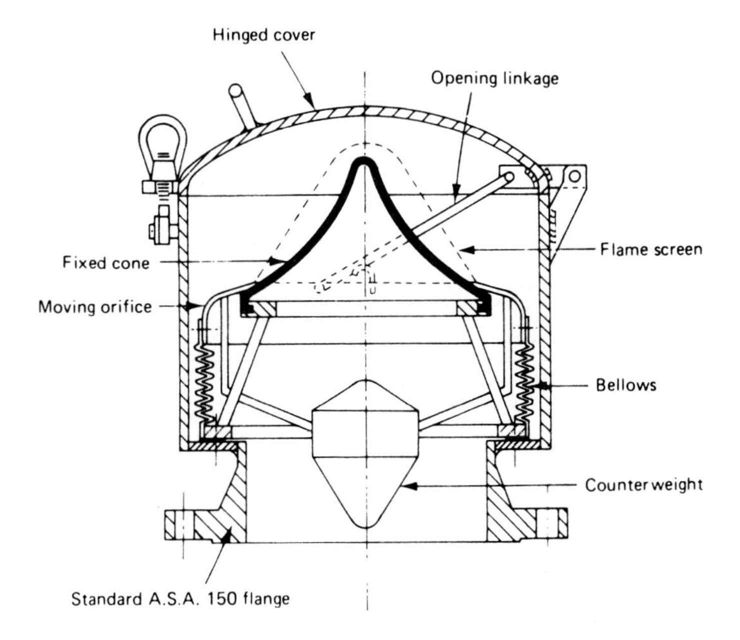

Figure 10.15 High velocity gas venting valve

tankers and a common venting line is led up a mast or samson post on smaller vessels.

During loading and discharging of the cargo the ventilation requirements are considerable. Air must be drawn in or removed in quantities equivalent to the cargo oil discharged or loaded. In addition, during the loading operation the hydrocarbon vapours issuing from the tank must be dispersed well above the deck. This is achieved by the use of high velocity gas venting valves. One type is shown in

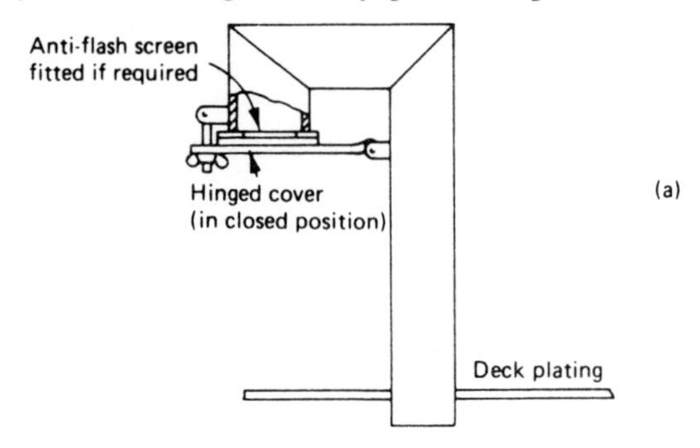

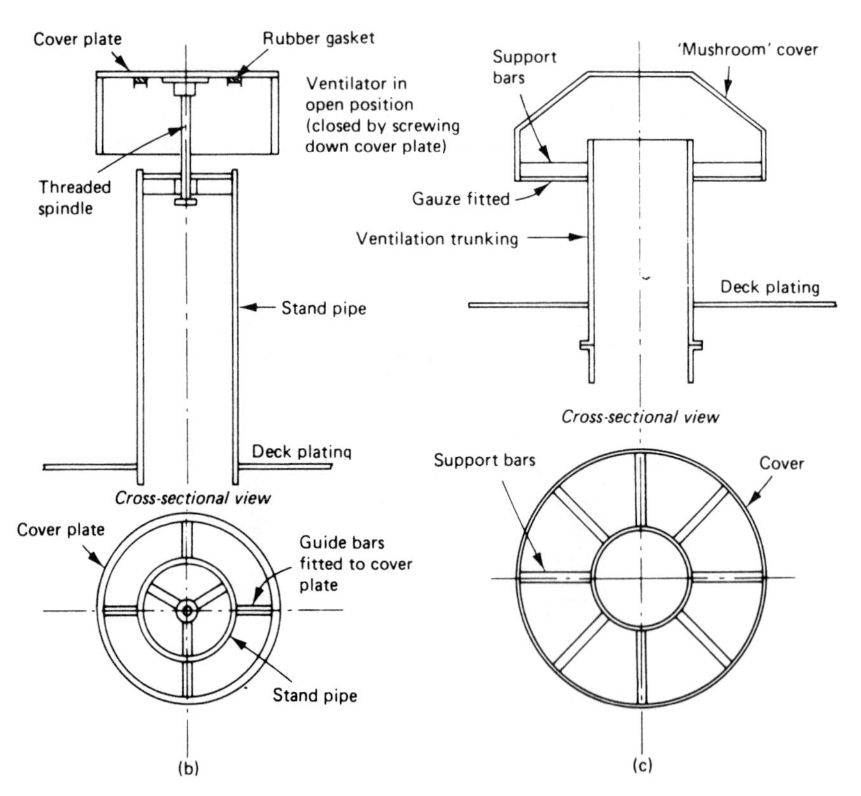

Figure 10.16 Ventilator heads: (a) gooseneck type; (b) mushroom type; (c) fixed mushroom type

Figure 10.15. The arrangement consists of a fixed cone around which is a movable orifice plate. A counterweight holds the orifice plate closed until sufficient gas pressure builds up to lift the plate. The gas is throttled through the orifice and issues at high velocity, dispersing into the atmosphere well above the deck. During discharge the cover is opened and a linkage from the cover holds the orifice plate in the fully open position.

Types of ventilator head

Various different types and arrangements of ventilator head are in use. *Figure 10.16* shows a selection of the more common designs.

11

Organisations and Regulations

The construction of merchant ships is considerably influenced and regulated by a number of organisations and their various requirements.

Classification societies, with their rules and regulations relating to classification, provide a set of standards for sound merchant ship construction which have developed over many years. These rules are based on experience, practical knowledge and considerable research and investigation.

A vast amount of legislation is applied to ships and is usually administered by the appropriate government department. The load line rules and tonnage measurement are two particular legislative requirements that are outlined in this chapter.

The International Maritime Organisation (IMO) is an international organisation which is attempting to develop high standards in every aspect of ship construction and operation. It is intended ultimately to apply these standards internationally to every ship at sea.

Classification societies

A classification society exists to classify or 'arrange in order of merit' such ships as are built according to its rules or are offered for classification. A classed ship is therefore considered to have a particular standard of seaworthiness. There are classification societies within most of the major maritime nations of the world and some are listed below.

Lloyd's Register of Shipping (UK)
American Bureau of Shipping (USA)
Bureau Veritas (France)
Det Norske Veritas (Norway)
Germanischer Lloyd (Germany)
Registro Italiano (Italy)
Register of Shipping (USSR)
Nippon Kaiji Kyokai (Japan)

Consultation between the societies takes place on matters of common interest through the International Association of Classification Societies (IACS).

The classification societies operate by publishing rules and regulations relating to the structural efficiency and the reliability of the propelling machinery and equipment. These rules are the result of years of experience, research and investigation into ship design and construction. They are in fact a set of standards. There is no compulsion on a shipowner to have his ship classified. However, the insurance premiums depend very much upon the class of a ship—the higher the standard the lower the premium. Also, by being classified a ship is shown to be of sound construction and a safe means of transport for cargo or passengers. There is no connection between the insurance companies and the classification societies.

The operation and organisation of Lloyd's Register of Shipping, the oldest classification society, will now be considered. Throughout this book all references to classification society rules are to those of Lloyd's Register of Shipping. This society is run by a general committee composed of members of the world community and the industry which it serves. National committees are formed in many countries for liaison purposes. A technical committee advises the general committee on technical problems connected with the society's business and any proposed alterations in the rules. The society publishes its '*Rules and Regulations for the Classification of Ships*' in book form, which is updated as necessary, and also '*Extracts*' from these rules and '*Guidance Notes*' relating to more specific structures and equipment. The society employs surveyors who ensure compliance with the rules by attendance during construction, repairs and maintenance throughout the life of classed ships.

To be classed with Lloyd's, approval is necessary for the constructional plans, the materials used and the constructional methods and standards, as observed by the surveyor. The rules governing the scantlings of the ship's structure have ben developed from theoretical and empirical considerations. Lloyd's collect information on the nature and cause of all ship casualties. Analysis of this information often results in modifications to the rules to produce a structure which is considered to be adequate. Much research and investigation is also carried out by the society, leading likewise to modifications and amendments to the rules.

The assigning of a class then follows acceptance by the general committee of the surveyor's report on the ship. The highest class awarded by Lloyd's is ✠ 100 A1. This is made up as follows:

100 A refers to the hull when built to the highest standards laid down in the rules.

1 refers to the equipment, such as the anchors and cables, being in good and efficient condition.

✠ indicates that the vessel has been built under the supervision of the society's surveyors.

It is also usual to name the type of ship following the classification, e.g. ✠ 100 A1 Oil Tanker. Machinery is also surveyed and the notation LMC (Lloyd's Machinery Certificate) is used where the machinery has been built according to the society's rules and satisfactorily proved on sea trials. This information regarding the classification of a ship is entered in the *Register of Ships*. The *Register of Ships* is a book containing the names, classes and general information concerning the ships classed by

Lloyd's Register of Shipping, and also particulars of all known ocean-going merchant ships in the world of 100 tons gross (a capacity measure) and upwards.

The maintaining of standards is ensured by the society in requiring all vessels to have annual surveys or examinations. Special surveys are also required every four years from the date of the first survey for classification. More detail with regard to these surveys is given in Chapter 13.

The society is also empowered to act as an assigning authority. This means that it acts as the agent for the government in administering certain of the mandatory requirements for shipping, e.g. the load line rules.

Governmental authorities

Legislation regarding the safety of ships is the responsibility of the government of the country concerned with registering the ship. In the UK this originally came under the Board of Trade and at the present time is the concern of the Department of Transport. This department is empowered to draw up rules by virtue of a number of Merchant Shipping Acts extending back more than a hundred years. The Department of Transport employ surveyors who examine ships to verify that they are built in accordance with the regulations. Some of the matters with which the Department of Transport is concerned are:

Load lines
Tonnage
Master and crew spaces
Watertight subdivision of passenger ships
Life-saving appliances
Carriage of grain cargoes
Dangerous cargoes

Some of these topics are now the subject of international regulations, e.g. load lines, tonnage and regulations relative to passenger ships. Load lines and tonnage will be considered in more detail as they have significant effects on ship design and construction.

IMO

The international nature of sea-borne trade has led finally to the organisation of an international body to provide intergovernmental co-operation on matters concerning ships, shipping and the sea. Under the auspices of the United Nations the International Maritime Organisation (IMO), formerly IMCO, was formed. Following its formal approval by 21 states, the first assembly met in London in 1959.

The governing body of IMO is the Assembly, which meets once every two years and consists of all the member states. IMO has one-hundred and thirty-seven members and one associate member. In the period between the sessions of the Assembly a council exercises the functions of the Assembly in running the affairs of the organisation. At the moment the council consists of thirty-two member governments elected for two year terms by the Assembly. The organisation's technical work is carried out by a number of committees, the most senior of which is the Maritime Safety Committee (MSC). This has a number of sub-committees whose titles indicate the subjects with which they deal. They are the sub-committees on safety of navigation; radio communications; life-saving appliances; standards of training and watchkeeping; carriage of dangerous goods; ship design and equipment; fire protection; stability and load lines and fishing vessel safety; containers and cargoes; and bulk chemicals. The sub-committee on bulk chemicals is also a sub-committee of the Marine Environment Protection Committee (MEPC), which deals with the organisation's anti-marine pollution activities. Because of the legal issues involved in much of its work the organisation also has a legal committee while the committee on technical co-operation coordinates and directs IMO's activities in this area. The facilitation committee, which deals with measures to simplify and minimise documentation in international maritime traffic, is a subsidiary body of the council.

In order to achieve its objectives IMO has, in the last thirty years, promoted the adoption of thirty-one conventions and protocols. It has also adopted a larger number of codes and recommendations on various matters relating to maritime safety and the prevention of pollution. The initial work on a convention is normally done by a committee or sub-committee. A draft instrument is then produced which delegations from all states within the United Nations, including states which may not be IMO members, are invited to comment upon. The conference adopts a final text, which is submitted to governments for ratification.

An instrument so adopted comes into force after fulfilling certain requirements which usually include ratification by a specified number of countries. Generally speaking, the more important the convention, the more stringent are the requirements for entry into force. Observance of the requirements of a convention is mandatory for countries which are parties to it. Codes and recommendations, which are adopted by the IMO Assembly, are not so binding on governments. However, their contents can by just as important, and in most cases they are implemented by governments through incorporation into their legislation.

Safety and the prevention of pollution are the two chief concerns of IMO and the work done in these two areas will now be considered in detail.

Safety

The first conference organised by IMO in 1960 was, appropriately enough, concerned with safety matters. In 1948 an 'International Convention on the Safety of Life at Sea' had been adopted at a conference convened by the United Kingdom, but developments during the intervening years had made it necessary to bring this up-to-date without delay.

The conference adopted a new 'International Convention on the Safety of Life at Sea', which came into force in 1965 and covered a wide range of measures designed to improve the safety of shipping. They include subdivision and stability; machinery and electrical installations; fire protection, detection and extinction; life-saving appliances; the carriage of grain; the carriage of dangerous goods; and nuclear ships.

The 'Safety of Life at Sea Convention' (SOLAS) became the basic international instrument dealing with matters of maritime safety and in response to new developments it was amended several times. In 1974 IMO convened a conference to adopt a new 'International Convention of the Safety of Life at Sea' which would incorporate the amendments adopted to the 1960 Convention as well as introduce other necessary improvements.

The 1974 Convention entered into force on 25 May 1980. In the meantime a considerable amount of work had been done on updating it. A protocol adopted in 1978 entered into force in May 1981 and the first of a series of important amendments was adopted in November 1981. The amendments entered into force in September 1984. A second set of amendments was adopted in June 1983 and entered into force on 1st July 1986.

In 1966 a conference adopted the 'International Convention on Load Lines'. Limitations on the draught to which a ship may be loaded, in the form of freeboards, are an important contribution to its safety. An international convention on this subject had been adopted in 1930 and the new instrument brought this up to date and incorporated new and improved measures. It came into force in 1968.

The system of tonnage measurement of ships can also affect safety and this has been one of the most difficult problems in all maritime legislation. Tonnage is used for assessing dues and taxes and because of the way in which it is calculated it has proved possible to manipulate the design of ships in such a way as to reduce the ship tonnage while still allowing it to carry the same amount of cargo. But this has occasionally been at the expense of the vessel's stability and safety.

Several systems of tonnage measurement were developed over the years, but none of them was universally recognised. IMO began work on this subject soon after coming into being, and in 1969 the first ever international convention on the subject was adopted. It is an indication of the complexity of this aspect that the convention, which had a very high requirement for entry into force (twenty-five states with not less than 65% of the world's gross tonnage of merchant shipping) did not receive the required number of acceptances until mid-1980. It entered into force on 18 July 1982.

The adoption of the conventions such as those described above is perhaps the most important of IMO's activities, but its work involves many other aspects. In addition to the conventions, whose requirements are mandatory for nations which ratify them, the organisation has also produced numerous codes, recommendations and other instruments dealing with safety. These do not have the same legal power as conventions, but can be used by individual governments as a basis for domestic legislation or as guidance.

Some of the most important of these deal with bulk cargoes, the carriage of dangerous goods; the carriage of bulk chemicals; liquefied gases; noise levels on board ships and special purpose ships.

Prevention of pollution

The 1954 'Oil Pollution Convention' was the first major attempt by the maritime nations to curb the impact of oil pollution. The 1954 convention was amended in

1962, but it was the wreck of the *Torrey Canyon* in 1967 which fully alerted the world to the great dangers which the transport of oil posed to the marine environment. Following this disaster, IMO produced a whole series of conventions and other instruments and in 1969 the 1954 convention was again amended.

In 1971 the 1954 'Oil Pollution Convention' was further amended: one amendment was intended to limit the hypothetical outflow of oil resulting from an accident, while the other aimed at providing special protection for the Great Barrier Reef of Australia.

In 1973 a major conference was called to discuss the whole problem of marine pollution from ships and resulted in the adoption of the most ambitious anti-pollution convention ever drafted. The 'International Convention for the Prevention of Pollution from Ships' dealt not only with oil but other forms of pollution, including that from garbage, chemicals and other harmful substances.

The convention greatly reduces the amount of oil which can be discharged into the sea by ship, and bans such discharges completely in certain areas (such as the Black Sea, Red Sea and other regions). It gives statutory support for such operational procedures as 'load on top' (which greatly reduces the amount of mixtures which have to be disposed of after the tank cleaning) and segregated ballast tanks.

In practice certain technical problems meant that progress towards ratifying this convention was very slow, and a series of tanker accidents which occurred in the winter of 1976–77 led to demands for further action. The result was the 'Conference on Tanker Safety and Pollution Prevention' in February 1978.

This conference could well prove to be one of the most important ever held by IMO. Not only did it complete its work in a remarkably short time (barely ten months after the first call to IMO to convene the conference was made) but the measures adopted are already having a profound effect on tankers.

The measures include requirements for such operational techniques as crude oil washing (a development of the earlier 'load on top' system) and inert gas systems, but also include constructional requirements such as segregated ballast tanks for much smaller ships than stipulated in the 1973 convention. The most important of the new measures are incorporated in protocols to the 1974 'Convention on the Safety of Life at Sea' and the 1973 'Marine Pollution Convention'. The SOLAS protocol entered into force in May 1981 and the MARPOL protocol, which in effect absorbs the parent convention (the combined instrument is usually referred to as MARPOL 73/78) entered into force on 2nd October 1983.

Annexes II, III and IV of the MARPOL 73/78 Convention entered into force in 1987, 1992 and 1988 respectively. They relate to pollution by chemicals, harmful substances carried in packaged form, e.g. containers, and garbage. The Marine Environment Committee has adopted major amendments to the regulations governing the design and construction of both new and existing tankers. They are expected to enter into force in July 1993.

Two amendments will be added to Annex I which relates to accidental pollution by oil. Oil tankers of 600 dwt and above must be fitted with double bottom tanks and the size of each tank is limited to 700 cubic metres, unless a double hull is fitted. Tankers of 5,000 dwt and above must be fitted with double bottoms and wing tanks extending the full depth of the ship's side. Mid-height deck tankers with double hulls are also permitted as an alternative.

Existing crude carriers of 20 000 dwt and above and product carriers of 30 000 dwt and above must comply with regulations which are expected to enter into force in July 1995. An enhanced programme of inspections will be required, particularly for tankers which are more than five years old. Tankers which were delivered after 1 June 1982 must comply with the double hull requirements not later than 30 years after their delivery date. Tankers built before the above dates must have side or bottom protection to cover at least 30% of the cargo tank area, not later than 25 years after their delivery date.

Tanker construction and equipment

The construction and equipment of oil tankers will continue to be a source of much investigation since large quantities of oil have been, and are still being, discharged from damaged or foundered ships. Efforts are being made with the object of preventing or limiting pollution of the sea (and shore) by oil. Two particular avenues of approach are currently being adopted. The first deals with preventing the escape of the cargo oil in the event of a collision or grounding. The second approach is to attempt to limit sizes of centre tanks and wing tanks.

The first arrangement utilises segregated or clean ballast tanks (SBT or CBT). Proposals for the fitting of double-bottom tanks over the cargo tank length and wing ballast tanks have been put forward. These tanks are to be segregated, that is, for the carriage of clean water ballast only. The second method aims at restricting cargo tank sizes to 50 000 m^3 for centre tanks and 30 000 m^3 for wing tanks. This would limit the extent of pollution in the event of damage to a particular tank.

Other proposals following the 1973 Marine Pollution Convention which are now in force include:

(1) For new crude carriers over 20 000 deadweight tonnes, segregated ballast tanks (SBT), crude oil Washing (COW) and an inert gas system (IGS) will be required.
(2) For existing crude carriers over 40 000 deadweight tonnes, CBT, SBT, or COW will be required.
(3) For existing crude carriers over 70 000 deadweight tonnes, IGS will be mandatory.
(4) For products carriers over 20 000 deadweight tones, IGS will be required.
(5) For products carriers over 30 000 deadweight tonnes, SBT will be required.

The fitting of double bottoms and wing tanks extending over the full depth of the ship's side will soon be compulsory for oil tankers over 5 000 dwt, as outlined in the previous section. Other structural or operational arrangements, such as hydrostatically balanced loading, may be accepted as long as they provide the same level of protection against pollution in the event of a collision or stranding.

Fire safety in ships

Fire at sea is an ever-present and much feared hazard. For passenger ships the recommendations, rules and regulations following the 1974 'International Convention on the Safety of Life at Sea' are extensive. They cover the many aspects of detection, restriction and extinguishing of fires. Cargo ships, particularly in the accommodation areas, must likewise have arrangements to deal with fires.

The arrangements for fire protection, by virtue of details of arrangement of construction, as detailed in the 1974 'International Conference on Safety of Life at Sea' and Lloyd's Rules, are applicable to passenger ships carrying more than 36 passengers and cargo ships of more than 4000 tons gross. The following principles are the basis of the regulations:

(1) The use of thermal and structural boundaries to divide the ship into main vertical zones.
(2) Thermal and structural boundaries are used to separate the accommodation spaces from the rest of the ship.
(3) The use of combustible materials is to be restricted.
(4) Any fire should be detected, contained and extinguished where it occurs.
(5) Access must be provided to enable fire fighting and a protected means of escape.
(6) Where inflammable cargo vapour exists the possibility of its ignition must be minimised.

Various definitions are given for the special terms used. Non-combustible material means a material which neither burns nor gives off inflammable vapours in a sufficient quantity to self-ignite when heated to 750°C in an approved test. Any other material is combustible. A standard fire test is when specimens of the relevant bulkheads or decks are exposed in a test furnace to a particular temperature for a certain period of time.

The 'A' class divisions are those divisions formed by bulkheads and decks which comply with the following:

(1) They shall be constructed of steel or other equivalent material.
(2) They shall be suitably stiffened.
(3) They shall be constructed to prevent the passage of smoke and flame for a one-hour standard fire test.
(4) They must be insulated such that the unexposed side will not rise more than 139°C or any point more than 180°C above the original temperature within times as follows: class A-60, 60 minutes; A-30, 30 minutes; A-15, 15 minutes; A-0, 0 minutes.

The 'B' class divisions are those divisions formed by bulkheads which are constructed to prevent the passage of flame for a half-hour standard fire test. They must be insulated so that the unexposed side will not rise more than 139°C, or any point 225°C, above the original temperature within times as follows: class B-15, 15 minutes and B-0, 0 minutes.

The 'C' class divisions are made of non-combustible materials but meet no other requirements.

The main vertical zones are those sections into which the hull, superstructure and deckhouses are divided by 'A' class divisions, the mean length of which should not exceed 40 m.

The hull, superstructure, bulkheads, decks and deckhouses must be of steel or other material which has structural and fire integrity properties equivalent to steel. Pipe materials affected by heat must not be used for outlets near the waterline. The use of combustible materials should be kept to an absolute minimum. Paints, varnishes, etc., with a nitrocellulose base must not be used.

The hull, superstructure and deckhouses must be subdivided into main vertical fire zones of 40 m length or less. 'A' class fire-resisting divisions are to be used from deck to deck and shell or other boundaries. 'A' class boundary bulkheads above the bulkhead deck should, where possible, be in line with watertight bulkheads below.

Any openings in 'A' class bulkheads must be made good for fire-resisting purposes. Dampers must be fitted in vent trunks and ducts and should be operable from either side of the bulkhead; indicators should also be fitted. Doors in 'A' class bulkheads must be as fire resistant as the bulkhead and should be capable of being opened from either side by one person. Fire doors must be self-closing, even in an inclined position of 3.5 degrees.

Other bulkheads in main vertical fire zones must be of 'B' class fire-retarding material. Boundary bulkheads and decks separating the accommodation from holds or cargo spaces or machinery spaces must be A-60 class fire-resisting divisions. Deck coverings within the accommodation spaces should be of non-ignitable material.

Stairways and lifts are to be steel-framed and within enclosures formed by 'A' class divisions. Self-closing doors with positive means of closure should be fitted at all openings, and be as effective as the bulkhead in which fitted, for fire containment. Control stations, such as the radio room, bridge, etc. must be surrounded by 'A' class divisions. Skylights in machinery spaces should have means of closing from outside the space and also steel shutters permanently attached.

Ventilation systems other than cargo and machinery spaces must have two independent control points where all machinery can be stopped in the event of a fire. Machinery space ventilation must be capable of being stopped from outside the space. All inlets and outlets must be able to be closed from outside the space. Air spaces in the accommodation behind ceilings, linings, etc. must be fitted with draught stops not more than 14 m apart.

The above arrangements are made to ensure that a fire on board ship will be contained within the zone in which it occurs. Attempts can then be made to extinguish the fire or, at worst, escape. Stairways and lift trunks act as chimneys which encourage the fire and 'A' class bulkheads are used here to ensure that this does not occur.

The load line rules—freeboard

Freeboard is the distance measured from the waterline to the upper edge of the deck plating at the side of the freeboard deck amidships. The load line rules set out the requirements for a minimum freeboard which must be indicated on the ship's side by a special load line mark. This minimum freeboard is a statutory requirement under the Merchant Shipping (Loadline) Rules of 1968. These rules are based on the

1966 International Loadline Convention called by IMO and ratified by each of the countries taking part.

A minimum freeboard is required principally to ensure that the ship is seaworthy when loaded. The minimum freeboard provides the ship with a reserve of buoyancy which enables it to rise as it passes through waves and thus remain largely dry on its decks. This reserve buoyancy also improves the vessel's stability and in the event of damage will enable it to remain afloat indefinitely, or at least for a time, to effect the escape of the crew.

The assigning of freeboard follows a calculation which considers the ship's length, breadth, depth and sheer, the density of the water and the amount of watertight superstructures and other features of the ship. Additional conditions of assignment are also made relating to certain openings and fittings. The ship is assigned a basic minimum freeboard on the assumption that it is correctly loaded, with adequate stability and strength. A number of terms and dimensions are used in the computation of freeboard.

Freeboard deck This is the uppermost continuous deck exposed to the weather and the sea which has permanent means for the watertight closure of all exposed openings on the deck and in the side shell below.

Deck line This is a horizontal line 300 mm long and 25 mm wide which is positioned amidships port and starboard. The upper edge of the line is located level with the upper surface of the freeboard deck plating on the outer shell.

Length The freeboard length is the greater of the following two measurements: (1) on a waterline at 85% of the least moulded depth, 96% of the length along the waterline; or (2) on the same waterline, the distance from the fore side of the stem to the axis of the rudder stock.

Breadth Measured at amidships, this is the maximum breadth to the moulded line.

Depth moulded This is the vertical distance between the upper edge of the keel and the upper edge of the freeboard deck beam measured at the ship's side.

Displacement This is the moulded displacement of the ship, excluding bossings, measured at 85% of the least moulded depth.

Block coefficient This is determined using the values of displacement, length, breadth and a value of draught which is 85% of the least moulded depth, i.e.

$$\text{block coefficient, } C_b = \frac{\text{displacement}}{\text{length} \times \text{breadth} \times \text{draught}}.$$

Superstructure. This is a structure of adequate strength on the freeboard deck which extends transversely to at least within 0.04 times the breadth from the ship's side. The superstructure length, S, is taken as the mean length of that part of the superstructure within the freeboard length of the ship.

Freeboard categories

In order to assign freeboards, ships are divided into Types A and B. Type A ships are those designed specifically for the carriage of liquid cargoes in bulk. The cargo tanks have only small openings for access which are closed by watertight covers of adequate strength. Type B ships are all those which are not of Type A. The greater freeboard required for the Type B ship may be reduced in certain circumstances. In ships where steel hatch covers are fitted, special subdivision arrangements exist, improved water freeing arrangements are provided and better protection for the crew is given, and a reduced freeboard is permitted. This reduction can result in an almost equivalent value to that of a Type A ship. Where this value is almost equivalent the notation Type B-100 is used, indicating a 100% reduction of the freeboard difference between Types A and B. The notation Type B-60 is used where a 60% reduction of freeboard difference is obtained. Bulk carriers particularly benefit from this reduction in freeboard.

The freeboard is determined from a calculation where a tabular freeboard figure based on the ship's length and type is adjusted by several corrections. These corrections are to account for the variations between the actual ship and the standard ship on which the tabular freeboard is based.

Flush deck correction

A Type B ship of less than 100 m length having superstructures with an effective length, E, of up to 35% of the freeboard length, L, may have its freeboard increased by

$$7.5(100 - L)\left(0.35 - \frac{E}{L}\right) \text{ millimetres}$$

where E is the effective length of the superstructure, in metres. With the superstructure length, S, known the effective length, E, may be found from the load line rules.

Block coefficient correction

Where the actual block coefficient, C_b, of the ship exceeds 0.68, the freeboard amended by the flush deck correction, if relevant, is multiplied by the ratio

$$\frac{C_b + 0.68}{1.36}$$

where C_b is obtained as defined earlier.

Depth correction

The formula for the freeboard depth, D, is given in the rules. Where D is greater than the freeboard length, L, divided by 15, the freeboard is increased by

$$\left(D - \frac{L}{15}\right)R$$

where $R = L/0.48$ for ships less than 120 m in length, or 250 for ships greater than 120 m in length. If D is less than $L/15$ no deduction is made, except where there is an enclosed superstructure extending $0.6L$ at midships. This deduction would be determined as for the flush deck correction.

Superstructure correction

For an effective length of superstructure, E, equal to the freeboard length, L, the freeboard may be reduced by 350 mm for a 24 m ship length, 860 mm for an 85 m ship length and 1070 mm for all ship lengths greater than 122 m. Intermediate length deductions are obtained by interpolation; with effective lengths less than $1.0L$ the deduction is a percentage of the values given.

Sheer correction

The differences between the actual sheer profile and a standard sheer profile are determined. The correction is then the deficiency or excess multiplied by

$$\left(0.75 - \frac{S}{2L}\right)$$

where S is the mean length of the superstructure.

For a deficiency of sheer, the correction is added to the freeboard. With an excess, a deduction is permitted where the superstructure covers $0.1L$ aft and $0.1L$ forward of midships. For lesser lengths of superstructure, the deduction is obtained by interpolation. A maximum deduction of 125 mm per 100 m of ship length is permitted.

With the tabular value amended by the corrections, the freeboard value will be that for the maximum summer draught in sea water. This value may be further amended if, for instance, the bow height is insufficient as defined in the rules, cargo ports or openings are fitted in the sides below the freeboard deck or the shipowner requests a freeboard corresponding to a draught less than the maximum permissible.

Load line markings

The maximum summer draught, as determined above, is indicated by a load line mark. This consists of a ring of 300 mm outside diameter and 25 mm wide, intersected by a horizontal line 450 mm long and 25 mm wide. The upper edge of this line passes through the centre of the ring. The ring is positioned at midships and at a distance below the upper edge of the deck line which corresponds to the assigned minimum summer freeboard. This value may not be less than 50 mm.

A series of load lines are situated forward of the load line mark and these denote the minimum freeboards within certain geographical zones or in fresh water. The summer load line is level with the centre of the ring and marked S. The tropical, T, and winter, W, load lines are found by deducting and adding, respectively, 1/48 of the summer moulded draught. For a ship of 100 m length or less a Winter North

Atlantic (WNA) zone load line is permitted. This line is positioned at the winter freeboard plus 50 mm. The fresh water freeboards F and TF are found by deducting from the summer or tropical freeboard the value

$$\frac{\text{displacement in salt water}}{4 \times TPC} \text{ millimetres}$$

where TPC is the tonnes per centimetre immersion in salt water at the summer load waterline.

These markings are shown in *Figure 11.1*. In all cases, measurements are to the upper edge of the line.

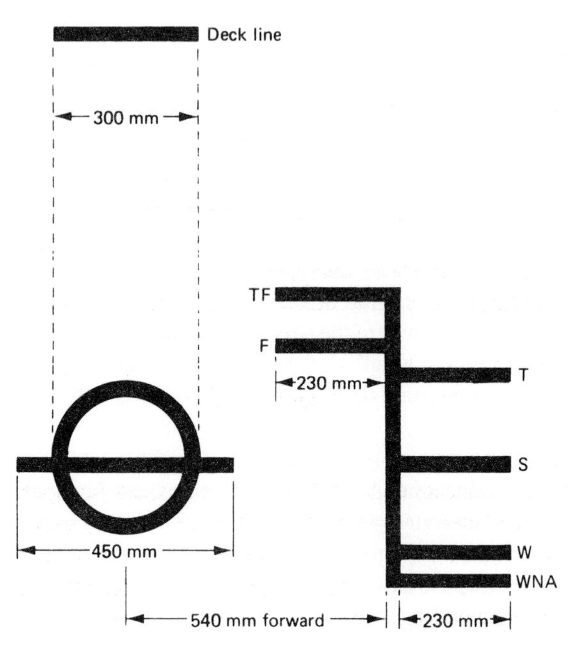

Figure 11.1 Load line markings (all lines 25mm thickness)

Conditions of assignment

Mention was made earlier of the conditions of assignment relating to freeboard. These are certain requirements which must be met to ensure the watertightness of openings and the ability of the ship to rapidly free itself of water on its decks. Reference will be made to two particular positions which are now defined.

Position 1 Exposed freeboard, superstructure and raised quarter decks within one-quarter of the ship's length from the forward perpendicular.

Position 2 Exposed superstructure decks outside one-quarter of the ship's length from the forward perpendicular.

Structural strength and stability

The ship is required to have the necessary structural strength for the freeboard assigned. Certain criteria with regard to stability must be met and an inclining experiment must be carried out in order to ensure compliance.

Superstructure end bulkheads

Such bulkheads for enclosed superstructures must be adequately constructed. Any openings must have a minimum sill height of 380 mm above the deck.

Hatchways

Portable covers secured by tarpaulins

Substantial coamings of mild steel or equivalent material must be fitted to all hatchways. Minimum heights are 600 mm in position 1 and 450 mm in position 2. Requirements must be met in respect of thickness of covers, strength, loading of covers and beams, carriers or socket design, cleats, battens, wedges, number of tarpaulins and securing arrangements.

Watertight steel covers

There are similar requirements for coamings, but these may be reduced in height or dispensed with where the safety of the ship is not affected. Again requirements must be met in respect of cover strength, construction and watertight securing arrangements.

Machinery space openings

Machinery space openings in position 1 or 2 must be efficiently framed and plated for strength. Openings are to have watertight doors with sill heights of 600 mm in position 1 and 380 mm in position 2. All other openings are to have attached steel covers which can be secured weathertight if required.

Other openings in freeboard and superstructure decks

Manholes and scuttles (portholes) must have covers fitted to efficiently secure them. All doorways are to have a minimum sill height of 600 mm in position 1 and 380 mm in position 2. All openings other than hatchways, machinery space openings, manholes and scuttles, where in an exposed position, must be enclosed by a structure of equivalent strength and watertightness to an enclosed superstructure.

Ventilators

Coamings on ventilators must be 900 mm above deck in position 1 and 760 mm in position 2. Where exposed to severe weather or in excess of 900 mm high, coamings are to be suitably bracketed to the surrounding structure or deck. Some means of permanent closure, either attached or close by, is required for all ventilators except those of height in excess of 4.5 m in position 1 or 2.3 m in position 2.

Air pipes

These pipes must be of efficient construction and have a permanently attached means of closing. The opening height must be a minimum of 760 mm on the freeboard deck and 450 mm on the superstructure decks.

Cargo ports and similar openings

Any cargo ports must be fitted with doors and frames which maintain the structural and watertight integrity of the ship. No door is to be fitted with any part of its opening below the load line decks.

Scupper, inlets and discharges

All discharges from above or below the freeboard deck from enclosed spaces are to have an efficient non-return arrangement fitted. Arrangements and their control are specified according to the discharge distance from the summer load waterline. Manned machinery space inlets and outlets are to have readily accessible controls and valve position indicators. Scuppers from open spaces may be led directly overboard.

Side scuttles (portholes)

Every side scuttle below the freeboard deck is to be fitted. Arrangements and their control are specified according to the discharge distance from the summer load waterline. Manned machinery space inlets and outlets are to have readily accessible controls and valve position indicators. Scuppers from open spaces may be led directly overboard.

Side scuttles (portholes)

Every side scuttle below the freeboard deck is to be fitted with a hinged cover-plate or deadlight which may be securely closed and made watertight. No side scuttles may be fitted below 2.5% of the ship's breadth or 500 mm, whichever is the greater, above the load waterline.

Freeing ports

Where bulwarks on any exposed decks form wells they must be provided with efficient means for rapidly freeing the decks of water. Special formulae are given for the determination of the freeing area in relation to the length of the bulwark, its height and the shear of the deck. The lower edge of the freeing port should be as close to the deck as possible. Two-thirds of the freeing area should be located near the lowest point of the sheer curve where sheer exists on the deck. Openings are restricted in height to 230 mm by bars being placed across them. Where shutters or flaps are fitted to these openings they should be prevented from jamming.

Protection of the crew

All exposed freeboard and superstructure decks must have bulwarks or guard rails fitted at their perimeter with a minimum height of 1 m. Where rails are fitted the deck and lower rail spacing must not exceed 230 mm and other rails 380 mm. Effective protection and safety in the form of gangways, passages and other means of access required in the course of their work must be provided for the crew.

Special conditions of assignment for Type A ships

Machinery casings

An enclosed poop, bridge of standard height or a deckhouse of equivalent strength and height must protect the machinery casing. An exposed casing is allowed without doors or with a double-door arrangement, provided it is of weathertight construction.

Hatchways

All exposed hatchways are to have efficient watertight covers of steel or equivalent strength materials.

Freeing arrangements

Open rails must be fitted for at least half of the exposed length of the deck. The upper edge of the sheer strake should be kept as low as possible. Where a trunk connects parts of the superstructure, open rails should be fitted at the perimeter of the deck in way of the trunk.

Protection of the crew

Where separate superstructures exist they should be connected by a raised gangway at the level of the superstructure deck. An acceptable alternative would be a passageway below deck. With a single superstructure, adequate safe arrangements should exist for access to all work areas on the ship.

Tonnage

Tonnage, as discussed in this section, is a measure of cubic capacity where 1 ton represents 100 ft^3 or 2.83 m^3. Tonnage is a measure of the ship's internal capacity, with two values being used. The gross tonnage is the total internal capacity of the ship and the net tonnage is the revenue-earning capacity. Tonnage values are also used to determine port and canal dues, safety equipment and manning requirements and are a statistical basis for measuring the size of a country's merchant fleet. All ships prior to registry must be measured according to their country's tonnage regulations. The differences in the various measuring systems have led to ships having several tonnage values and to unusual designs which exploited aspects of tonnage measurement. The 1969 IMO 'International Conference on Tonnage Measurement of Ships' led to an international review of the subject and a system which will ultimately be universally adopted. Reference will now be made to the British tonnage measurement system and also the 1969 convention measurement system.

British tonnage

The current regulations governing tonnage measurement are the Merchant Shipping (Tonnage) Regulations 1967(11). The measurement of tonnage follows from various specialist terms and values which will now be defined in turn.

Tonnage deck This is the second deck, except in single-deck ships.

Tonnage length An imaginary line is drawn across the ship at the stem and stern on the inside of the hold frames or sparring. The tonnage length is the distance between these lines measured along the ship's centreline on the tonnage deck.

Tonnage depth This is measured from the upper surface of the tanktop to the underside of the tonnage deck at the centreline, with a deduction of one-third of the camber. The height of flooring, double or single, is limited.

Tonnage breadth The breadth of the ship to the inside of the hold frames or sparring.

Underdeck tonnage This is the tonnage of the space below the tonnage deck. It is found by dividing the tonnage length into a specified number of parts. At each cross-section formed by this division, the tonnage depth is similarly divided up. The tonnage breadths at these points are then measured. The measured distances are then put through Simpson's rule to provide the underdeck volume which is converted into a tonnage value.

Gross tonnage

This is the total of the underdeck tonnage and the tonnage of the following spaces:

(1) Any tween-deck spaces between the second and upper decks.
(2) Any enclosed spaces above the upper deck.
(3) Any excess of hatchways over 0.5% of the gross tonnage.
(4) At the shipowner's option and with the surveyor's approval, any engine light and air spaces on or above the upper deck.

The term gross register tonnage (GRT) is also used.

Exempted spaces

These are spaces which are not measured for the gross tonnage calculation. Such spaces may be above or below the tonnage deck and include:

(1) Wheelhouse, chartroom, radioroom and navigation aids room.
(2) Spaces fitted with and for the use of machinery or condensers.
(3) Safety equipment and battery spaces.
(4) Stability tanks and machinery.
(5) Galley and bakery spaces.
(6) Skylights, domes and trunks.
(7) Washing and sanitary accommodation forming part of the crew accommodation.

Deducted spaces

The tonnage of these spaces must first be measured and may then be deducted from the gross tonnage of the ship to give the net tonnage. Examples of deducted spaces are:

(1) Master's accommodation.
(2) Crew accommodation and an allowance for provision stores.
(3) Chain locker, steering gear space, anchor gear and capstan space.
(4) Space for safety equipment and batteries below the upper deck.
(5) Workshops and storerooms for pumpmen, electricians, carpenter, and boatswain.
(6) Donkey engine and donkey boiler space if these are outside the machinery space.

(7) Pumprooms, where these are outside the machinery space.
(8) Water ballast tanks, where they are for the exclusive carriage of water ballast; a maximum limit of 19% of the gross tonnage is imposed.
(9) Propelling power allowance—this is the largest deduction and is determined according to certain criteria, as follows:

If the machinery space tonnage is between 13% and 20% of the gross tonnage, the propelling power allowance is 32% of the gross tonnage. If the machinery space tonnage is less than 13% of the gross tonnage then the propelling power allowance is the amount expressed as a proportion of 32% of the gross tonnage. Where the machinery space tonnage is more than 20% of the gross tonnage, the propelling power allowance is $1^3/4$ times the machinery space tonnage. There is a maximum limit of 55% of the gross tonnage for the propelling power allowance. If any part of the light and air space is included in the gross tonnage then it may also be included in the machinery space tonnage.

Net tonnage

This is the tonnage value obtained by deducting from the gross tonnage the total value of the deducted spaces. The net tonnage is considered to represent the earning capacity of the ship. The term net register tonnage (NRT) is also used.

Tonnage mark scheme

The tonnage mark scheme was devised to exempt from tonnage measurement the tween deck space between the uppermost complete deck and the second deck, provided a special tonnage draught mark was not submerged. The position of this mark on the ship's side was to generally correspond to the draught which would be obtained if the freeboard had been calculated for the second deck being the freeboard deck. A special mark is used and is shown in *Figure 11.2*. The position of the mark on the ship's side is given in the amendment to the load line rules dealing with the tonnage mark scheme.

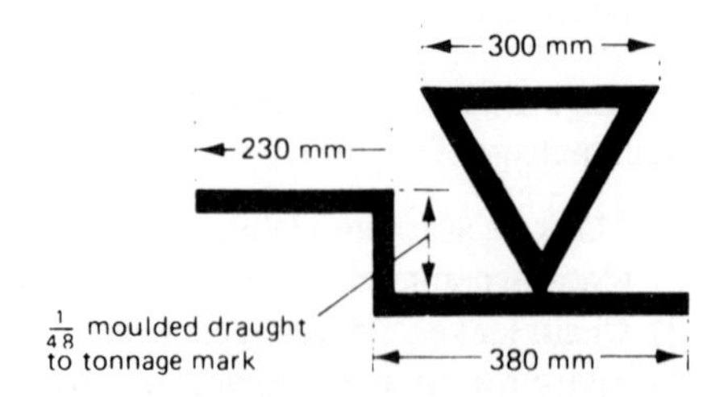

Figure 11.2 Tonnage mark (all lines 25mm thickness)

When the tonnage mark is at or above the waterline the ship is considered to have a modified tonnage. When the tonnage mark is below the waterline the ship is considered to be at its full tonnage.

The International Convention of Tonnage Measurement of Ships

This convention, which was the first successful attempt to create a universal tonnage measurement system, came into force on 18th July 1982. The shelter-deck concept and the tonnage mark scheme are abandoned. Gross and net tonnage are the only two parameters now used. Gross tonnage is determined in relation to the volume of all enclosed spaces. Net tonnage is the sum of the cargo space plus any volume of passenger spaces multiplied by a coefficient to bring the value close to existing tonnages. Each measurement is determined by a formula as follows:

$$\text{gross tonnage } (GT) = K_1 V$$

$$\text{net tonnage } (NT) = K_2 V_c \left(\frac{4d}{3D}\right)^2 + K_3\left(N_1 + \frac{N_2}{10}\right)$$

where V = total volume of all enclosed spaces of the ship in cubic metres

K_1 = $0.2 + 0.02 \log_{10} V$

V_c = total volume of cargo spaces in cubic metres

K_2 = $0.2 + 0.02 \log_{10} V_c$

K_3 = $1.25 \dfrac{GT + 10\,000}{10\,000}$

D = moulded depth amidships in metres

d = moulded draught amidships in metres

N_1 = number of passengers in cabins with not more than eight berths

N_2 = number of other passengers

$N_1 + N_2$ = total number of passengers the ship is permitted to carry as indicated on the ship's passenger certificate
when $N_1 + N_2$ is less than 13, N_1 and N_2 shall be taken as zero

GT = Gross tonnage of the ship.

In the above the factor $(4d/3D)^2$ is not to be taken as greater than unity and the term $K_2V_c(4d/3D)^2$ is not to be taken as less than $0.25GT$.

The volumes referred to in these formulæ are to be calculated to the inside of plating and include the volumes of appendages. Volumes of spaces open to the sea are excluded.

The main features of this convention can be summarised as follows:

(1) Measurements of gross and net tonnage are dimensionless numbers. The word ton will no longer be used.
(2) New ships are defined as ships whose keel is laid, or are at a similar stage of construction, on or after 18th July 1982.
(3) Existing ships may retain their current tonnages until 18th July 1994. After this date they may retain their existing tonnages only for the purpose of the application of international conventions.

(4) Excluded spaces are those which are open to the sea and therefore not suitable for the carriage of perishable cargoes.
(5) Cargo spaces are defined as compartments for the transport of cargo which is to be discharged from the ship. They are to be permanently marked with the letters CC.
(6) Alterations to the parameters of the net tonnage formula which would result in a reduction of net tonnage are restricted to once a year.

The application of this convention and the use of the above formulæ will mean that open shelter-deck vessels and others with large exempted spaces will have larger gross tonnages. Roll-on roll-off ships and ferries will have significant increases in both their gross and net tonnages. Bulk carriers, ore carriers and other ships designed to carry high density cargoes will have their net tonnage values reduced.

Other tonnage systems

A ship will carry a tonnage certificate which indicates the values of tonnage for the vessel, calculated according to the relevant system. Other special tonnages exist which are calculated in a slightly different way and are shown on special certificates. These are used for ships passing through the Suez and Panama Canals. The charges levied for the use of these canals are based upon their particular canal tonnage.

1	Merchant Ship Construction	£14.00
1	UK Postage	£ 1.20
TOTAL		£15.20

Payment received with thanks by cheque for the sum of £15.20. If you have any queries please do not hesitate to contact me at the above address.

Best Regards,

Joan Murphy

Joan Murphy
Publication Sales Department.

Enc.

Marine Management (Holdings) Ltd

THE MEMORIAL BUILDING, 76 MARK LANE, LONDON EC3R 7JN

Tel: 071-481 8493 Telex: 886841 Fax: 071-488 1854

Our ref: *Your ref:*

DELIVERY NOTE

To : Mr Clark
Country : UK

Order No : Mail order
Dated : 13th May 1993

Method of Payment: Cheque

Date : 20th May 1993

Thank you for your order.

12

Corrosion and its Prevention

The prevention of corrosion on board ship is an immense ongoing process demanding the attention and skills of considerable numbers of personnel. The ship because of its size, its physical environment and the materials used in its construction is subject to attack from the various forms of corrosion.

Corrosion

Corrosion is the wasting of metals by chemical or electrochemical reactions with their surroundings. Erosion is a term often associated with corrosion and refers to the destruction of a metal by abrasion. Erosion is therefore a mechanical wastage process that exposes bare metal which can then corrode.

Iron and steel corrode in an attempt to regain their oxide form which is in a balanced state with the earth's atmosphere. This oxidising, or rusting as it is commonly termed, will take place whenever steel is exposed to oxygen and moisture. The prevention of corrosion therefore deals with the isolation of steel from its environment in order to stop this oxidation taking place.

In addition, the presence of a ship almost constantly in sea water enables an electrochemical reaction to take place on unprotected steel surfaces. A corrosion cell is then said to have been formed. This is often referred to as a 'galvanic cell', since its current flow is a result of a potential difference between two metals (not necessarily different) in a solution such as sea water. This current flow results in metal being removed from the anode metal or positive electrode, while the cathodic metal or negative electrode is protected from corrosion. Most common metals can be arranged in what is known as a galvanic series, according to their electrical potential in sea water, as shown in *Table 12.1*.

A simple example of a corrosion cell would be a plate of copper and one of iron placed in a sea water solution and joined by a wire. Reference to *Table 12.1* will show that copper will become the cathode or protected end and the steel will become anodic and corrode. This is shown in *Figure 12.1*. The chemical reaction taking place and the electron flow occurring will result in the anodic metal combining with dissolved oxygen to form its stable oxide form (rust).

Table 12.1 GALVANIC SERIES OF METALS AND ALLOYS IN SEA WATER

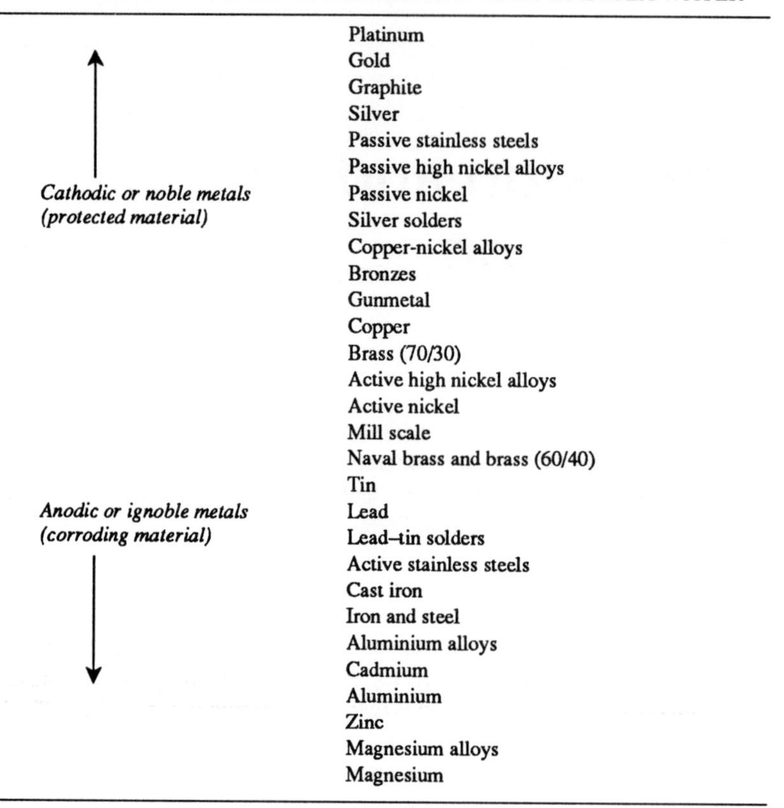

↑	Platinum
	Gold
	Graphite
	Silver
	Passive stainless steels
	Passive high nickel alloys
Cathodic or noble metals	Passive nickel
(protected material)	Silver solders
	Copper-nickel alloys
	Bronzes
	Gunmetal
	Copper
	Brass (70/30)
	Active high nickel alloys
	Active nickel
	Mill scale
	Naval brass and brass (60/40)
	Tin
Anodic or ignoble metals	Lead
(corroding material)	Lead–tin solders
	Active stainless steels
	Cast iron
	Iron and steel
	Aluminium alloys
	Cadmium
	Aluminium
	Zinc
	Magnesium alloys
↓	Magnesium

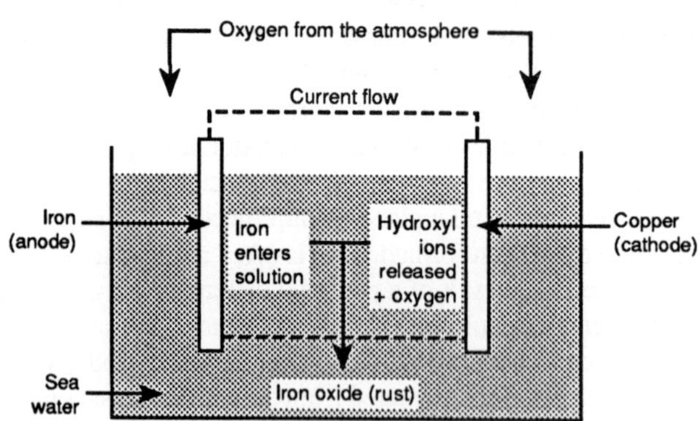

Figure 12.1 Corrosion cell

Corrosion can also occur as a result of stress, either set up in the material during manufacture or as a result of its 'working' in the sea. The effects of stress and fatigue are to provide areas where cracking may occur, but even these sometimes minute cracks create conditions under which galvanic corrosion will proceed. The combined action of the two has a considerable effect on the material.

Corrosion prevention

The prevention of corrosion deals in the first place with the provision of an adequate protective coating for the ship's structural steel and its continued maintenance. Secondly, a means of preventing electrochemical wastage is required, which is known as cathodic protection. The two distinctly different types of corrosion prevention are usually complementary to one another in that both are normally fitted on modern ships. Finally, it should be noted that a knowledge of the processes of corrosion can ensure the reduction or prevention of corrosion on board ship, particularly on the internal structure, by the use of good design and arrangement of structural members.

Paint

Protective coatings refer to the application of a suitable paint system. Paint is a mixture of three ingredients—the pigment, the binding agent or vehicle and the solvent. The pigment is responsible for the colour and covering capacity and may also refer to certain additives, depending upon the properties required of the final product. The binding agent or vehicle, depending on its proportion in the paint, will decide the consistency and ease of application of the paint. The solvent or thinner is added to make the paint flow easily.

Most paints consist of solid pigments, usually in a finely divided form, suspended in a liquid binder or vehicle which, when spread thinly over a surface, will eventually dry out. A thin dry film is then left adhering to the surface. The 'drying' process associated with ships' paints is usually the evaporation of the solvent from the vehicle. Good ventilation is therefore essential and moisture-laden atmospheres are to be avoided during the drying process. The coating applied must also be thin to ensure that it dries out correctly. The appropriate solvent is essential to ensure the correct drying time; too quick and blistering can occur, too slow and the paint may end up immersed before it is dry.

The common vehicles in use are:

(1) Bitumen or pitch—bitumen or pitch in a white spirit solvent, or blends of pitch with other materials.
(2) Oil based—vegetable drying oils, e.g. linseed oil, dehydrated castor oil.
(3) Oleo-resinous—natural or artificial resins mixed into drying oils.
(4) Alkyd-resin—a special type of (3).
(5) Chemical resistant—chlorinated rubber, epoxide resins and coal tar/epoxide are examples.

All the above vehicle types are suitable for above-water use. Only types 1 and 5 and certain types of 3 are suitable for underwater use, because of the need to resist alkaline deposits formed at the anodes of corrosion cells.

Anti-fouling paint

Fouling is the covering of a ship's underwater surface with marine organisms such as green slime, weeds and barnacles. Fouling occurs usually only when the ship is at rest and is dependent on water temperature, salinity, the season, the place, etc.

The slower speeds of the larger tankers and bulk carriers has resulted in increased fouling problems, since some marine organisms can survive and grow at speeds of 10–15 knots. The result of fouling is increased hull resistance and subsequent loss of the ship's speed or increased fuel consumption.

Anti-fouling paints function by slowly releasing a poison into the laminar sea water layer surrounding the ship. This sea water soluble poison is toxic to marine organisms which must pass through this laminar layer in order to attach themselves to the ship. The poison is released at a controlled rate, determined by the type of toxin and also the degree and rate of solubility of the binder.

Two basically different types of anti-fouling paint currently exist—non-polishing and self-polishing.

Non-polishing anti-fouling may have either a soluble or insoluble matrix. The soluble matrix consists mainly of rosin (colophony) which is slightly sea-water soluble. The bio-active materials (poisons) are released in sea water together with the binder. The insoluble matrix type uses a large proportion of polymeric binders which are insoluble in sea water. The bio-active materials are released together with other components which act as leaching aids. This leaves behind a released layer of insoluble binder. The release rate of the bio-active materials in each type will decrease with time in service of the vessel. The bio-active materials will include cuprous oxide and organotin compounds.

The amount or 'loading' of these materials is varied according to the vessel's requirements. Small amounts would be used for vessels trading in cold and temperate climates with short idle periods and long sailing times. Large amounts would be used for vessel trading world-wide in warm climates with short-to-medium idle time and varied sailing periods. Different strengths of binder result in the use of one- or two-coat systems to achieve a particular dry film thickness. The dry film thickness determines the quantity of bio-active materials available and the system life time. For any particular dry docking interval a suitable life time must be selected. It should be noted that the bio-active materials in the system are consumed faster during high speed sailing.

Self-polishing anti-fouling paint is designed to wear down smoothly while maintaining a bio-active interface between the coating and the water. One type of this paint uses a tributyltin copolymer binder and reinforcing bio-active compounds which produce a synergistic (assisting one another) effect with tributyltin anti-foulants. The tributyltin copolymer produces tributyltin oxide (TBTO) in a hydrated form by hydrolysis (ionic dissociation) with sea water. The reinforcing bio-active compounds comprise cuprous oxides and organotin compounds. They leach as the tributyltin copolymer releases its tributyltin content. The copolymer then becomes water soluble and is washed off. This renews and activates the next layer of tributyltin molecules.

The release of tributyltin (TBT) from anti-fouling paint has raised environmental concerns over possible damage to the marine ecology. Legislation has so far only been enacted against smaller vessels of less than 25 metres in length, but tighter controls are expected on dry dock discharges which may effectively stop the use of

TBT anti-fouling paints. Paint manufacturers have therefore developed TBT-free anti-foulings in anticipation of possible legislation banning the use of TBT. Controlled depletion polymer (CDP) technology is used to ensure the controlled release of biocides. These TBT-free biocides are exposed as a series of physical and chemical reactions polish away the paint film to expose them.

The self-polishing rate is determined during paint manufacture by the nature of the copolymer binder. One manufacturer provides three self-polishing rates which, together with two possible degrees of fouling protection, results in six possible types of coating. The fouling protection may be either normal or severe. The three self-polishing rates relate to low-to-medium speed, medium-to-high speed and very high speed hulls. The degree of hull roughness acceptable increases in the same order and dry film thicknesses are 100 μm, 80 μm and 60 μm per coat minimum respectively. The self-polishing rate will increase with speed and average hull roughness.

Painting the ship

The paint used must be appropriate for the degree of protection required at the particular area or section of the ship. The principal areas requiring different forms of treatment are the underwater plating and boot topping region, the topsides, the superstructure and the weather decks (*Figure 12.2*).

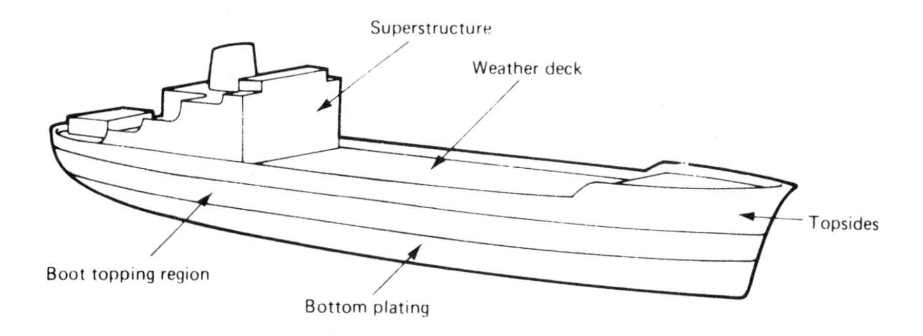

Figure 12.2 Principal painting areas

Preparation and priming

The surface preparation of the steel plate must be good in order to ensure the successful operation of the applied painting system. The steel plates used in ship construction are first shot-blasted to remove all traces of rusting and mill scale which may be present. The plating is then immediately primed with a quick-drying prefabrication primer. This all takes place as part of a continuous undercover process under controlled conditions. This coating is usually adequate to protect the plate during the various fabrication processes leading to its incorporation into the hull of the ship. Final painting will progress with the construction of the ship.

Underwater areas

The underwater and boot topping plating region will have paint types applied after consideration of the presence and type of cathodic protection applied to the hull and the degree of anti-corrosive and anti-fouling paint which is required. Highly alkaline conditions are to be found near the anodes of cathodic protection systems, and paints of an epoxide type are therefore required to resist these chemical conditions. Anti-fouling properties are also required for paints used in this region to emit poisons that will kill the marine organisms which tend to collect on ships' hulls. While fouling in the main increases ship resistance there are certain bacteria which reduced sulphates in sea water and release oxygen which can then take part in the corrosion process. The anti-fouling properties of a paint for the underwater regions are therefore important. The actual choice of paint type and its particular composition is usually made by the shipowner bearing the above factors in mind.

Modern practice makes little or no distinction between the paint used on the bottom shell and that used around the boot topping region. The boot topping region is, however, more likely to suffer damage due to mechanical abrasion (erosion) and the action of waves. Some suitable vehicle types of paint for this region would be bitumen or pitch, oleo-resinous epoxide, coal tar/epoxide resin and chlorinated rubber. A compatible primer would be applied first, then the particular paint type and a final coat of anti-fouling paint if it is to be used.

Topsides and superstructures

Topsides and superstructures are usually adequately coated with primer, an undercoat and a finishing paint. Paint based on alkyd resins, modified alkyd resins and enamels are used in this region. Since appearance is of some importance, good colour- and gloss-retaining properties of the paints used on these parts is essential.

Weather decks

The paint for the weather deck area requires exceptionally good resistance to wear and abrasion and some non-slip quality. The deck coating should also be resistant to any oils or chemicals carried as cargo or fuel. Initial protective coatings topped by grit-reinforced oleo-resinous paints have been used successfully, as have primers and chlorinated rubber deck paints. Certain metallic final coats have been tried with considerable success, more particularly on naval vessels. The constant abrasion on weather decks from traffic, cargo handling and general ship operation makes long-term protection by paint alone almost impossible. Self-sealing coatings utilising epoxide resins have been used with some success on top of epoxide resin paint for a hard-wearing deck covering.

Tanks

Ballast, cargo/ballast and fresh water tanks require special coatings, depending upon the nature of their contents. Treatments used include two coats of epoxide resin or a three-coat phenolic resin-based paint, with care taken to ensure compatibility with the tank contents. Fresh water tanks can be satisfactorily protected by bitumen or tar paints. Drinking water tanks must have a non-taint coating such as artificial bitumen to BS 3416 Type 2.

Cathodic protection

When a metal is in contact with an electrolyte, e.g. the steel of a ship's hull in sea water, small corrosion cells may be set up due to slight variations in the electrical potential of the metal's surface. Electric currents flow between the high and low potential points, with the result that metal is corroded from the point where the current leaves the metal (the anode). At the point where the current re-enters the metal (the cathode) the metal is protected. Cathodic protection operates by providing a reverse current flow to that of the corrosive system. With current then entering the metal at every point, the whole metal surface becomes a cathode, and it is therefore cathodically protected.

When the potential over the immersed hull surface is 0.80–0.85 V more negative than a reference silver/silver chloride electrode in the water nearby, then the hull is adequately protected. Current density of the order of 20–100 mA/m^2 is usually sufficient on a painted hull to reverse any corrosion current and cease further metal corrosion. Current density necessarily increases for a poorly painted hull and therefore cathodic protection should be regarded as an additional protection to painting and by no means a substitute.

Two means of cathodic protection are in general use on ships—the sacrificial anode type and the impressed current type. The sacrificial anode type of cathodic protection uses metals such as aluminium and zinc which form the anode of a corrosion cell in preference to steel (see *Table 11.1*). As a consequence, these sacrificial anodes are gradually eaten away and require replacement after a period of time. The impressed current system provides the electrical potential difference from the ship's power supply through an anode of a long-life highly corrosion-resistant material such as platinised titanium.

Sacrificial anode system

Sacrificial anodes are, in practice, arranged as blocks and are securely bolted or welded to the ship's hull by their steel core to give a good electrical connection. Their metal composition is aluminium or zinc, usually in alloyed form. They are designed to ensure uniform wearing away and to provide a constant current to the protected steel. The amount of anode material should provide a protective current of 12–20 mA/m^2. Modern sacrificial anodes have a life of 3–4 years before requiring replacement.

Impressed current system

An impressed current system comprises several anodes, reference electrodes and a

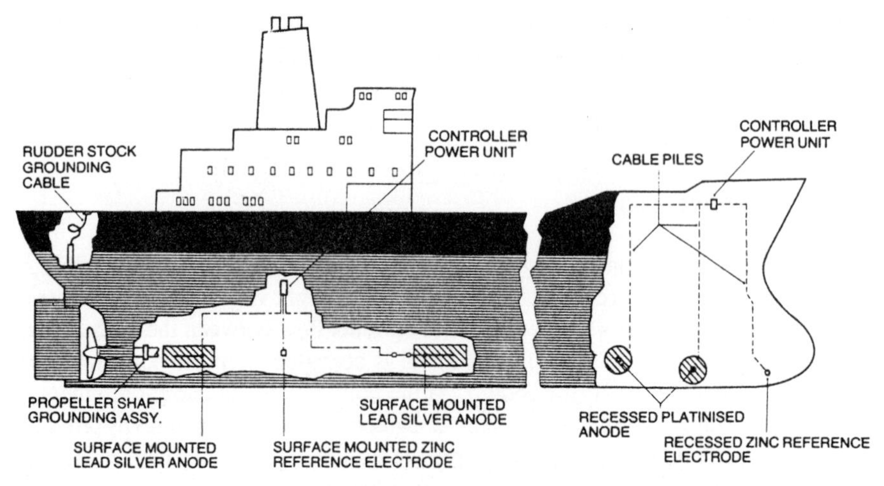

Figure 12.3 Typical location of impressed current system

controller power unit. A typical installation for both large and small vessels is shown in *Figure 12.3*. The type and sizes of the various components and their position on the ship's hull will be decided according to design parmaters. These will include vessel size and the assumed fluctuation of the protection current during sea-going service.

The aft end system arrangement is used for all vessels, whereas the forward end system is only required on larger, longer vessels. Recessed anodes are fitted at the forward end in order to reduce drag and minimise damage. Where a bow thruster is fitted a separate immersed current system may be fitted to protect the housing tunnel and thruster components.

The propeller, exposed shafting and the rudder must also be protected in addition to the hull. The propeller and shafting are electrically grounded to the hull structure with a shaft slipring. A flexible cable is used to ground the rudder. When electrical continuity is established between these components and the hull, the impressed current system will protect them all.

Anodes used in the system may be of a lead/silver alloy or a platinised carrier metal, both of which are relatively inert. Vessels engaged in normal sea-going trades are usually fitted with lead/silver anodes which are encapsulated in glass reinforced resin holders. The anodes are bolted to doubler plates which have been welded to the hull. The doubler plate is surrounded by a dielectric shield of glass reinforced resin which is bonded to it during manufacture (*Figure 12.4*).

Platinised anodes have a platinum coating on a carrier metal plate which may be titanium or niobium. The anode is encapsulated in or mounted on a reinforced resin holder and may be surface mounted or recessed as required. Platinised anodes have their immediate surrounding area protected by a dielectric shield of an epoxy mastic material which has been applied to the shot blasted hull.

All anodes have a cofferdam with a double gland assembly to ensure a watertight hull penetration for the cable.

A minimum of two reference anodes are fitted which may be surface mounted or recessed (*Figure 12.5*). They are made of high purity zinc which is both robust

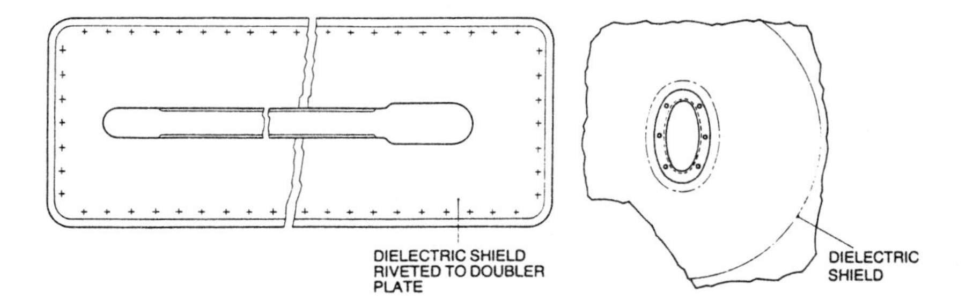

Figure 12.4 Surface mounted and recessed anodes. That on the left is lead/silver; on the right, a platinised anode

and has stable electrochemical characteristics. The reference electrode will continuously monitor hull potential as a measure of the protection being provided. Signals from the electrodes are fed to the controller power unit which adjusts the current output as required.

The reference electrode is fitted into a glass reinforced resin holder and bolted to a doubler plate which is welded to the hull.

The recessed reference electrode is similarly mounted but in a recess. Again, cofferdam arrangements are used to ensure watertight hull penetration for the cable.

The controller power unit is self contained in a cabinet which may be positioned in the machinery space or any other convenient location. The ship's a.c. mains supply is transformed and rectified in the controller power unit into the d.c. current which is used for cathodic protection. A graphic display can be provided for the recording of readings or a microprocessor unit can be provided to carry out self checking, monitoring and data output to computers and printers.

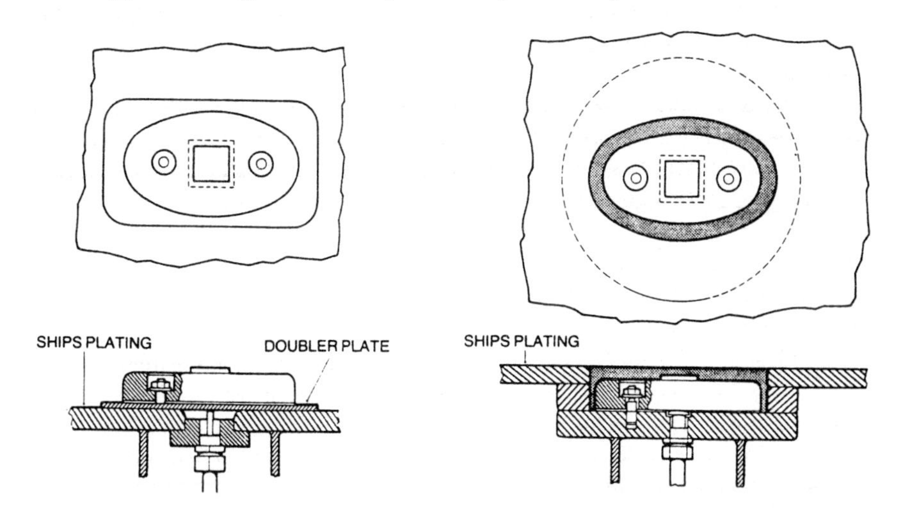

Figure 12.5 Surface mounted and recessed reference electrodes

The propeller shaft slipring assembly ensures a good electrical contact between the propeller, shafting and the ship's hull. This will inhibit dezincification of bronze propellers and also protect propellers of other materials. The shaft bearings are also protected from corrosion. A silver inlaid copper band is clamped to the propeller shaft and a brush assembly of high silver content brushes runs on it to give electrical continuity to the hull (*Figure 12.6*).

The rudder and rudder stock must also be bonded to give electrical continuity. a flexible cable is fitted between the rudder stock and the hull for this purpose.

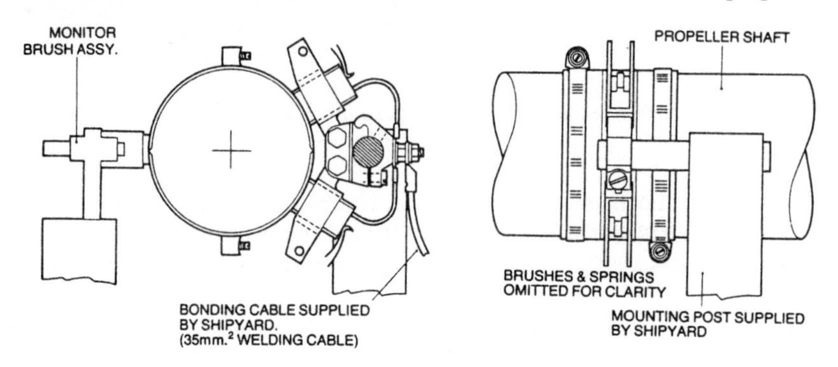

Figure 12.6 Propeller shaft slipring assembly

Cathodic protection of tanks

The cathodic protection of ballast and cargo/ballast tanks is only ever of the sacrificial anode type using aluminium, magnesium or zinc anodes. The use of aluminium and magnesium anodes is restricted by height and energy limitations to reduce the possibility of sparks from falling anodes. Magnesium and aluminium anodes are not permitted at all in cargo oil tanks or tanks adjacent to cargo oil tanks. The anodes are arranged across the bottom of a tank and up the sides, and only those immersed in water will be active in providing protective current flow. Current density in tanks varies from 5 mA/m^2 for fully-coated surfaces to about 100 mA/m^2 for ballast-only tanks. Deckheads cannot be cathodically protected, since tanks are rarely full; they are therefore given adequate additional protective coatings of a suitable paint for the upper 1.5 m of the tank.

Sea water circulation systems

Corrosion and also marine growth can be controlled in sea water circulation systems by an impressed current arrangement. The different metals of pipes, valves and fittings will be affected by electrochemical corrosion, since sea water is an electrolyte. This corrosion is also accompanied by marine incrustation or the growth of marine plants and animals within the sea water system. Chemical methods, such as the introduction of hypochlorite, to release chlorine, have been used, but this can lead to metal pitting and possible environmental problems.

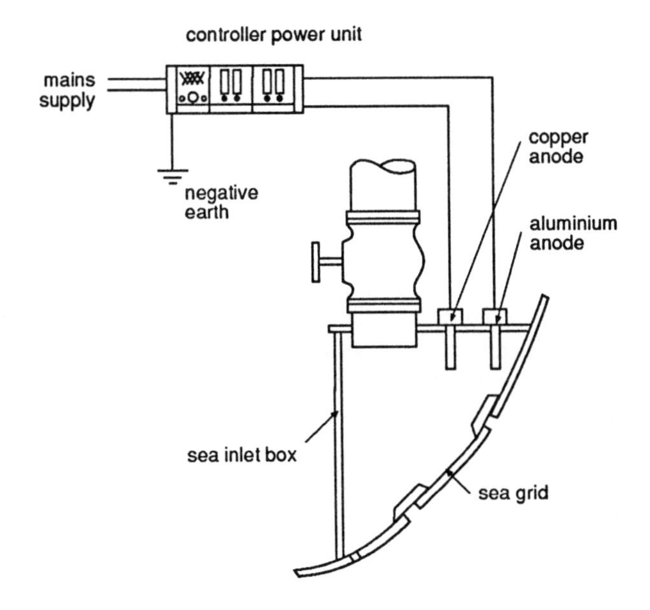

Figure 12.7 Corrosion protection of a sea water circulation system

The impressed current cathodic protection principle can be used where direct current is applied to one or more copper anodes (*Figure 12.7*). Copper ions are then released at a controlled rate into the system and will create an environment in which primary forms of marine life cannot exist. Iron anodes can be used, in a similar way to protect a system with copper alloy piping.

A second aluminium anode releases a 'floc' or precipitate of aluminium hydroxide which collects the copper ions released from the copper anode and distributes them around the sea water system, in particular to low flow rate areas. The aluminium hydroxide precipitate also forms a fine coating over all the inner surfaces of the sea water circulation system. This coating acts as a current dispersing film to protect the system from the possible corrosive action that can occur due to copper ion deposition.

A controller power unit converts the a.c. mains supply to a suitable low voltage d.c. current. The sea water circulation system is connected to the negative terminal of the controller power unit and the protecting anodes to the positive terminal. All anodes have a cofferdam with a double gland assembly to ensure a watertight hull penetration for the cable.

Corrosion prevention by good design

The third method of corrosion prevention is by good design based on a knowledge of the corrosion processes. Good design, therefore, should avoid the trapping of corrosive agents or the setting up of corrosion cells in places which cannot be reached, are poorly ventilated, or rarely protected or maintained.

Small pockets, crevices, etc., where salt spray, water, etc., can collect will result ultimately in severe rusting. Since this involves an increase in volume of the material it will be followed by distortion or fracture of the structural members. Sealing of such crevices by welding or concrete, or their avoidance in the design stage, should be ensured. Dripping water as a result of poorly designed discharges or scuppers should be avoided. Condensed moisture on the underside of enclosed structures will cause corrosion and good design should ensure adequate ventilation of these areas. Steel decks covered by wood will corrode unless the steel is suitably protected and the wood is 'sealed' with a bitumen coating. All joints should be sealed by a suitable filler and any bolts through the wood should have washers under the nuts to prevent the entry of water. Paint, to be an effective protection, requires an adequate thickness over the metal surface. The surface should be made as accessible as possible to enable good coverage and a uniform dry paint thickness. Welding can be used to fill small crevices; however, any welded surface must be suitably prepared prior to painting to ensure protection against corrosion. Smooth rounded surfaces are always easier to paint and less liable to damage and subsequent corrosion.

The atmosphere of machinery spaces and boiler rooms, with the presence of heat, moisture, vibration and foul air, presents ideal conditions for the corrosive process to take place. Surfaces should therefore be kept water-free and as cool as possible by good drainage, insulation of steam pipes, etc., and good ventilation. Inaccessible places such as machinery seats should be well protected by painting before any machinery is fitted. Double-bottom tanks under boilers are sometimes left empty and specially coated with heat-resistant paint. All double-bottom tanks should be regularly inspected and maintained but only after adequate ventilation has been ensured. Maintenance should take the form of painting with bitumastic paint mixtures or in some cases cement wash. Any double-bottom tanks regularly used for oil will have little or no need for corrosion protection.

Two different metals in contact in the presence of an electrolyte such as rain, spray or condensation, can result in a corrosion cell. This can create problems in areas where light alloy members such as aluminium are in contact with steel, as in the superstructure of passenger ships. Modern practice with such joints is to use a transition plate as described in Chapter 4, but older vessels may have bolted joints with insulating ferrules, such as neoprene or some inert filler, between the metal surfaces. Problems do still arise where such joints are made by bolting or riveting, and regular maintenance and attention is required.

Where stainless steel is used in a marine environment the passive mode should be selected, since it is almost immune to electrochemical action.

13

Surveys and Maintenance

In common with all machinery a ship requires regular overhaul and maintenance. The particularly severe operating conditions for an almost all-steel structure necessitate constant attention to the steelwork. The operations of berthing, cargo loading and discharge, constant immersion in sea water and the variety of climatic extremes encountered all take their toll on the structure and its protective coatings. The classification societies have requirements for examination or survey of the ship at set periods throughout its life. The nature and extent of the survey increases as the ship becomes older.

Periodic surveys

All ships must have an annual survey, which is carried out by a surveyor employed by the classification society. This survey should preferably take place in a drydock but the period between in-dock surveys may be extended up to 2½ years. Such an extension is permitted where the ship is coated with a high resistance paint and an approved automatic impressed current cathodic protection system is fitted. In-water surveys are permitted for ships which are less than 10 years old and greater than 38 m in breadth and have the paint and cathodic protection systems already referred to. Special surveys of a more rigourous nature are required every 4 years. Continuous surveys are permitted where all the various hull compartments are examined in rotation over a period of 5 years between consecutive examinations.

During an annual survey the various closing appliances on all hatchways and other hull openings through which water might enter must be checked to be in an efficient condition. Water-clearing arrangements, such as scuppers and bulwark freeing ports, must also operate satisfactorily. Guard rails, lifelines and gangways are also examined.

When surveyed in drydock the hull plating is carefully examined for any signs of damage or corrosion. The sternframe and rudder are also examined for cracks, etc. The wear in the rudder and propeller shaft bearings is also measured.

The fire protection, detection and extinguishing arrangements for passenger ships are examined every year and for cargo ships every two years.

For a special survey, the requirements of the annual survey must be met together with additional examinations. A detailed examination of structure by removing covers and linings may be made. Metal thicknesses at any areas showing wastage may have to be checked. The double-bottom and peak tanks must be tested by filling to the maximum service head with water. The decks, casings and superstructures, together with any areas of discontinuity, must be examined for cracks or signs of failure. All escape routes from occupied or working spaces must be checked. Emergency communications to the machinery space and the auxiliary steering position from the bridge must also be proved.

Continuous surveys are permitted during which all compartments of the hull are opened for survey and examination in turn. An interval of five years is permitted between the examination of each part. Continuous surveys are a means of simplifying special surveys.

For tankers, additional special survey requirements include the inspection of all cargo tanks and cofferdam spaces. Cargo tank bulkheads must be tested by filling all, or alternate, tanks to the top of the hatchway. The greater the age of a ship the greater will be the detail of examination and testing of suspect or corrosion-prone spaces.

Liquefied gas tankers have requirements for annual surveys, as mentioned earlier, and several additional items. All tanks, cofferdams, pipes, etc., must be gas freed before survey. Where the maximum vapour pressure in the tanks is 0.7 bar or less the inner tank surfaces are to be examined. In addition, the tanks must be water tested by a head of 2.45 m above the top of the tank. All tank level devices, gas detectors, inerting arrangements, etc., must be proved to be operating satisfactorily. The special survey requirements are as previously stated, together with the examination internally and externally where possible of all tank areas. Tank mountings, supports, pipe connections and deck sealing arrangements must also be checked. Samples of insulation, where fitted, must be removed and the plating beneath examined. Pressure-relief and vacuum valves must be proved to be efficient. Refrigeration machinery, where fitted, must be examined.

All ships must be surveyed annually to ensure that they comply with the conditions of assignment (see Chapter 11) as stated in the Merchant Shipping (Load Line) Rules of 1968.

Hull surveys of very large crude carriers

The very size of these ships necessitates considerable planning and preparation prior to any survey. Large amounts of staging are necessary to provide access to the structure. Good lighting, safe access and some means of communication are also required. Surveys are often undertaken at sea, with the gas freeing of the tanks being one of the main problems. In-water surveys of the outer hull are also done. Some thought at the design stage of the ship should enable the stern bush, pintle and rudder bush clearances to be measured in the water. Provision should also exist for unshipping the propeller in the water. Anodes should be bolted to the shell and therefore easily replaced. Blanks for sealing off inlets should be carried by the ship,

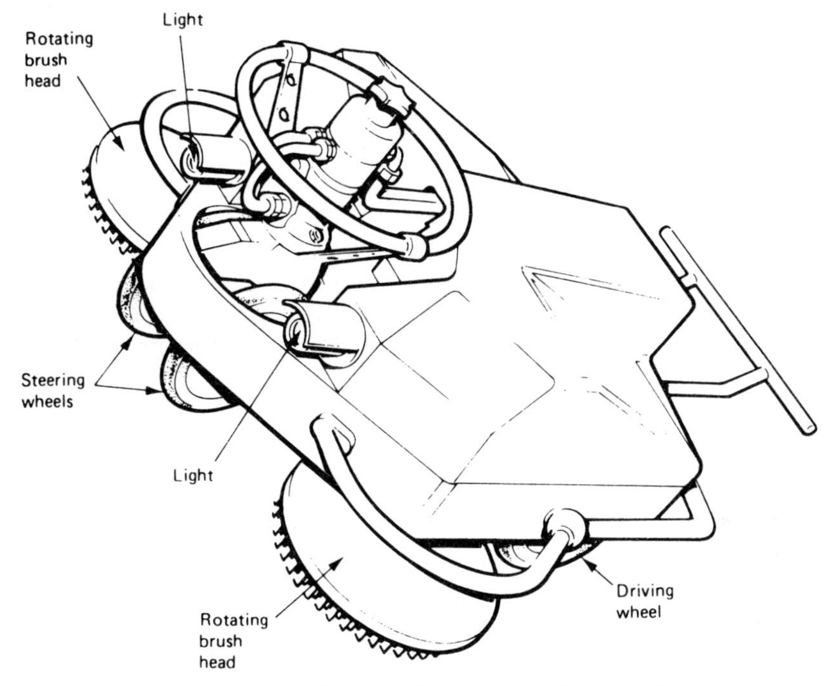

Figure 13.1 'Brush Kart' underwater cleaning vehicle

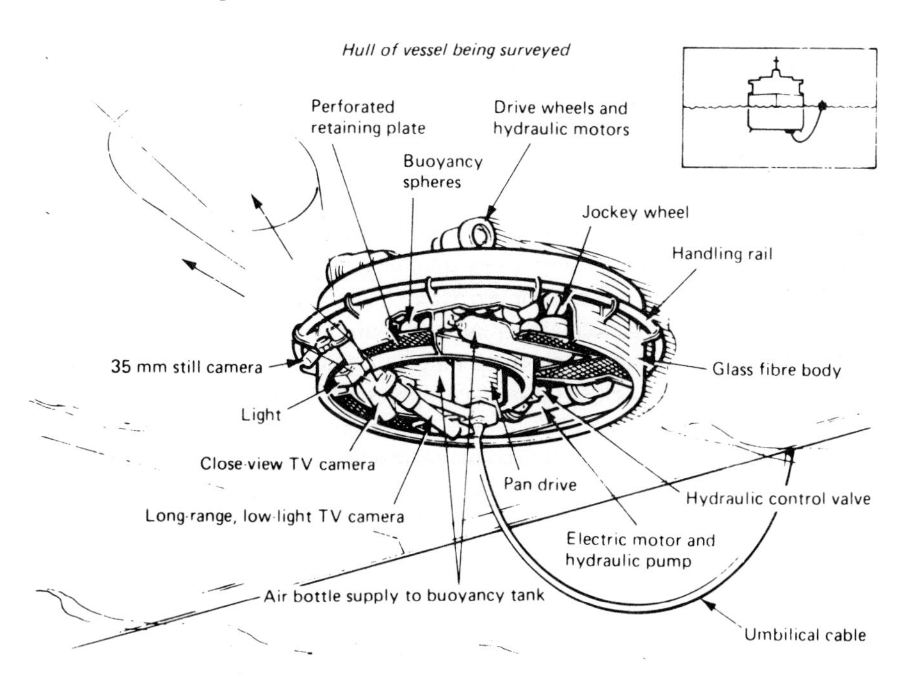

Figure 13.2 'Scan' underwater survey vehicle (from 'Wet-docking of large ships', in In-Water Maintenance Conference, 1975, by D F Jones)

to enable the overhaul of shipside valves. The frame markings should be painted on the outside of the ship at the weather deck edge to assist in identifying frames and bulkheads. An in-water survey plan should be prepared by the shipbuilder. The hull plating surface must be clean prior to survey. This can be achieved by the use of rotary hand-held brushes which may be hydraulically or pneumatically powered. In-water cleaning of the hull is possible, with divers using these brushes or specially designed boats with long rotating brushes attached.

One particular system uses a 'Brush Kart'. This is a hydraulically-powered vehicle with three brushing heads. It is driven by a diver over the surface of the hull to clear the plating of all forms of marine fouling. The Brush Kart is shown in *Figure 13.1*. The shell plating may then be surveyed by using an underwater survey vehicle such as the 'Scan' unit shown in *Figure 13.2*. The various camera units enable close scrutiny of all the areas of the shell plating by the surveyor observing the monitoring units. The Scan unit is fully manœuvrable over the hull surface.

Bulk carrier surveys

Mechanical damage during cargo handling can lead to side shell failure. Cargoes such as iron ore and coal can bring about corrosion of the structure which can likewise bring about failure. High losses of this type of vessel in recent years have resulted in classification societies paying particular attention to problem areas during surveys.

Main side frames with end connections are prone to cracks beginning at the toe or root of the lower bracket connection to the hopper tank. These cracks mat propagate during heavy weather movements of the ship and bring about separation and then similar action at the upper bracket connections. The unsupported shell plating then begins to crack and a major failure may follow.

The cross deck strips between hatches provide the upper support to vertically corrugated bulkheads. If this welded joint cracks the bulkhead may buckle, possibly upwards, causing the hatch covers to become detached. Corrosion may also occur where the bulkhead joins the deck or its stool or the stool joins the tank top. The bulkhead ay then fail in shear due to excessive loading on one side.

Transition zones are particularly prone to cracking. The change in cross-section forward and aft of the cargo hold areas may be significant. It may be that these regions have been hand welded during the ship's construction making them further suspect. The ends of the upper and lower hopper tanks are also problem areas. Cracks may begin at the termination points against the transverse bulkheads. Water leaks may then occur causing corrosion which will hasten the failure.

Ballast tanks may corrode if the protective coatings fail or are not maintained. Where these ballast tanks act as support for other structural elements, they must be inspected very carefully. The various areas which should be examined are summarised in *Figure 13.3*.

Examination in drydock

The drydocking of a ship provides a rare opportunity for examination of the

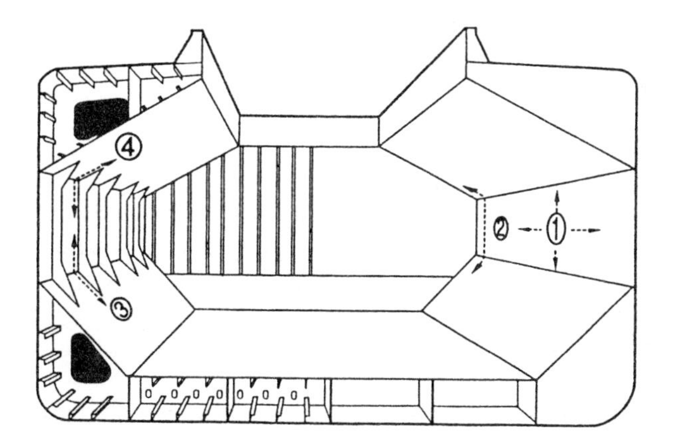

1 side shell plating
2 connection of bulkhead plating to side shell
3 connection of side shell frames and end brackets to shell plating and hopperside tank plating by close-up inspection
4 connection of side shell frames and end brackets to the shell plating and topside tank plating

Figure 13.3 Bulk carrier survey points

underwater areas of a ship. Every opportunity should therefore be taken by the ship's staff, the shipowner and the classification society to examine the ship thoroughly. Some of the more important areas are now listed.

Shell plating

The shell plating must be thoroughly examined for any corrosion of welds, damage, distortion and cracks at openings or discontinuities. Any hull attachments such as lugs, bilge keels, etc., must be checked for corrosion, security of attachment and any damage. All openings for grids and sea boxes must also be examined.

Cathodic protection equipment

Sacrificial anodes should be checked for security of attachment to the hull and the degree of wastage that has taken place. With impressed current systems the anodes and reference anodes must be checked, again for security of attachment. The inert shields and paintwork near the anodes should be examined for any damage or deterioration.

Rudder

The plating and visible structure of the rudder should be examined for cracks and any distortion. The drain plugs should be removed to check for the entry of any water. Pintle or bearing weardown and clearances should be measured and the security of the rudder stock coupling bolts and any pintle nuts should be ensured.

Sternframe

The surface should be carefully checked for cracks, particularly in the areas where a change of section occurs or large bending moments are experienced.

Propeller

The cone should be checked for security of attachment and also the rope guard. The blades should be examined for corrosion and cavitation damage, and any cracks or damage to the blade tips. It is usual to examine any tailshaft seals and also measure the tailshaft weardown.

Anchors and cables

Cable should be laid out or 'ranged' in a drydock and the various lengths (shackles) transposed. The individual links should then be examined for wear and the joining shackles should be opened up and examined. Every link should be hammer tested to ensure it is sound. The chain locker should meanwhile be thoroughly cleaned out and the cable securing arrangement overhauled.

The anchor should be cleaned and examined, in particular to ensure the free movement of the head pivoting mechanism. The mechanism should be suitably greased after examination.

Paintwork

The shell plating should be examined for areas of paintwork which must be repaired. The whole surface of the shell will then be cleaned and prepared for recoating with paint. In some instances the hull may be cleaned down to the bare metal and completely recoated; most situations, however, will only require preparation of the surface for recoating.

Preparation

Several methods are used for cleaning the ship's hull prior to recoating. Some of the more common ones will now be discussed.

Manual wire brushing and scraping with steel scrapers usually takes place on the wet surface as the water level drops in the dock. The finish is poor, the operation slow and the effectiveness varies according to the skill and effort of the operatives involved.

Power discing or wire brushing uses either an electrically or pneumatically driven machine which is hand held. The method is slow but provides a relatively good finish.

High pressure water jetting is being increasingly used for hull cleaning. Water at pressures of 150–500 bar is directed on to the hull by a tubular steel lance. The lower pressure is sufficient to remove weak fouling growths, while the higher pressure will clean the hull down to the bare metal. The results from this method are excellent and very fast, although time is lost while waiting for the hull to dry. It is, however, a skilled operation requiring competent trained personnel for efficient safe performance.

Shot-blasting or abrasive-only cleaning utilises a jet of abrasive at 5–7 bar pressure fired from a nozzle on to the ship's hull. This method rapidly produces a clean dry surface ready for painting. The dusty, dirty nature of the work, however, stops any other activities in the area.

Abrasive and water-blasting combines in effect the foregoing two methods and claims the advantages of each. The method is fast, clean and effective, the abrasive speeding the cleaning and the water suppressing the dust. With this method and water jetting, corrosion inhibitors are added to the water to allow time between cleaning, drying and painting.

Painting

The successful application of paint requires the correct technique during painting and suitable conditions during which the application takes place.

Painting should take place in warm dry weather but not in direct sunlight. The presence of moisture in the air or on the metal surface may damage the paintwork or slow down its curing process. Where poor conditions are unavoidable, specially formulated paints for curing under these conditions should be used. The use of shelters or awnings perhaps supplied with warm air will greatly improve curing and adhesion of the paint. Any scuppers, discharges or overflows which may direct water on to the surface to be painted should be blocked or diverted before work is begun.

The principal methods of paint application are the airless spray, the air-assisted spray, the roller and the brush. Brush and roller application is employed where rough surfaces exist and small often inaccessible areas are to be covered. The method is slow, labour intensive and difficult with certain types of paints. Air-assisted spraying has been largely replaced by the airless spray technique for which most modern paints are formulated. Airless spray is the fastest and cleanest application method. High build materials are suitable for this method of application with dry film thicknesses up to 300μm possible in one application.

Throughout the preparation and painting of a ship the need for good safe, suitable means of access is paramount. Freedom of movement to maintain the appropriate distances for water jetting and paint spraying, for example, is essential. Free-standing scaffolding is used to some extent and also hydraulically operated mobile platforms.

A final mention on the subject of safety is required. Paints in their various forms can be poisonous, skin irritants and of a highly inflammable nature. Adequate protection and ventilation is therefore necessary. In addition, care is required in the location and operation of equipment to avoid the possibility of fires and explosions. Most manufacturers apply their own symbols to paint containers to indicate the various hazards, in addition to any mandatory requirements on labelling.

14

Principal Ship Dimensions and Glossary of Terms

Principal ship dimensions

A ship is defined and described in size, shape and form by a number of particular terms, which are listed below and some of which are shown in *Figure 14.1*.

Forward perpendicular An imaginary line drawn perpendicular to the waterline at the point where the forward edge of the stem intersects the summer load line.

After perpendicular An imaginary line drawn perpendicular to the waterline, either (1) where the after edge of the rudder post meets the summer load line, or (2) in cases where no rudder post is fitted, the centreline of the rudder pintles is taken.

Length between perpendiculars (LBP) The distance between the forward and after perpendiculars, measured along the summer load line.

Length overall (LOA) The distance between the extreme points of the ship forward and aft.

Amidships The point midway between the forward and after perpendiculars. A special symbol is used to represent this point (*Figure 14.1*).

Extreme breadth The maximum breadth over the extreme points port and starboard of the ship.

Extreme draught The distance from the waterline to the underside of the keel.

Extreme depth The depth of the ship from the upper deck to the underside of the keel.

Moulded dimensions are measured to the inside edges of the plating, i.e. they are the frame dimensions.

Base line A horizontal line drawn along the top edge of the keel from midships.

Moulded breadth The greatest breadth of the ship, measured to the inside edges of the shell plating.

Moulded draught The distance from the summer load line to the base line, measured at the midship section.

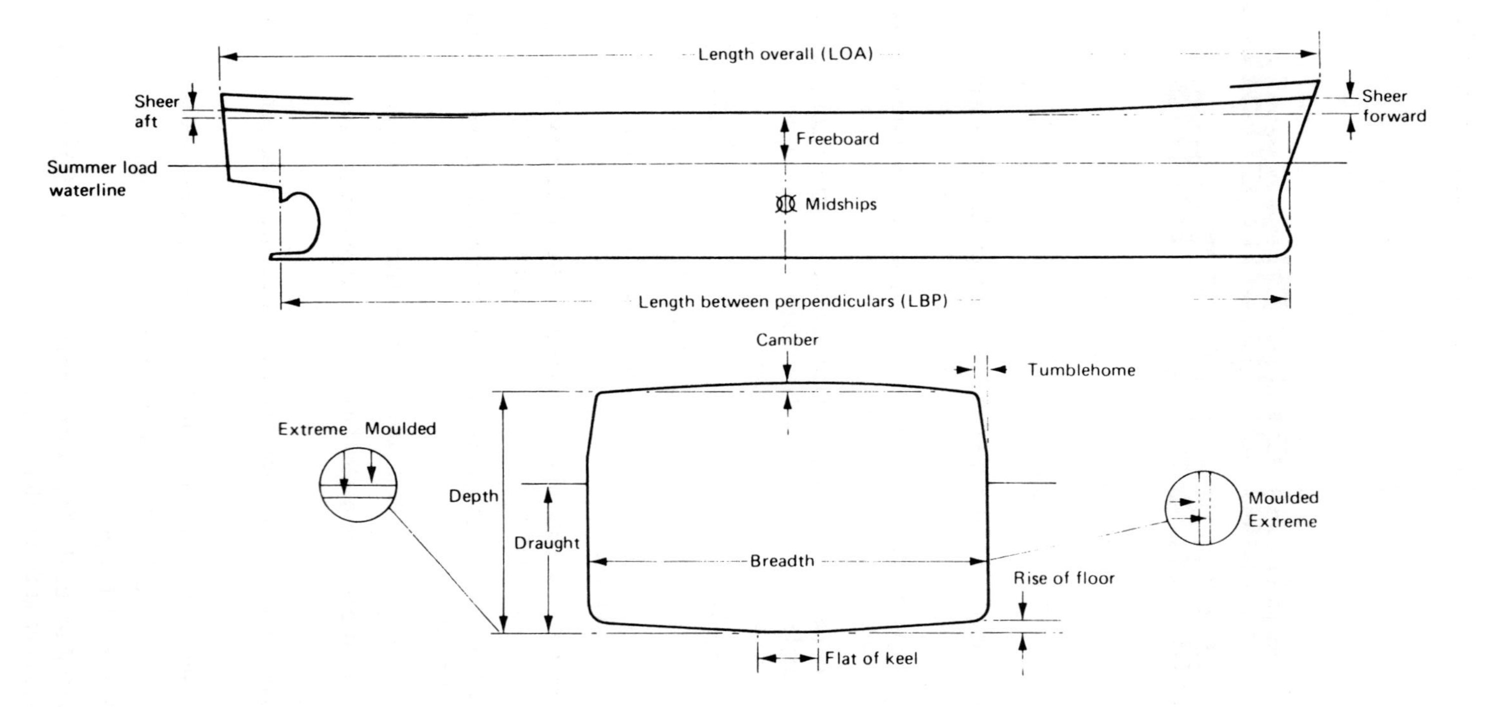

Figure 14.1 Ship terms and definitions

Moulded depth The depth of the ship from the upper deck to the base line, measured at the midship section.

Half-breadth At any particular section half-breadth distances may be given since a ship is symmetrical about the longitudinal centreline.

Freeboard The vertical distance from the summer load waterline to the top of the freeboard deck plating, measured at the ship's side amidships. The upper-most complete deck exposed to the weather and the sea is normally the freeboard deck. The freeboard deck must have permanent means of closure of all openings in it and below it.

Sheer The curvature of the deck in a longitudinal direction. It is measured between the deck height at midships and the particular point on the deck.

Camber The curvature of the deck in a transverse direction. Camber is measured between the deck height at the centre and the deck height at the side.

Rise of floor The height of the bottom shell plating above the base line. Rise of floor is measured at the moulded beam line.

Bilge radius The radius of the plating joining the side shell to the bottom shell. It is measured at midships.

Flat of keel The width of the horizontal portion of the bottom shell, measured transversely.

Tumblehome An inward curvature of the midship side shell in the region of the upper deck.

Flare An outward curvature of the side shell at the forward end above the waterline.

Rake A line inclined from the vertical or horizontal.

Parallel middle body The ship's length for which the midship section is constant in area and shape.

Entrance The immersed body of the ship forward of the parallel middle body.

Run. The immersed body of the ship aft of the parallel middle body.

Displacement The weight of the ship and its contents, measured in tonnes. The value will vary according to the ship's draught.

Lightweight The weight of the ship, in tonnes, complete and ready for sea but without crew, passengers, stores, fuel or cargo on board.

Deadweight The difference between the displacement and the lightweight at any given draught, again measured in tonnes. Deadweight is the weight of cargo, fuel, stores, etc., that a ship can carry.

Tonnage A measure of the internal capacity of a ship where 100 ft^3 or 2.82 m^3 represents 1 ton. Two values are currently in use—the gross tonnage and the net tonnage.

Glossary of terms

Aft In the direction of, at, or near the stern.

Aft peak A watertight compartment between the aftermost watertight bulkhead and the stern.

Athwartship In a direction across the ship, at right-angles to the fore and aft centreline.

Ballast A weight of liquid positioned in a ship to change the trim, increase the draught or improve the seaworthiness.

Bilge Rounded region between the side and shell plating; the space where water collects after draining down from cargo holds, etc.

Bitter end The end of the anchor cable which is secured in the chain locker by the clench pin.

Bollard A pair of short metal columns on a rigid baseplate which are used to secure the mooring ropes or wires.

Bow The forward end of a ship.

Bracket A plate which is used to rigidly connect a number of structural parts; it is often triangular in shape.

Break The point at which a side shell plating section drops to the deck below, such as the poop or forecastle.

Bulkhead, aft peak The first major transverse watertight bulkhead forward of the sternframe.

Bulkhead, collision or forepeak The foremost major watertight bulkhead.

Coaming The vertical plate structure around a hatchway which supports the hatchcover. The height is dictated by the Merchant Shipping (Load line) Rules of 1968.

Cofferdam A void or empty space between two bulkheads or floors which prevents leakage from one to the other.

Cowl The shaped top of a natural ventilation trunk which may be rotated to draw air into or out of the ventilated space.

Deep tanks Tanks which extend from the shell or double bottom up to or beyond the lowest deck. They are usually arranged for the carriage of fuel oil or water ballast but may be fitted with hatches and used for cargo.

Devil's claw A stretching screw with two heavy hooks or claws. It is used to secure the anchor in the hawse pipe.

Dog A small metal fastener or clip used to secure doors, hatch covers, etc.

Erection The positioning and temporary fastening together of units or fabricated parts of a ship prior to welding.

Fabrication The various processes which lead to the manufacture of structural parts for a ship.

Fair To smoothly align the adjoining parts of a ship's structure or its design lines.

Fairlead An item of mooring equipment used to maintain or change the direction of a rope or wire in order to provide a straight lead to a winch drum.

Flange The portion of a plate or bracket bent at right-angles to the remainder; to bend over at right angles.

Flat A minor section of internal deck often without sheer or camber, also known as a platform.

Forepeak A watertight compartment between the foremost watertight bulkhead and the stem.

Forward In the direction of, at, or near the stem.

Frame A transverse structural member which acts as a stiffener to the shell and bottom plate.

Gasket A joint, usually of flexible material, which is positioned between metal surfaces to prevent leakage.

Girder A continuous stiffening member which runs fore and aft in a ship, usually to support the deck.

Gooseneck A fitting on the end of a boom or derrick which connects it to the mast or post and permits a swivel motion.

Grommet A ring of soft material positioned beneath a nut or bolthead to provide a watertight joint.

Gudgeon A solid lug on the sternframe or rudder which is drilled to take the pintle.

Gussett plate A bracket plate usually positioned in a horizontal or almost horizontal plane.

Holds The lowest cargo stowage compartments in a ship.

Inboard In a direction towards the centreline of the ship.

Intercostal Composed of separate parts, non-continuous.

Offsets The co-ordinates of a ship's form.

Outboard In a direction away from the centreline of the ship.

Panting The in and out movement of a ship's plating.

Pintle The hinge pin on which certain types of rudder swing.

Port The left-hand side of a ship when facing forward.

Samson post A rigid vertical post used in place of a mast to support derricks.

Scantlings The dimensions of the structural items of a ship, e.g. frames, girders, plating, etc.

Scuppers Deck drains to remove sea water, rain water or condensation.

Seat The structural support for an item of machinery or equipment.

Seaworthy A term used to describe a ship which has adequate strength, freeboard and stability in order to carry and deliver its cargo in good condition.

Spectacle frame A large casting which projects outboard from the ship and supports the ends of the propeller shafts in a twin screw ship. The casting is plated into the surrounding shell.

Starboard The right-hand side of a ship when facing forward.

Stays Wires or ropes from the deck to the head of a mast, samson post or boom to provide support or prevent movement.

Stealer strake A single wide plate which replaces two narrow plates in adjacent strakes.

Stern The after end of a ship.

Stiffener A flat bar, section or built-up section used to stiffen plating.

Tarpaulin A tough waterproof canvas-type cloth cover used to cover non-watertight hatch covers.

Tiller A casting or forging which is keyed to the rudder stock and used to turn the rudder.

Topping wire A wire used to raise, lower or fix the position of a boom and to support it.

Transverse A direction at right-angles to the centreline of the ship or an item of structure in this position.

Tripping bracket A flat bar or plate fitted to a deck girder, stiffener, beam, etc., to reinforce the free edge.

Trunk A passage extending through one or more decks to provide access or ventilation to a space.

Tunnel A watertight access passage surrounding the propeller shaft which is fitted on a ship where the machinery space is positioned towards midships.

Tween decks The upper cargo stowage compartments or the space between any two adjacent decks.

Uptake A metal casing or large bore piping which carries exhaust gases up through the funnel to the atmosphere.

Web frame A deep-section built-up frame which provides additional strength to the structure.

Well A space into which bilge water drains.

Winch A machine which utilises the winding or unwinding of rope or wire around a barrel for various cargo and mooring duties.

Windlass A machine used for hoisting and lowering the anchor.

Index